OREGON WATER

AN ENVIRONMENTAL HISTORY

ELIZABETH ORR
WILLIAM ORR

PORTLAND • OREGON

To A&J; E&Z
Two generations of water users.

PREFACE

The idea for this book came about after the authors helped to form a watershed council in the northern Willamette Basin. While serving on the council, they became aware that Oregon faced serious water issues. With this awareness came the realization that the long-held notion of the state's abundant and clean resource was no longer true and that it wasn't just other regions of the country, which had to deal with shortages and pollution. What started as a brief look at water conditions grew into a book covering such broad areas as the history of Oregon's past water use, the impact of development on the state's water resources, and the present day conditions.

In researching such an all-encompassing subject, the authors read through thousands of agency reports, some literally dusty, dating back to early 1900s. Newspapers, with no index, were searched, court cases examined, and personal interviews conducted. Because of the variety of sources, errors are bound to have crept in, for which the authors take credit. A lengthy bibliography, included at the end, resulted from the frequent frustrations encountered when attempting to find a reference in the "Notes at the End" for each chapter.

We would like to thank the following persons for their assistance in contributing information and reviewing chapters: John Beaulieu, Oregon Department of Geology and Mineral Industries, Portland; Audrey Eldridge, Oregon Department of Environmental Quality, Medford; John Falk, Oregon Water Resources Department, Salem; Richard Heinzkill, Library, University of Oregon, Eugene; Bobbi Lindberg, Oregon Department of Environmental Quality, Eugene; Carol McKillip, Southern Oregon College, Coos Bay; Dave Predeek, U.S. Forestry Service, Eugene; Karen Russell, WaterWatch of Oregon, Portland; and Eileen Webb, Geologist, Tualatin.

Eugene, 2005

TABLE OF CONTENTS

MT. ANGEL, OREGON, A TOWN WITHOUT WATER

Sometimes when they visit our country home on a hot August day, our grandchildren are surprised to find that no water appears when they turn on the faucet. The well has run dry, but "miraculously" the water returns over-night. To these city children, water always comes out when the handle is turned. In late summer we worry about our water supply, always making sure there's a container full for morning coffee. The flowers are carefully watered along their roots, and some plants, especially the hydrangeas, are checked in the late afternoon for signs of wilting. We keep a close eye on my grandson, who mischievously likes to turn on all the outside spigots, empty-ing the well. After showing our grandchildren the pump, the well, and the spring, we satisfy their curiosity.

Familiar with the idiosyncrasies of our well and our water cycles, we know how to conserve, but what happens when a town, an industry, or even a wide geographic region runs out of water? A simple pump and shallow well aren't enough to produce the many thousands of gallons consumed for every single need, and for cities and businesses to run dry is no longer exceptional, even in rainy western Oregon. Mt. Angel, a community situ-ated in the northern Willamette Valley, currently faces this dilemma. Its surface rivers and streams are diminished and polluted, and its regional groundwater levels are dropping. In the search for an adequate source, pan-icky administrators and farmers are deepening existing wells, drilling new ones, or building dams for storage.

For our family, the arrival of the first rains in late September allays our worry, bringing the illusion that the well is now full and the spring is renewed.

But the same concerns will return again next fall. Will we end up like Mt. Angel with our well polluted and empty?

Every year toward the middle of September, the town of Mt. Angel, Oregon, celebrates its German beginnings with an Oktoberfest. Men wear Lederhosen, tubas oompah, sausages and sauerkraut are consumed, and gallons of beer are drunk to toast the festivities. Oktoberfest is a traditional Old World expression of thanks for the bountiful harvest, and the center-piece in the town square is a two-story-high totem of farm fruit, vegetables, and other crops. Such a celebration is particularly appropriate for Mt. Angel, which has been a farming town since its beginning around 1850.

Pioneers who first came to this region of Marion County in Oregon's Willamette Valley found a land ideal for agriculture. The soils were fertile, and the climate mild. Cool winters with rare snowfalls were followed by dry summers when temperatures averaged in the low seventy to eighty degrees during the warmest afternoons. But most of all, water was plentiful. Mt. Angel might experience up to fifty inches of rain a year, mainly coming during the interval from November through May. Precipitation swelled the rivers and replenished the groundwater, which was part of a seemingly end-less supply percolating through the sands, silts, and gravels beneath the re-gion. The meandering Pudding River passed to the west of town, Abiqua Creek was on the south, while Zollner Creek flowed north and westward. These Oregon creeks, whose beds were filled year-round, would be called "rivers" anywhere else in the United States.

A community of 3,400 persons today, Mt. Angel lies approximately twenty miles northeast of the state capital at Salem and thirty miles south-east of the largest metropolis of Portland. From the intersection of Main and Charles streets, three landmarks on the skyline rise above the town: the Benedictine Abbey atop a prominent butte, the Gothic spire of St. Mary's parish church, and the seven-story Wilco grain elevator. These three sym-bolize the character of Mt. Angel, a strongly Catholic agricultural town, where farming and religion have come together to dominate the past and present.

Mt. Angel is situated in the shadow of an elongate butte, visible for fifty miles. Two and one-half miles long with an elevation of 485 feet at its highest point, Mt. Angel Butte has always had something of a mystical aura. To the Indians, who called it *Tapalamaho*, it was a place to commune with the spirits. Benedictine Father Adelhelm Odermatt, arriving from Switzerland in 1882, was instantly drawn toward its dominating presence but was prevented from building a monastery on its summit because there was no immediate supply of water. The Benedictines did, however, purchase 1,600 acres that included the butte, converting the surrounding "howling wilderness covered with timber" to "waving grain fields, orchards, vineyards, and vegetable gardens, dotted here and there at convenient points with flour and saw mills and shops."[1] Shortly after this, the Benedictine Sisters acquired thirty acres near the base of the butte, "where good water could be obtained." [2]

Hardy emigrants to the region were also drawn to the butte and its surroundings. They liked what they saw and immediately set to work plowing the ground and planting apple, cherry, pear, and plum trees along the creeks. Within ten years the acreage around the butte was yielding fruit along with wheat and oats. Stalks of wheat grew over seven feet tall "and large enough otherwise to make a respectable rail."[3] George Settlemeir, a frontiersman from Missouri, claimed a large parcel of property to the northeast of the butte that included the site of the present city of Mt. Angel, while Robert Zollner settled on the creek that would bear his name. Mathias Butsch, who emigrated in 1878, was an important addition to the village. Since most of his 213-acre parcel was covered with fir and oak, he placed a waterwheel on Zollner Creek, using its power to operate a sawmill. Cutting 6,000 to 7,000 board feet a day, the "up and down" mill operated only during the rainy season, when water was plentiful.

The formal coming together as a community began with a school and a church in the 1850s. A railroad station was the first actual building placed within the present day city limits, and, after the addition of a store, a restaurant, and a hotel, the village was incorporated in 1893. Municipal regulations concerning saloons, weapons, animals running at large, sidewalks, and street lamps were soon enacted.

Hand-dug wells furnished each farm with water, but for the growing community the need for a municipal supply soon became apparent. Two systems, one for fresh domestic water and one to rid the town of waste, were planned. The first well was drilled in 1905 on land owned by City Recorder Peter Meese. Meese offered a small tract "for the purpose of sinking a well to obtain water for city purposes."[4] The Meese family and heirs were to have perpetual access to a two-inch stream of water. At the same time a reservoir was placed southeast of town. The complete system of pipes, a tank, and hydrants cost $2,963, and Joseph Zollner was appointed water pumper with a salary of 20 cents an hour.

As the town increased to around 1,000 inhabitants, a second municipal well was drilled in 1925 to a depth of 235 feet, and a third just over ten years later reached 117 feet into gravels and clays. The Benedictines' original hand-dug, sixty-foot-deep well was extended to 173 feet in 1907 and deepened again to 183 feet in 1939.

Sewage disposal lagged far behind the necessity for supplying clean drinking water. In times past, the effluent problem was solved simply by collecting the waste and piping it into the nearest wetlands or stream. Businesses and homes sent their offal into Mt. Angel streets, where it sat until dispersed by rains. During the summer of 1908 the city constructed a ten-inch-diameter tile pipe, placed five feet underground, which was to carry sewage from the north side of Charles to Main Street, thence to an open ditch, and from there into a gully southwest of town. This clearly was only a temporary solution, but the antiquated pipes and ditch remained in use after the population increased and more businesses came to Mt. Angel's downtown. A creamery, slaughterhouse, feed mill, cannery, stockyard, and produce warehouses were among the fourteen or so commercial establishments utilizing the same system.

By 1911 the tile drain was shown to be inadequate when Anna Ulmen brought suit complaining that the municipal collecting system ended within sixteen feet of her private well west of town. During a January 5th hearing, Robert Zollner testified that the tile drain collected water and refuse from all of the streets as well as the businesses along Main. Another witness certified that during the dry summers water emerging from the pipe was dark, smelling of street offal, and wasn't carried along the ditch but sank into the ground. Water from Ulmen's well had acquired a similar smell and color.

Mt. Angel officials responded, "Of course when there is a heavy rain, the water is not clean. Everybody knows that." Another assured the court that the city had stopped the practice of running house sewage directly out into the street because, "There was a smell when walking along the sidewalk." [5] Ruling in Ulmen's favor, the judge enjoined the city from discharging into the gully but had no power to enforce any processing or cleanup of what emerged from the pipe.

Just ten years later community leaders once again found themselves in court for much the same problem. A drain field running from the municipal septic tanks directly west of town ended in a small unnamed creek, which flowed through private land owned by Clara Houghman and Martin Horst. During the trial in October, 1921, Dr. Wrightman of Silverton testified that animal feces may have entered the creek from cattle, and not from the septic line. He added that, "The water from the septic tank was as pure as any mountain stream." However, when the jury went out to inspect the septic system, they found it wasn't working properly and awarded $4,000 to the plaintiffs. Vowing to appeal, Mt. Angel officials instead agreed to extend the drain tile an additional half-mile "and no doubt eliminate for all time any chance for trouble from this source." Once again, the nuisance was removed from the immediate area, but the problem wasn't solved.

In 1937, Mt. Angel was among several cities that dumped its unprocessed sewage directly into state owned wetlands and streams. As part of the effort to abate water pollution in the Willamette Basin, the State Board of Consulting Engineers and the State Planning Board recommended that the city install a complete treatment plant. But after some public discussion the Mt. Angel City Council decided in July, 1938, that "so large a burden [$40,000] would be impossible to carry at this time." Instead the council proposed lengthening the tile and ditch all the way to the Pudding River. This "splendid piece of work," funded by the Federal Works Progress Administration, widened the ditch to eighteen feet across at the top and twelve at the bottom, thus solving the "much unpleasant odor" problem when the tanks overflowed. [7]

The community served as the agricultural center for the surrounding farming enterprises. Over the years the large original farms were broken up into smaller, more numerous parcels, with diversified crops such as berries, vegetables, grain, hops, and especially flax. The expanding number of individual farms meant heavier demands on the surrounding water resources

XII | ELIZABETH ORR & WILLIAM ORR

during long dry summers. Water from wells and dammed streams was pumped through canals to irrigate the crops. From the beginning, irrigation was mainly used during the hottest ten to fifteen dry days of July and August, and very little land was actually watered. In what was termed an innovation, Nebraskan William Schwartz, who purchased property south of Mt. Angel in 1936, installed a sprinkler system. Pumping from Abiqua Creek, he reported, "the Rain Birds throw water over approximately 60-foot widths."[8]

The growing and production of flax for linen cloth began in 1915, and twenty years later it dominated the fields in Marion County. A processing plant at the state penitentiary in Salem was followed by a second facility just north of Mt. Angel on Zollner Creek, which provided the necessary water. The storage sheds and soaking tanks had the capacity to handle all the flax grown on the surrounding farms. During the retting stage, the plants were packed into water-filled, heated tanks, in which a temperature of eighty-five degrees was maintained by the addition of cold water. Once the plants had soaked and decomposed for over a week, the foul water was drained off into Zollner Creek, and the tanks refilled. After the flax fibers dried, a machine crushed or scrutched them, before they were sold to spinning mills.

By the 1930s flax was heralded as on its way to becoming Oregon's top crop. "Hope is held by the industry's friends that the time is not far distant when a large part of the linen now gracing the homes of American women will be grown, processed and manufactured in the Willamette Valley."[9] Flax became such an important commodity to Mt. Angel that an annual flax festival was held, a precursor to the Oktoberfest celebration. A flax king and queen were chosen for the event that included a grand floral and industrial parade, fireworks, flaxville shows, flaxtown frolics, and a baseball game in which the players all rode bicycles.[10]

For the next twenty years the region remained focused on agriculture and its accompanying industries. The Farmers Union Warehouse, a grain-marketing service, the Marion County Farmers Union Oil Company, and the Mt. Angel Cooperative Creamery, employing seventy-five people, accounted for most of the enterprise. The Benedictine Abbey continued extensive farming on its lands around the butte, supporting its own blacksmith, dairy, and hop house. The flax operation and creamery eventually closed, while new businesses opened. One of the state's largest egg producers was to open in buildings once housing the flax plant.

A flax-cutting machine, a common sight in Willamette Valley fields during the early 1900s, resembles a World War I tank. (The Oregon Magazine, 1936)

As businesses and farms came to depend more and more on wells, surface streams dried up and groundwater reservoirs dropped considerably. By the mid-1950s, the search for new deeper well sites was under way. Failing to reach water after drilling through 300 feet of volcanic lava during the dry August of 1956, city councilmen suggested abandoning that location in favor of another. However, Mayor Jacob Berchtold called upon his beliefs. "Let the drilling continue for another 100 feet; this is the month of the Blessed Virgin and if Mt. Angel needs water, she will see that we get it." [11] Water began to flow into the new well within days. Six years later another municipal well plumbed depths over 600 feet.

In the surrounding countryside farmers, faced with similar problems, turned to damming creeks to supplement their supply. Sprinkler irrigation, which came into wide use after World War II, drew tremendous amounts of water, and storage behind dams was one way of ensuring there was enough for late summer demand. In 1952 the first impoundment of any size blocked Zollner Creek north of Mt. Angel. The reservoir, constructed by Edward A. Hammer, held five acre-feet of water. [12] One acre-foot is equal to an area of one acre with a foot of water atop it, or about one-third million gallons.

An increased awareness of water quality throughout the state, and especially in the Willamette Basin, came after 1940, when Oregon set more stringent standards for controlling and abating pollution. To begin the task of purifying public waters, a newly created State Sanitary Authority notified cities and businesses, which had failed to install adequate treatment facilities, that it would no longer be legal to dispose of waste and raw sewage in public waterways. During the early 1950s, the Authority charged a number of cities with noncompliance, and Mt. Angel was one of these. At that time the city still relied on septic tanks built in 1915, but by 1955 it operated with a filter system authorized by the Department of Environmental Quality.

As the population approached 3,000 in the 1980s, Mt. Angel was still firmly based in agriculture. There were new industries such as Coachman RV manufacturers, which remained only a short time, GEM Equipment, manufacturers of commercial food processors, and the Mt. Angel Beverage Company, taken over by Pepsi-Cola.

For the most part, excessive water practices didn't change. The community, businesses, and farms found themselves impinging on each others' rights as they competed for the same water. Regional users faced two serious water issues. The first was finding a sufficient amount of the diminishing supply, and the second was to locate an unpolluted source.

Endeavoring to deal with its dwindling supply, the community began construction of a million-gallon reservoir in the mid-1980s. The project was praised by City Manager Alan Bengyel as paving the way "to residential and industrial development that could double its population." [13] Negotiating with the Benedictine Abbey, officials placed the reservoir tower on top of Mt. Angel Butte, where it was filled from city-owned wells. Two reservoirs there with a capacity of 400,000 gallons already served the residents.

Solving the municipal contamination problem was not as easy. Pollution of Mt. Angel's domestic source had become apparent in 1978, when tests by the U.S. Environmental Protection Agency found counts of fecal bacteria so high that they violated safe standards. Mt. Angel City Manager Phil Misener dismissed the possibility that the condition posed a health hazard: "It could have been the period of time they took their sample … It has its ups and downs but it's nothing to issue a 'boil water' order over." [14]

Searching for a long-term solution in 2000, Mt. Angel officials were considering buying and piping water from the nearby community of Silverton. Mt. Angel wasn't large enough for its own water treatment plant, and its wells were in danger of being polluted from adjacent properties. Administrator Paul Koch remarked, "Well No. 6 is in an agricultural zone that could be highly susceptible to contamination. The reason for this was due to the fact that the city lacks any control over what is deposited on the nearby soil." [15]

Something of a water crisis arose for Mt. Angel in 2002. Of its three producing wells, one was surrounded by "an auto salvage yard," giving officials concerns over contamination, the second was drying up, and the third was in an agricultural region, also subject to pollution. All had a "sulfur smell ... It's very potable; it's not terrible water," was the judgment of John Yarnall, a consultant from Westech Engineering.[16] Mt. Angel Beverage Company, one of the area's major employers, was not happy with the water quality and attempted to find its own source, while the city sought a new well on the grounds of the middle school.

Meanwhile, farmers were experiencing their own water deficiencies. Since agriculture remains by far the largest consumer of Oregon's water, the expansion of the nursery business brought serious consequences. By 1993 the growing of ornamentals took over the top slot as the state's leading farm commodity. The number of nurseries in Marion County jumped from around twenty in the 1980s, to fifty-three in 1999, and to seventy-three in 2000. Woodburn Ornamentals was incorporated in 1984, Kraemer's Nursery in 1979, Mt. Angel Nursery, also owned by the Kraemer organization, started in 1990, and the Wooden Shoe Bulb Company in 1989. Such operations draw inordinate amounts of water required to keep the individual pots wet. Separate plastic pots, exposed on all sides, dry out rapidly. Watered by sprinklers that shoot a spray high into the air, evaporation can reach forty percent on hot days. Contaminated water, which covers bare gravel sections between the containers, drains into the ground or evaporates from a perimeter ditch.

The increasing use of sprinklers, combined with the growth of container nurseries, brought an even greater reliance on groundwater regionally. In 1992, inroads into the quantity of the surface and underground flow

In a photograph taken on a hot August day in 2002, water, sprayed from a sprinkler system, evaporates from a bed of gravel or is drained off into the perimeter ditch of a Mt. Angel plant nursery. Algae blooms in the nutrient-rich water-filled moat.

had become so serious that the Water Resources Department declared approximately fifteen square miles of the Mt. Angel area as groundwater limited. This meant the underlying basalt aquifer was badly depleted by the number of wells servicing the community, the surrounding homes, and the farm fields. In the Abiqua Creek basin southeast of town, over 400 wells are concentrated within a one-mile radius. But neither this density nor the new groundwater regulations slowed the deepening and drilling of wells or the erection of dams. Between 1971 and 1990, Kraemer farms, an agribusiness based in Mt. Angel, drilled four wells near Mt. Angel, and in 2004 the Water Resources Department granted it a certificate for yet another.[17] As its most recent operation was to be placed within the groundwater limited region, the nursery was restricted from penetrating the water-bearing basalt layer. Consequently the well came up dry.

Several years earlier the same agribusiness had applied to the department for a right to construct a reservoir on the already-impounded and debilitated Zollner Creek. The stated purpose of the reservoir was "42.5

A.F. [acre-feet] for wildlife and 102.5 A.F. for supplemental irrigation." [18] When the dam was still unfinished seven years later, Water Resources granted a time extension. Justification for the project was the storage of water "that would otherwise flow to the ocean and benefit no one," a frequent rationale for building impoundments.[19]

Community leaders and businesses, who also saw dam construction as an answer, favored an impoundment of Rock Creek in Clackamas County. Mt. Angel's Mayor Randy Traeger expressed his feelings in a 1994 letter to the Marion County Board Commissioners: "This is to seek your support on behalf of the City of Mt. Angel for ... this project ... We are located in a ground water limited area and our City's primary economic base, agriculture, is seriously threatened by the lack of a dependable water source. Further, our City is dependent on ground water ... and that source has been determined to be inadequate, even for current needs." [20]

Vice President Rick Jacobson of NORPAC Foods, a processing facility, stated the same fears: "NORPAC Foods, Inc. solicits your support of this application as the development of adequate water resources are so critical to the economic viability of the Willamette Valley ... NORPAC Foods, Inc., and its grower/owners depend on a reliable source of irrigation water." [21] NORPAC operates from eight groundwater wells.

The Oregon Water Resources Department approved a water right permit for the Rock Creek dam, but the project proved too costly when it was realized that around 200 to 300 acres of wetlands, which would be destroyed by its construction, had to be mitigated. Other dam sites are currently being examined.

Since these measures aren't producing the much-needed water quickly enough, aquifer injection is being considered. Hop farmer Glenn Goschie suggested that, "Groundwater recharge may not prove a long-term solution, but does look like a good possibility for the short term for those properties that are most desperate." [22]

Today waters of the basin in and around Mt. Angel are so badly degraded from past practices and agricultural runoff that a treatment plant worker noted, "The wastewater is cleaner than that of the [Pudding] River into which it is discharged." [23] The Department of Environmental Quality has identified waterways in the basin as below standards set by the state, and because of the impaired condition, it is evaluating and establishing limits for each contaminant. An overall assessment of regional conditions, currently undertaken by the Pudding River Watershed Council, will demonstrate more specifically the problems of the watershed and will suggest what can be done to benefit and contribute to its health.

On a dry July or August afternoon, the bed of Zollner Creek below the dam has no water. Dave Predeek remembers how it was when he grew up here: "It saddens me to hear about Zollner Cr[eek]. The stream flows through a narrow ravine that widens northwest of Mt. Angel. At this point there used to be islands with lots of beaver dams. A flock of wood ducks spent the year there. We had an old row boat which we would float through the channels. My older brother used to fish for trout and trap muskrat and beaver to sell the pelts. I remember one summer seeing dead trout floating in the brown water ... There were lots of wooded areas along the Pudding and for us it was a regular wilderness." [24]

In a photograph taken during the 1950s, the sun reflects off the surface of Zollner Creek wetlands. (Courtesy Dave Predeek)

Mt. Angel's present water plight is the result of past practices, and its predicament reflects what has taken place across the state. That story needs to be told, and this book relates the environmental history and use of Oregon's water from the state's beginning, millions of years ago, to the present day.

ENDNOTES: INTRODUCTION

[1] Sister Ursula Hodes, *Mt. Angel Oregon, 1848 – 1912* (Eugene, University of Oregon, Master of Science, 1932), 78.

[2] Ibid, 76.

[3] *Statesman Journal*, October 14, 1851

[4] Hodes, 1933, p.99

[5] Ulmen v. Town of Mt. Angel, 112 Pac. 529, 1911, 549

[6] *Mt. Angel News*, October 13, 1921, 1; December 15, 1921, 1.

[7] *Mt. Angel News*, July 14, 1938, 1; September 29, 1938, 1.

[8] *Mt. Angel News*, May 11, 1939, 1.

[9] U.S. Works Progress Administration, *Flax in Oregon*, nd., @1930, [1].

[10] *Mt. Angel News*, August 4, 1938, 1.

[11] *Statesman*, August 26, 1956, 10, Sect.2.

[12] Oregon Water Resources Department, Permit R-1371, 1953.

[13] *Statesman*, October 3, 1986, C2.

[14] *Statesman,* May 10, 1978, D7.

[15] *Silverton-Appeal Tribune and Mt. Angel News*, April 12, 2000, A3.

[16] *Silverton-Appeal Tribune and Mt. Angel News,* January 9, 2002, I2.

[17] Oregon Water Resources Department, Permit #G-13596, 2004.

[18] Oregon Water Resources Department, Permit R-72038, November 22, 1991.

[19] Oregon Water Resources Department, Application for Extension of Time, Permit R-72037, November 12, 1998.

[20] Mt. Angel Mayor Randy Traeger, Letter to Marion County Commissioner Mary Pearmine, May 31, 1994.

[21] Rick Jacobson, Vice President, Agricultural Services, NORPAC Foods, Inc., Letter to Craig Luedeman, Marion County Community Development, Salem, May 12, 1994.

[22] East Valley Water District, Minutes, April 14, 2003.

[23] Silverton Wastewater Treatment Plant, Personal communication, May, 2003.

[24] Email, Dave Predeek, July 21, 2004

CHAPTER 1

OREGON'S WATERY PAST

The Eozoic Ages: The dominion of heat has passed away; the excess of water has been precipitated from the atmosphere, and now covers the earth as a universal ocean.[1]

To tell the story of Oregon's waters it is first necessary to look at the state's beginnings, where water was an integral part of its legacy. The land known as Oregon was slowly assembled in distant oceans from widely scattered places and pieces of the earth's crust. Over 200 million years ago, the Pacific Northwest was covered by a vast sea, its shoreline running across Idaho and Nevada. Oregon was merely an embayment of this ocean.

Landscapes never remain static for long, and after millions of years had passed this geographic picture changed, as the Pacific Ocean shrank in size while a parade of oceanic volcanic islands and plateaus collided one-by-one with the western shoreline. Eventually the collage of islands would become the underpinnings of present-day of Oregon.

As recently as 100 million years in the past, not long ago in geologic time, at least three-fourths of Oregon still was covered by a wide expanse of shallow ocean spread over a continental shelf. The only land to project above the watery environment lay in the vicinity of the Klamath and Blue mountains at opposite corners of the state. The seas continued their gradual retreat, until ocean waters covered only the area that was to become the present-day Willamette Valley and Coast Range. Around 50 million years ago, unprecedented volcanic activity combined with torrential rainfall dominated the Oregon scene.

Late in this period the warm rains decreased and drier cooler conditions prevailed. Gradually the seaway, covering the Willamette Valley and Coast Range retreated westward, while the ocean shoreline moved close to its present site. The Cascade Mountains were elevated, cutting off moisture to eastern Oregon. By about 5 million years ago the modern geography of the state was established.

Once again climate changes worldwide brought profound alterations to the earth's surface. Nearly 2 million years ago, the Ice Ages began as an epoch dominated by water in all its forms – ice, rain, and snow. Rain increased, temperatures dropped, and continental glaciers, which grew to unimaginable size, began to move. Water, locked up as ice on land, caused global ocean levels to drop, exposing large tracts of the continental shelf. In the Pacific Northwest, thick sheets of ice ground a path down into northern Washington and Montana. High in the Oregon mountain ranges, snow built valley glaciers that deepened and straightened river channels. On both sides of the Cascades, rain accumulated in great pluvial lakes across previously dry basins.

THE FIRST OREGONIANS

This was the picture 15,000 years ago, when people first trudged across the Bering Straits from Asia to North America. If water hadn't been held in glaciers across much of the land, such a journey would have been improbable. But the severe freezing climate produced sheets of ice and lowered sea level, exposing a land route for the Archaic travellers.

Enduring the open Arctic-like tundra of the newly exposed continental shelf, small bands of ten to twenty people began the infinitely slow and difficult southward migration. Paleo-Indians reached the Northwest about 13,000 years ago, dispersing fairly evenly along the Oregon coast, into the Willamette Valley, and throughout the eastern part of the state. They found vast wetlands, and a cold constant rain, which were inhospitable. Precipitation swelled rivers over their banks, and lakes formed when volcanic sediments or landslides cut off tributary streams. Lakes, in turn, evolved into bogs as ash periodically mantled the ground from the newly-formed Cascades.

The location of waterways determined the placement of villages. Small family groups focused their lives around the resources of rivers, lakes, wetlands, or ocean. By learning then adapting to the natural successions of their particular surroundings, Paleo-Indians settled into a rhythm based on seasons when fish gorged the streams, when plants appeared or ripened, or when game was most plentiful. Living in sheltered bays or river estuaries, coastal Indians were favored by a rich supply of seals and sea lions, molluscs, and many kinds of fish. On the Columbia River, Chinook tribes depended on plump and delicious fish, arriving from the ocean in prime condition, and on both sides of the Cascade Mountains Indians were on the move constantly gathering a much broader harvest.

As the multitudes of fish thrust their way up the many rivers and tributaries to spawn, Indians lining the banks watched in eager anticipation. Migrating salmon and trout are anadromous. That is, they start and end their life in freshwater but travel to the ocean to mature. Once they have lived out their time in the sea and are ready to reproduce, the fish migrate back to spawn and die in the streams where they originated. Cutthroat or steelhead and rainbow trout, as well as chum, coho, sockeye, and Chinook salmon make this trek, moving determinedly upriver, crowding against then leaping waterfalls, and fighting the rapids to complete their instinctual journey. On the Columbia River, they made the epic voyage from the Pacific Ocean to the headwaters in British Columbia, a staggering distance of 12,000 miles.

Great fisheries were situated at the cascades of the Columbia and the falls on the Willamette River. On the Columbia, the Long Narrows and Celilo Falls near The Dalles were famous for their salmon. Here swiftly flowing cold waters of the river brought seasonal salmon runs of such magnitude that they sustained large, very prosperous, and permanent communities. With high hopes of a rich fish harvest, Indians crossed the Columbia Plateau to reach Celilo Falls. Standing on platforms, they speared or netted the salmon.

Willamette Falls at present-day Oregon City was equally well-known for its plentiful fishing. In 1841 John Wilkes, a government agent with the U.S. Exploring Expedition, reported, "The salmon leap the fall; and it would be inconceivable, if not actually witnessed, how they can force themselves up, and after a leap of from ten to twelve feet retain strength enough to stem the force of water above. About one in ten of these who jumped would succeed in getting by ... I never saw so many fish collected together before; the Indians are constantly employed in taking them. They rig out two stout poles, long enough to project over the foaming cauldron." [2]

To the Indians of the Great Basin, as well as to those tribes along the

Indians fishing at Celilo Falls on the Columbia River before erection of
The Dalles Dam in 1957. (Ralph Gifford, Oregon State Highway
Department)

coast, the salmon run was also of importance. Although they appeared in
lesser numbers during the spring, fish found their way to the Malheur River
by way of the Columbia and Snake channels. At the mouth of the river,
Indians caught and dried the salmon during the May run, which lasted several weeks. Coastal resources were among the most plentiful, but the deli-
cate salmon was still highly prized. Using hooks or spears, as well as great
woven nets, Indians snared the fish when they entered the estuaries for their
seasonal journey.

Along with fish, plants formed an essential part of the Indians' diet.
Three plants that favored a wetlands habitat, camas (*Camassia*), wappato
(*Sagittaria*), and wocus (*Nuphar*), assumed great importance when they
bloomed in the spring and early summer or went to seed during fall. Growing in boggy areas or near streams throughout much of Oregon, great fields
of the attractive purple to blue or white camas flowers indicated where the

bulb could be found. Using sharpened sticks or antlers women dug then gathered up the bulbs, which were roasted with hot stones.

Before it was diked and drained, the saturated ground of Sauvie Island, near the mouth of the Willamette River, was covered with the arrow-shaped leaves of wappato, Indian potato. On this poorly-drained island, dotted with marshes, lakes, and ponds, this water plantain grew so heavily that the Indians could use it for trade, bringing them a degree of wealth. Although not as abundant elsewhere, wappato could also be harvested in other lowlands across the Willamette basin.

In the Klamath marshes of southern Oregon, the large floating leaves of the yellow water lily, wocus, shaded and cooled the shallow waters, providing a habitat for insects, frogs, fish, and ducks. For the Klamath Indians, the seeds were considered a delicacy, and a thriving industry revolved around their harvest. In later years, white-introduced pots, coffee grinders, and skillets were incorporated into the gathering and processing, but after the 1940s, reliance on wocus became sporadic, following significant environmental alterations to the wetland habitat.

For the Northwest Indians, rivers and wetlands offered foods that set the rhythms of their days. Fish and plants, which sustained them, were never harvested to the extent that their own survival would be endangered. However, permanent and irreparable changes were about to be introduced by the advent of Europeans, whose lavish consumption of the resources would lead to the demise of the existing environment.

EXPLORERS BY WATER

Water was the main avenue by which European explorers came to the Northwest, some crossing the oceans in boats, others following the rivers overland from the East. The early explorers came from Russia, Spain, England or eastern North America. Each had their own reasons for seeking the west, but all wanted to establish a presence on the Pacific Coast. Returning to their home countries, they related the exciting news about a whole new region ready for the taking.

Efforts to delineate the Pacific coastline and discover inland waterways set the stage in the opening up of the Northwest. In 1728 Czar Peter the Great hoped to determine whether there was a land bridge between Asia and America. While this endeavor proved fruitless, Americans and British sought a water passageway through the continent from the Atlantic to Pacific Ocean. By the end of the 1700s, some twenty-one vessels were exploring up and down the Pacific Coast, but, hampered by fog, rain, and an unforgiving rocky shoreline, they failed to sight the broad entry to such a grand river as the Columbia. While not reaching across the continent, the Columbia River would have offered a passageway deep into the Northwest Territory. Several ships came close, but the clues were misread. In August, 1775, Bruno Heceta noted a large inlet, which he named Assumption Bay, remarking on the "currents and eddies," which caused him to think "that the place is the mouth of some great river." [3] Calling it Rio San Roque, Heceta failed to investigate further.

Scrutinizing the western shoreline from 1792 to 1794, Captain George Vancouver of the British Navy kept a strict watch for signs of harbors and navigable rivers, but, when actually passing by the mouth of the Columbia on April 27, 1792, he wasn't sufficiently impressed with the presence of flowing water to investigate. "The sea had now changed from its natural, to river coloured water, the probable consequence of some streams falling into the bay … Not considering this opening worthy of more attention, I continued our pursuit to the N.W." [4] Had either Heceta or Vancouver acted on this evidence, the future of the Northwest might have fallen under different flags.

A few days later, Captain Vancouver encountered Robert Gray's ship *Columbia*, and he sent an officer, Peter Puget, along with Dr. Archibald Menzies, over to question the American. A fur trader and consummate Boston businessman, Gray had actually found the mouth of the Columbia River the previous year, but the strong currents and heavy breakers prevented his entering. Although he hesitated to share his information with Vancouver, wanting, no doubt, to protect his business ventures, Gray eventually informed the British of the latitude of the river's entrance. Vancouver remained skeptical and kept on sailing north, while Gray turned south to cross between the two sandbars at the mouth of the Columbia on May 11, 1792. John Boit, a seventeen-year-old officer, described this remarkable achievement very matter-of-factly in his log: "This day saw an appearance of a spacious harbor abreast the Ship, haul'd wind for it, observ'd two sand bars making off, with a passage between them to a fine river … the Ship under short sail, carried in from ½ three to 7 fm. And when over the bar had 10 fm. water."[5]

Many canoes crowded alongside the *Columbia,* the natives astonished at the sight of the ship but anxious to trade. In his journal Boit wrote, "Soon after, above 20 canoes came off, and brought a good lot of furs and salmon, which last they sold, two for a board Nail. The furs we likewise bought cheap, for Copper and Cloth." The *Columbia* eventually arrived at a large village where "We purchas'd 4 Otter skins for a Sheet of Copper, Beaver skins, 2 spikes each, and other land furs, 1 spike each."[6] The Americans remained here trading for close to one week, at which time the ship was loaded with 3,000 skins to be sold in China. During their stay Gray and Boit went ashore to look around and, as noted by Boit, "to take possession" of the land for America.

Gray sailed away never to return, but his claim of land ownership for the Americans was to assume great importance later, when the government in Washington, D.C., maintained that the Northwest belonged to the United States and not to Great Britain. Of equal importance for the fur industry was Gray's report in Boston and the eastern states that some fifty Indian villages lining the magnificent river offered extensive trade possibilities.

The British-owned *Chatham*, which entered the Columbia River harbor in October, 1792, was only the second ship to cross over the sandbar at the entrance.

Learning of Gray's discovery that October while he was at Nootka Sound, Captain Vancouver wasted no time in sending one of his men, Lieutenant William Broughton, down to the mouth of the Columbia in a smaller ship, the *Chatham*. Although Broughton found the water at a low ebb since the rains had yet to begin, he crossed the bar and explored up as far as present-day Washougal, Washington. Along the way Broughton mapped and named land features, among them the Willamette and Sandy rivers. He called the Willamette the River Mannings after a crew member, and the Sandy was Barings River for a family of English bankers. Considering himself to be the first white man to visit here, Broughton felt justified in claiming the land for England.

While ships from European ports were obliged to sail some distance to reach the Pacific shores, Americans were favored with the additional advantage of being able to make their way overland from the Eastern Seaboard. Rivers were the highways by which they came. Rivers provided direction and ease of travel, until, ultimately, trading posts, forts, and missions lined their banks as pathways through the wilderness.

One of the first of these routes was forged by Meriwether Lewis and William Clark. Worried over British inroads into the Northwest and wanting to strengthen America's hold on this territory after Captain Robert Gray's somewhat casual act of possession, President Thomas Jefferson financed an expedition to the Pacific Ocean. Setting aside $2,500, he instructed Lewis and Clark to explore the Missouri River, its principal streams, and other tributaries in order to cross the continent and connect to the Columbia River and Pacific Ocean. In Jefferson's words to Congress, their course was to "offer the most direct & practicable water communication across this continent, for the purposes of commerce."[7] What the President had in mind was not only the acquisition of the huge Oregon territory, but he was desirous of establishing a trade route as well. In 1804, Lewis and Clark started from a point at St. Louis on the Missouri River, which they ascended, portaging around the great falls, until they reached the headwaters. Crossing the Rocky Mountain divide, they came to the Clark Fork and the Clearwater rivers, now in Idaho, where they feasted with the Nez Perce Indians. Canoes, constructed on the Clearwater, carried the party to the Snake River then down the Columbia, passing rapids and cascades, skimming past the mouth of the Willamette River, which they failed to notice, until the Pacific Ocean was sighted. This was more than a year after the explorers had set out.

From the outset, the rainy Northwest climate was the subject of comment among the men. Constructing a primitive shelter on the south bank of the Columbia River near what is now the Lewis and Clark River, the expedition spent a very rainy winter. Clark's journal for November 12th, Tuesday, 1805, reflected: "About three o'clock a tremendous gale of wind arose, accompanied with lightning, thunder, and hail: at six it became light … but a violent rain soon began and lasted during the day." On November 13th he recorded: "During the day we had short intervals of fair weather, but it began to rain in the morning, and continued through the day." Finally, Clark noted on Thursday, 14th: "It rained without intermission during last night and to-day." [8]

The expedition left camp on March 23, 1806, for their homeward journey. Once again Lewis and Clark failed to notice the Willamette River until a native informed Clark of the presence of a lengthy stream discharging into the Columbia. About this time they had reached the Sandy River, where the explorers halted. Taking several men, Clark canoed back to become the first white person to enter "this river … called Multnomah … from a nation who reside on Wappato Island, a little below the entrance." He proceeded several miles upstream, where his view was hampered by a mist so thick that he retreated.[9]

The most far-reaching consequence of these expeditions to the Northwest, whether by ocean-going vessels or by overland march, was the widespread publicity. The territory and all of its resources were rapturously praised. "But our mild climate, rich soil, good health, boundless grassy plains, vast forests of superior timber, rich minerals, large ocean navigation, pure fountains of living, gushing, cold water, delightful season … immense water power – all invite our fellow citizens … to come among us." [10] As fame and knowledge about the western lands spread eastward, excited Americans wanted to see for themselves.

FUR TRADERS; MARKETING THE RIVERS

The next wave of whites to the Northwest appropriated the natural riches of the new territory in just a few years. These men came with a purpose, bringing the need for profit, for exploitation, and for management of what they found. From the time when Captain Robert Gray spread the news in Boston about his discoveries, adventurers and financial entrepreneurs speculated about the money to be made from marketing fur-bearing otter, beaver, fox, mink or marten. Of these animals, the most sought after were the sea otter (*Lutra enhydra marina*) and beaver (*Castor canadensis*). Because sea otters were concentrated along the ocean shore and since beavers lived on rivers and streams, the task of trapping them was made easier. Without such easy access on waterways, fur exploiters would have faced the much more daunting task of thrashing through heavy forests of massive trees and thick underbrush in search of their prey. River corridors, penetrating the continent, offered the most obvious trapping routes, and the Columbia, that furnished access eastward into the depths of Oregon Territory, played a significant role in the expansion of the fur enterprise.

The first mammals to be sought were sea otters, marine members of the weasel family that once inhabited the rocky shores and reefs from the northern Japanese islands, through the Aleutians, to the West Coast of North America and down to Mexico. Hunting from ocean canoes with bow and arrow or harpoon, Indians were seldom able to kill more than one each trip. On the other hand, organized parties of whites slaughtered as many as 637,000 animals between 1790 and 1810. Overlooking just a few thousand in secluded coves of the Aleutians, fur traders eradicated otters from the entire Pacific region by the middle 1800s.

An engraving of a charming, but somewhat imaginative, beaver.

The next species to be targeted was the beaver, at one time the most prevalent of all the fur-bearing animals along Northwest streams and tributaries. In less than thirty years their numbers were greatly diminished by trappers, selling the furs in America and Europe. Famed botanist, David Douglas, who walked over much of the Willamette Valley, was content to see the demise of the beaver. In August of 1825 he wrote, "The beaver is now scarce; none alive came under my notice. I was much gratified in viewing the deserted lodges and dams of that wise economist." [11]

Initially the fur business was somewhat haphazard, but that picture soon changed. "The trade thus commenced was, for a time, carried on by individual adventurers, each of whom was alternately a seaman, a hunter, and a merchant... Eventually, however, some capitalists ... employed their funds in the pursuit; and expeditions to the islands were ... made on a more extensive scale ... Trading stations were established." [12] Instead of relying on sporadic exchanges from the deck of ships or on the vagaries of a single trapper, teams of men living in fur posts could carry on business year-round.

The presence of permanent trading stations along rivers and tributaries marked the turning point the escalating process of harvesting nature. The first posts were situated near the mouths of the Columbia or Willamette rivers, which provided freshwater and ready accessibility to the ocean. Once a site was selected, trees and brush were cleared away, residences and storehouses were constructed from logs, soil in a garden spot was prepared, then seed was planted. In 1841 Commander Wilkes described Hudson's Bay Company headquarters at Ft. Vancouver near the mouth of the Willamette River as consisting of a row of fifty or more comfortable log houses. A short distance away, the fort boasted additional dwellings, shops, a powder magazine, and a four-acre garden. One year later another trading post was successfully placed at Point George, the current site of the city of Astoria, by members of John Jacob Astor's company. Some members from Astor's Pacific Fur Company reached the coast by ship while others struggled overland.

By 1821, the British-owned Hudson's Bay Company gained a monopoly over fur trade in the Oregon Territory, and its agent John McLoughlin moved his administration upriver from Fort George to Fort Vancouver. Through a series of mergers the powerful McLoughlin dominated the fur enterprise for the next twenty years. Under his control, the company's influence extended across a vast domain from Alaska to California and from the Rocky Mountains to the Pacific Ocean.

As part of his reorganization, McLoughlin sent groups of trappers to outposts as far away as the Snake River. Travelling by canoe, the men would head to Snake River collection sites during the winter from December to January or in the summer from August to September. The extraordinary passageway of the Snake River between the Seven Devils Mountains of Idaho and the Wallowa Mountains of Oregon provided its own barrier to the fur adventurers as the river plunged between the steep walls of Hells Canyon and Box Canyon. In this, the deepest chasm in the United States, the riverbed drops 5,000 feet in seven miles, narrowing in places to a hundred feet.

The first trapper to risk a trip through this canyon was the sandy-haired, Donald Mackenzie. Setting out to organize trade in the Snake River country in 1819, Mackenzie began by erecting Fort Nez Perces (later to become Ft. Walla Walla) at the mouth of the Walla Walla River before scouting elsewhere. He needed to determine whether it would be practical to transport his furs down the Snake. A man of remarkable courage and size at 300 pounds, Mackenzie accompanied by four companions ascended the river from the mouth of the Clearwater near present-day Lewiston to Burnt River in a barge-like Canadian bateau. His route was hampered by "bold cut rocks" and hazardous whirlpools. At the end of his journey Mackenzie concluded that the currents and frequency of rapids made transit on the Snake too risky.[13]

The fur trading period lasted roughly sixty years, from 1780 to 1840, by which time the easy-to-come-by riches were gone, and permanent settlers were arriving into the Northwest. No longer was the region the "wild unknown." Maps had been made, and boundaries drawn. Because of the inroads made along river systems, much of the interior and coastline geography of Oregon country was mapped, and its topographic features drawn. Issued in 1844, Captain John Wilkes' *Map of the Oregon Territory* provided a detailed picture of the area, connecting and filling gaps with known regions of the continent. Compiling information from explorers and trappers, Wilkes delineated streams, tributaries, and mountain ranges, naming over 250 landmarks. Included with Wilkes' map was a large inset of the Columbia River from its mouth to Walla Walla. Thanks to those adventurous explorers and traders, settlers who next came westward had their way shown in guidebooks.

On the deficit side of the balance sheet, Europeans brought an end to ecosystems that had existed for thousands of years. Coastal and riverine animals had been hunted to the point of extinction, and fish runs diminished. These would never be reestablished, and the arrival of civilization meant permanent communities, a clearing of the land, and utilization of the water.

ENDNOTES: OREGON'S WATERY PAST

[1] J.W. Dawson, *The Story of the Earth and Man* (New York, The Booksellers Union, 1886), 15.

[2] Charles Wilkes, *Narrative of the United States Exploring Expedition* (London, Ingram, Cooke, & Co., 1852), 184.

[3] H.O. Lang, ed., *History of the Willamette Valley* (Portland, Oregon, Himes Publ., 1885), 81.

[4] T. C. Elliott, "The Oregon Coast as Seen by Vancouver in 1792," *Oregon Historical Quarterly*, v.30, 1920, 42.

[5] John Boit, "Log of the Columbia – 1790-1793," *Oregon Historical Quarterly*, v. 22, no.4, 1921, 309.

[6] Ibid.

[7] Lang, 1885, 135.

[8] Meriweather Lewis, *The Lewis and Clark Expedition* (Philadelphia, Lippencott v.2, 1814), 476-477.

[9] Ibid, 606.

[10] David Newsom, *David Newson: the Western Observer, 1805-1882* (Portland, Oregon Historical Society, 1972), 65.

[11] David Douglas, *The Oregon Journals of David Douglas* (Ashland, The Oregon Book Society, 1972), v.1, 46.

[12] Robert Greenhow, *The History of Oregon and California* (Boston, Little & Brown, 1844), 135.

[13] T.C. Elliott, "Earliest Travellers on the Oregon Trail," *Oregon Historical Quarterly*, 1912, v.13, 78.

CHAPTER 2

OREGON, THE END OF THE GREAT MEDICINE ROAD OF THE WHITES

The tale we have to tell is of … a progress still but begun, not to be ended until thousands of prospering citizens have joined the hundreds who have already found their way to the Pacific Northwest.[1]

The process of systematic consumption of the natural resources in the Pacific Northwest, begun by fur traders, was carried forward by pioneers. Settlers brought with them the notion that the water, land, trees, wildlife, and minerals could be found in such abundance that there was no need to conserve. There was plenty of everything for everyone who came to live within the territory. What's more, such resources needed only to be utilized for a profit to be made. "Large quantities of these desirable lands, mostly wooded, lie about the upper courses of nearly every one of the tributaries of the Willamette, and only await the hand of the energetic settler to produce abundantly."[2]

Declaring Northwest lands to be in the public domain, the government offered all of the riches free for the taking. Indians were viewed as having no ownership rights. The giveaway land schemes came about when legislators in Washington, D.C., enacted a number of regulations such as the Donation Land Act of 1850, the Homestead Act in 1862, the Mineral Land Act of 1866, the Timber Culture Act in 1873, the Desert Land Act in 1877, and the Timber and Stone Act of 1878. The Donation Land Act gave 320 acres to any citizen who cultivated it for four consecutive years. Because a spouse could claim an equal amount, a family could acquire 640 acres.

Under the Homestead Act, $10 had to be paid for 160 acres with similar provisions. These acts opened the floodgates to thousands of settlers desirous of reestablishing in the west.

Throughout the 1800s, the wheels of countless wagons wore grooves into the dirt of the 2,000-mile-long Oregon Trail, creating a broad highway with signs pointing out the "Road to Oregon." Called by the Indians the Great Medicine Road of the Whites, the trail remained in use until completion of the railroad late in the century. Those who arrived were farmers, and, unlike the earlier explorers and fur traders, who moved from place to place, they intended to stay. For purposes of homesteading, for ease of travel, or for commercial navigation, emigrants reaching the Northwest clustered along its water sources. Homes and subsequent towns were located on the fertile bottomlands of the rivers, near lakes, or by springs. Agriculture became dominant in Oregon, farm labor and wealth outstripping that of all other trades including timber, fishing, and mining.

Western Oregon

Having overcome the many hardships of the Oregon Trail, which ended with portages around the harrowing Columbia River rapids, the travellers reached their destination in the Willamette Basin. Whereas the surging Columbia River had directed the explorers and fur traders miles inland from the Pacific Ocean to the Snake River Plateau and Rocky Mountains, the calm waters of the Willamette River, meandering in a wide floodplain across a level valley, attracted dwellers to its surrounding fertile soils. More than any other river in Oregon, the Willamette saw the most activity early on as it became the highway southward into the unsettled regions. Of the 13,294 emigrants to Oregon after 1850, over ninety percent lived in the Willamette Valley. Even in 1900, sixty percent of the state's population was clustered there.

At the termination of the long wagon trail in western Oregon, pioneers encountered water in its many phases. Streams and lakes, snow and rainfall seemed to have no limits, and frequently there was too much water everywhere. Inordinate amounts of precipitation came down during the wet season making life miserable and greatly hampering settlement. Such disadvantages had not been mentioned by those eastern promoters, who touted Oregon as the Garden of Eden, and often unsuspecting travellers, arriving in the fall, left for the Sacramento Valley - once the weather permitted.

Rains began in October or November every year and frequently didn't let up until May or June. For anyone living in a wagon or in a hastily constructed rude dwelling, the weather was formidable. Clothing never dried, and leather tents rotted. Food molded and became scarce. Some cabins had neither doors, nor windows, nor fireplaces to keep away the weather. Having to live out in the open, with few comforts, it appeared to emigrants that the hostile conditions rarely diminished.

Elizabeth Greer, who kept a diary of her journey from Indiana, reached Oregon with her family late in October, 1847. Waiting over a week to raft past the cascades of the Columbia River, Greer's party consisted of three families. She wrote on November 14:

"Unloaded the boat, put our wagons together. Drizzly weather.

November 15: Rainy day.

November 16: Rain all day.

November 17: Rainy weather."

On November 18 Greer's husband became sick, but in spite of this she and her children began to walk in the rain and snow. Unable to keep warm or dry, he died on February 1st at Portland.

Unfortunately for Greer and her companions, the winter of 1846 to 1847 turned out to be remarkably severe. During mid-January, temperatures at Oregon City dropped to seven degrees below zero, and heavy snows blanketed the valley. Game animals and livestock along the upper Columbia died. A similar record cold in 1861 was responsible for a number of deaths among the settlers.

Intense rains in the Willamette Valley were seemingly slight when compared to those in the Coast Range. At Fort Umpqua, approximately two miles upriver from the beach, an isolated army post housed 167 men, who were to supervise Indians on the Siletz Reservation. During 1858 Fort Umpqua had the distinction of being the wettest military installation in the United States when over seventy-three inches fell. Stationed there, Lieutenant Lorenzo Lorain wrote to his wife, "Fort Umpqua I believe to be the Maximum point of aqueous condensation." [4]

Flooding was another disagreeable aspect of pioneer life. Farms and villages, placed on the rich soil of river floodplains or at river's edge, were

Flooding at Oregon City in 1890. (Courtesy Oregon State Archives)

particularly susceptible to the vagaries of the weather, especially when rising waters spilled over. Even the seemingly tranquil Willamette River could turn violent. In February, 1843, missionaries Gustavas Hines and William Gray, canoeing down to Champoeg, "rose early in the morning, the rain pouring down with increasing violence ... and borrowing a canoe, we struck out into the dashing current of the Wallamette. Already the banks of the river were full, and the rapidly increasing flood was rolling onward with fearful fury towards the Pacific," carrying trees and filled with debris. By keeping their "cockle-shell craft" in the center of the river, the men reached Rock Island, where they tied up the canoe and portaged down to the falls.[5]

During the "Great Flood" of December, 1861, waters covered a half million acres along the Willamette floodplain. The wharves at Portland were immersed, and numerous towns upriver destroyed. Rains of October and November brought the entire length of the river to the top of its banks, and when warm temperatures in December melted the snow at higher elevations, water rose at the rate of a foot an hour. The muddy current carried forest debris, the wreckage of households, and animals. Occupants of riverside communities fled to high ground, while those stranded were rescued by any ship that could manage the turbulence. On December 7th the river ceased to rise, but it was a week before the water receded. In some communities 200 to 300 structures washed away, many never to be rebuilt.

Floods in 1881 and 1890 destroyed dozens of bridges, ferry landings, and towns in both the Willamette basin and on the coast. A covered bridge across the Willamette at Springfield in Lane County was thought to be invincible. "When a flood comes high enough to take the bridge away, it will either be a second deluge or the end of the world." [6] The structure resisted gale-force winds but succumbed to high water in January, 1890. "The Springfield bridge passed Eugene again." [7] Spring flooding in 1894 inundated much of the lower Columbia region, enabling people in Portland to boat and fish in water that reached the thirty-three-foot-high mark.

On the other hand, water had its positive side. In the western part of the state pioneers found a continuous and serviceable supply of water, essential to domestic life, farming, and early industries. Flowing in seemingly endless quantities down the Columbia and Willamette, along their tributaries, and through countless valleys crisscrossing the territory, water was pure and free to everyone. In no time it was put to use. Farmers tapped groundwater for homes, livestock, and gardens. Ditches were dug to divert streams. Waterfalls were used to power mills, rivers moved logs or carried away sewage, and hindrances in their channels or rapids were altered or removed for ease of transportation.

Those first farmers found that rainfall was sufficient to grow wheat and oats, which became their main crops. Cattle and sheep were fattened on the grains, and the herds enlarged. Between 1850 and 1900 the number of head of domestic cattle increased from 41,729 to 531,980, and sheep from 15,382 to 1,961,355. Thirteen million bushels of cereals expanded to 23,200,000 by the turn of the century. These totals for crops were followed by those for vegetables and fruits, while flowers and nursery products accounted for the lowest production.

Farming began with Director John McLoughlin of Hudson's Bay Company, who cultivated several thousand acres near Ft. Vancouver. Adding to his fur trading and lumber empire, McLoughlin acquired cattle, hogs, and horses, which were imported by ship or herded overland from California. Although he planted orchards and grew a variety of fruits and vegetables, most of his acreage was in wheat.

McLoughlin was also instrumental in bringing agriculture to the fertile plains of the Willamette River just above the falls. Released from Hudson's Bay Company, French-Canadian fur traders, along with their wives and children, took the first tentative steps toward a permanent establishment in Oregon Territory at French Prairie, now Champoeg State Park. In 1829 McLoughlin gave the Canadians permission to farm, even though this area was technically to become American soil. Many were not in favor of moving to the south side of the Columbia River, but, as with others, they found the Willamette Valley highly desirable. After just one year, the village boasted of hogs, horses, and cows, with wheat, barley, and vegetables planted in the cleared fields. "The multitude of hogs, which at first lived on the grasses, camas and oak mast [acorns], were the chief destroyers of roots, which were the chief foods of the natives." [8]

Americans, arriving shortly afterward, were also attracted to land along the verdant Willamette, although it soon became apparent to them that the lower reaches of the river were swampy and less desirable. By-passing this region, they sought the open prairies of the upper stretch. Below the falls, the banks were "exceedingly wild," the shores rocky and lined with a dense cover of trees, reeds, and grasses, the transparent waters home to ducks, geese, cranes, and other water birds. Dark with evergreens, cottonwoods, and alder, the river here stood in contrast to the upper, which " resembles a grand picture. We have not here the heavy forests of the Columbia River region, nor even the frequently recurring fir-groves of the Middle Wallamet [Willamette]. The foothills … are rounded, grassy knolls, over which are scattered groups of firs, pines, or oaks, while the river bottom is bordered with tall cottonwoods … with pines of a lofty height and noble form." [9]

Missionaries and their families, who came to aid the Indians, ended up farming as well. In 1840 Jason Lee, of the Methodist Mission Society, chose a beautiful prairie about ten miles north of Salem to situate his establishment. Hoping to Christianize the natives, he constructed a house and turned to planting crops and raising cattle in order to sustain the group. Proselytizing elsewhere in Oregon, Lee and fellow missionary Gustavas Hines travelled to Fort Umpqua in late August, 1840. Riding in canoes handled by Indians, the two started out in the rapidly flowing Umpqua River, heading west toward the ocean. "We ran a number of narrow shoots where the current is at least twelve knots an hour, and in some instances shot past the rocks which projected into the stream within six inches, with the velocity of an arrow … Fifteen miles below the fort, the river rushes over a ledge of rocks in a number of narrow channels, and falling about twenty-five feet in so many rods," before reaching the Pacific.[10] As a result of this journey, Lee concluded that the country along the Umpqua was so rocky and mountainous that it would sustain no population or agriculture.

Farming required cleared land for the plow and pasturage for cows. Although extensive forests stood in the way, settlers soon realized that the trees themselves were valuable if they could be turned into lumber and sent to outside markets. In 1877 the Corvallis *Gazette* reported, the land around Alsea is "covered with a heavy growth of valuable timber," [but], when cleared of trees, would produce "immense crops of vegetables and grain. There is room in this valley for a large number of farms." [11] As the forests of 300-foot-high Douglas Fir trees fell to the axe, farmers and loggers worked together to free up the soil for production.

Those men and women who travelled to western Oregon found what they were seeking in land, in fertile soils, with a new life, and with profits to

In 1886 the Ludeman & McMillan shingle and lumber mill on Mill Creek above Alsea floated logs to its water-powered operation. (Courtesy Lincoln County Historical Society)

be made. If occasionally the rainfall seemed relentless, temperatures were mild, and surface water plentiful. The same could not be said of the high desert east of the Cascade Mountains where the only readily available water was coveted, confiscated, and frequently the cause of violence.

EASTERN OREGON

Eastern Oregon was the scene of battles and defeats over water. Today the landscape is pockmarked with dry trenches and empty reservoirs, testimonials to human efforts to conquer the desert with water. Since the volcanic rocks are porous and sponge-like, the soil failed to hold water reserves, which drained away into the ground. Water was such a precious commodity that legal wrangling at best and shootings at worst were fought to own it.

Because of the barrier of the 10,000-foot-high Cascade Mountains, Oregon is divided into two regions of widely varying geographies and climates. Extending from south to north across the state, the mountain range combs moisture from incoming Pacific storms before it reaches the eastern region, cutting off most of the precipitation. Elevation of the range some 20 million years ago turned eastern Oregon into a desert province. In the eyes of weary travellers seeking the Northwest, this was the most feared stretch of their journey.

Facing a hot, seemingly endless expanse of sand, sagebrush, and juniper, those pioneers on wagon trains hurried through this hostile environment as quickly as possible in favor of their destination in the Willamette Valley. "Its waterless deserts, severely hot in summer and cold in winter, inspire the overland tourist with dread; and many a trapper and voyageur meets his death from want in crossing them." [12] Moving from spring to spring or from river to river, camping often without water, emigrants endured daytime temperatures, which could easily soar over 100 degrees, as well as nights, which frequently turned chilly. A rare summer shower or even a heavy cloudburst provided temporary relief.

Although it might not have appeared so to anyone crossing the region with all possible haste, the entire province wasn't without water. Streams replenished with snowmelt flowed through deep canyons, cold springs emerged from basalt, and playa lakes filled depressions. Occasional river valleys, with tall waving grasses, tempted some settlers to remain, but they were eventually dissuaded because no winter supplies were at hand. "Nevertheless by the 1st of October the main body of the immigration had arrived at Grand Rond [*sic*] Valley, which appeared so beautiful, set in its environing pine-clad hills, with its rich pasturage and abundant watercourses, that a portion of the immigrants were deterred from settling there only by the impossibility of obtaining supplies for the colony during the coming winter." [13]

Not everyone found the climate unpleasant. In a letter to his church in 1881, Benedictine Father Lambert Conrardy praised the area for its weather in comparison to that of the Willamette Valley. "I don't see a better place to start a monastery than Eastern Oregon … I came in 74. Since I saw here [only] two winters where the snow lay on the ground for over two weeks … and I can affirm I like Eastern Oregon better than the climate of Belgium, France, East Indies, Africa, a thousand times more than that of Willamette Valley." [14]

The lives of those who came to eastern Oregon depended on the proximity to a river, spring, or well. The lack of readily available water, combined with the extremes of climate, made the prospect of ranching or farming difficult, and permanent settlement lagged fifteen to twenty years behind that in the western part of the state. Those whites to remain for any length of time were cattlemen, who drove their herds across the Cascades to the lush bunchgrass of the Deschutes River basin. As early as 1857 stockmen wintered over, living in rude huts or caves. Deciding to bring their families across the mountains to stay permanently, they built cabins near water sources. Not only was water necessary for households and livestock, but hay, which was grown to feed cattle during snowy winters, required irrigation. Cold spring water, that bubbled from the ground, was frequently enclosed by small sheds, where vegetables, milk, and butter could be refrigerated. On the road to Willow Creek in the John Day drainage, the Eakin family characterized the countryside. "What few scattered farmers or ranchmen there is on these small streams have splendid stock. Grass is very plenty and of an excellent quality. There is *no farmers only in these little valleys as yet* [*sic*]." [15]

Unrestrained by fences, herds of cattle multiplied, while ranchers increased the acreage they controlled. During the late 1800s, vast land holdings and numbers of cattle reached well into the thousands. Taking over the best selection of pasturage and sometimes the only water, ranchers lived miles apart. The Teal and Coleman Ranch dominated the John Day River valley and its tributaries. The Hay Creek Ranch of 300,000 acres in the Ochoco Mountains relied on water from Hay Creek, which flows east of Madras, and Peter French's empire Malheur County utilized springs from Steens Mountain. To the south, many of the soldiers, who had mustered out of the army at Fort Klamath, came to operate ranches of 400 acres or more along the rivers.

Subsequent waves of permanent homesteaders, seeking free land under federal regulations, broke up the big spreads. Claims under the Timber and Stone Act of 1878, for example, permitted a settler to buy 160 acres covered with timber or stone but supposedly "unfit for cultivation." [16] Since access to springs or riverbanks was the key to success, farmers also located in the watered areas needed by the stockmen. Taking advantage of these acts as well, cattle barons fought back by having their own men buy "swamps" or useless "stony ground" and living on the land for the legal number of months. Frequently the acres claimed were not actually wetlands. When the General Land Office sent the property title to the "dummy" in residence, it was then appropriated by the rancher to expand his own holdings. Controlling hundreds of thousands of the most choice acres as well as the water supply, big cattlemen thus attempted to "freeze out" homesteaders.

Finally claimants to the smaller land parcels appealed to the governor and courts to retain their property. The case of Peter French, owner of the French-Glenn Livestock Company, took a somewhat different twist when settlers asserted their rights to land abutting Malheur Lake, which French held as part of his ranch. In May, 1897, both parties appeared in court, Alva Springer for the numerous property owners. The issue was a mere 160 acres that had a boundary drawn at the shoreline of the lake. French held that the lake water had diminished over the years and that the area where the settlers "squatted" was originally submerged. Springer, on the other hand, introduced evidence that "the water of the lake had been, from a time prior to 1877, of about the same height as it was at the date of trial." [17] The legal decision hinged on whether the lake had ever changed dimensions.

Malheur Lake lies in a landlocked basin with no drainage to the sea. The many lakes in this depression are supplied by rainfall or streams entering from higher mountains. At the same time, these bodies of water experience unusual amounts of evaporation during dry intervals, causing their shorelines to fluctuate considerably. In wet years Malheur Lake fills to overflow westward into Mud then Harney lakes, whereas during drought it becomes a marsh. Historic records of the level in Malheur Lake are skimpy, but, existing data show that the water body often went to extremes. Following a low period in 1873, the water rose to medium, then to very high over the next ten years, and back to very low from 1887 to 1889.[18] Supposedly basing its conclusion on the lake levels, the court found for the settlers, even on appeal, although the judicial decision was probably incorrect.

Both owners of the French-Glenn corporation were murdered. Hugh James Glenn from San Francisco, a financial partner only, was shot by a bookkeeper, who had been discharged. In that winter following the trial, French was killed by Ed Oliver, a local landowner, who was said to have no connection to the lawsuit. Even in death, French lost in court. In spite of testimony by witnesses that French had been attacked and shot in the back, the jury found Oliver not guilty.

As with ranching, farming without water was impossible, and those newcomers, who were fortunate, gained access to a spring or river. Minnie McCaffery recalled that the cabin where she and her husband lived was two

Her wagon loaded with seven 50-gallon barrels, a young girl on North Agency Plains siphons water for her cows. (Courtesy Jefferson County Historical Society)

miles from the Deschutes River, their only source of water. For a supply, they attached five-gallon coal oil cans by a wooden handle across the back of their horse. "We led the pony and away we went on our four mile trip for water." [19] Another practice was for a waterman to fill barrels at the nearest river and carry them to any village, where each sold for around 25 cents. On the other hand, Howard Maupin used summer runoff from Antelope Creek in Wasco County for his fields and stage stop, while Solomon Tetherow tapped the Deschutes River near his home.

Anyone with a source of water shared with others, who carried home enough to fill their cisterns. When the railroad came to Opal City on Agency Plains, the company drilled a 1,600-foot-deep well and erected a huge storage tank, from which it allowed settlers to draw water. Tapping Opal Springs south of Madras on the Crooked River, ranchers installed a water wheel and pump, thereby raising the water 500 feet to send it into troughs for their cattle. Having water for a farm "meant an endless procession of tired horses and men down the dusty road to the well. It meant waiting their turn at the old hand-pump, and sometimes it meant making the trip at night, after the homesteader and his horses had worked in the field all day." [20]

Percolating springs occur frequently in eastern Oregon, where water moves slowly for long distances through layers of basalt or between lava flows to emerge at surface openings. On the Deschutes plateau some of the springs have a tremendous output of thousands of gallons of cold water per minute, while others closer to the Cascade Range are thermal. Warm Springs in Jefferson County reaches over 100 degrees Fahrenheit, and its lodge and restaurant were a popular stopping off place for travellers from Walla Walla or The Dalles. Californian Aubrey Angelo found in the 1860s: "In the rear of the building, on the opposite side of the stream, which is crossed on a plank, is the great attraction and comfort of man and women, viz: three warm sulphur springs, one of which has been fitted up for bathing purposes … by standing under the fall, and receiving on the back the first deluge, the effect is not only delicious, but magical to the system." [21]

In the particularly arid Harney County, ranchers and farmers didn't hesitate to defend their rights to springs, even with violence. Providing the only source of year-round water for livestock, the springs emerging from Wagontire Mountain were the cause of a celebrated murder when sheep owner Bill Brown shot a local cowhand. The acquisitive Brown and his brothers, controlling an empire of sixty sections or 38,400 acres that took in both sides of the mountain and the Sinks of Lost Creek, had not fenced in the springs but generously shared the water. However, when the disputed waterhole was enclosed by cattlemen, keeping out Brown's sheep, he protested. An argument ensued between Brown and an aggressive Texas cowboy named John Overstreet, during which Brown was told to "take your woolies and get the hell out of the country." Accounts vary, but both men took up arms and while still some distance apart began shooting at each other. After six rounds had been fired on the afternoon of April 1, 1886, Brown eventually killed his opponent. As Brown was on his way to Canyon City, Overstreet's friends attempted to lynch him, but he escaped and was later acquitted at a local hearing. A jury refused to indite Brown on the grounds that he was defending himself and his home place.[22]

The livelihood of stockmen, miners, sheepherders, and farmers not only revolved around water but depended on the weather as well. The lack of rainfall during the summer, too much snow in the wintertime, or flash flooding almost anytime could mean financial disaster or worst. Some winters found only a light dusting, but heavy amounts of snow could obscure the ground for months on end. In the early 1800s, when four feet fell trapping animals in isolated corrals, several thousand sheep died on Willow Creek in Wasco County before horse teams broke trails through the crusted top layer. Alvin Cyrus recounts that in 1890 in Deschutes County, "Winter came early with a deep snow. It stayed on for awhile then when it went away the grass began to green up and the stock began to scatter all over ... Then in February it started to rain and rained for three days and nights. Most of the cattle died during the rain. Then it snowed two feet deep and the temperature went thirty degrees below zero. Most of the sheep died that night, being in such poor condition ... Those that did survive kept on dying." The sheepherders set juniper trees on fire in an attempt to keep the coyotes away from the flock.[23]

In spite of a seeming scarcity of water, pioneers also had to contend with flooding when summer thunderstorms high in the mountains sent torrents of water down steep-sided canyons to the lower flatlands. On June 2, 1884, roaring waters from a cloudburst came over the cliffs near Mitchell in Wheeler County, washing away houses and filling the streets. Sweeping along the bed of Bridge Creek, the torrent spread out into a lake across the lowlands of the Painted Hills. Along the road from The Dalles to Canyon City, the home of the Carroll family was engulfed, drowning one of the married daughters and three of her children. Two children were rescued, one pulled out by the family dog.

Flooding along the Columbia River took place roughly every five to ten years when waters might rise fifty to seventy feet. During the disastrous event of 1894, waters reached close to sixty feet above normal, inundating the communities of The Dalles and Umatilla to depths of two feet. At The Dalles, Edward Crate, an employee of Hudson's Bay Company, "landed his bateaux at a pine tree near where the Methodist Church is now located." [24]

With water in short supply in southern and eastern Oregon, the discovery of gold during the mid-1850s brought farmers and ranchers into conflict with miners over its use. One year after gold was found on the Illinois River in the Klamath Mountains, the town of Jacksonville became most populous in the state. The same invasion occurred in the Blue Mountains some ten years later once gold was struck on Canyon Creek in the John Day watershed of Grant County and on Griffin Gulch in Baker County.

Almost all stories of gold mining praise the size of nuggets uncovered, the fabulous wealth realized, or the rugged adventurism of the men. But few tell how streambeds were laid bare, how tremendous amounts of water were transported through canals to the mines, or how thousands of tons of rock and dirt were torn from hillsides to smother adjacent environments. Rudimentary ditches dug to irrigate fields of grain did not come close to being as elaborate as those constructed by men in search of gold. No obstacle, even the lack of water, stood in the way of the sheer numbers of miners and their fanatic determination to wrest the ore from the ground. Superhuman efforts went into moving water great distances to operations, where one miner boasted, "Money is our only stimulus and the getting of it our only pleasure." [25]

Initially miners panned for placer gold in streambeds, but they soon turned to extracting the lode metal from hillsides with powerful streams of water in what was an extraordinarily destructive process. Water, sent downhill through wooden flumes and shot out of a hose, moved mountains of soil and rock, which choked rivers and gullies with debris. In 1862 a gigantic landslide carried off what hadn't been hydraulically stripped away at the

Rock Creek mines in Baker County. A seventy-five-foot-wide and 200-foot-long mass of water-saturated mud, rubble, and trees broke away from the mountainside, sweeping down to the creek and up the side of the opposite hill. The tremendous noise of the slide could be heard for miles.

In order to deliver water to the gold fields, a system of ditches drained the closest river or stream. Near the John Day River, the Lone Star, Humboldt, and Rawhide were public ditches, from which miners could obtain water for 50 cents per inch each twelve-hour day. Payment was made to those miners who owned the land where the ditches crossed or who had dug the channel. The Rawhide Ditch was named because it was lined with animal hides, since no lumber was available. Most famous were the twenty-three-mile-long Sterling Ditch in Jackson County, as well as the thirty-mile-long Auburn Ditch and the thirty-two-mile-long Sparta Canal, both in Baker County.

Running from the South Fork of Burnt River to the mines in Rye Valley, the Eldorado channel was the largest of all. Begun in 1863, it was not completed until ten years later by Chinese laboring with shovels or picks. Five feet wide at the bottom, seven across at the top, around 134 miles long, and big enough to float logs to the mines, the ditch was filled with water from Burnt River. Ranchers sabotaged the Eldorado, and after the mines played out, they looked for ways to utilize the canal. In 1911 it was taken over by the Eastern Oregon Land Company, a California-based organization that purchased large plots to control water. When local residents realized that the company intended to divert water to its Malheur County land holdings, they went to court. The resulting legal decision put so many conditions on the use of the ditch that it became impractical for the company to go ahead with its plans. Today the abandoned channel is filled only with grass.

Formal companies to control water sometimes resulted when miners organized together. The Auburn Water Company in Baker County, begun in 1862 by businessmen interested in procuring water for "mining, mechanical, and other purposes," drew up a constitution and by-laws.[26] A board of trustees, stockholders, and paid superintendent ran the company, letting contracts for the construction of the Auburn Canal. One year later the company completed the main section to Pine Creek, built a large reservoir above the town, and made side ditches to distribute water to various mines – all for $225,000. After the company was sold to a California mining and water organization in 1875, the ditch was lengthened.

The digging and location of canals for diverting water to the mines sparked numerous disagreements, many of which ended in court. Typically, one person interfered with or contaminated the stream flow at a point above the source of another. In Baker County A.P. Brown brought suit in 1906 against the Gold Coin Mining Company to halt the pollution and diversion of Rith Creek, a tributary of Burnt River. The creek flowed through properties owned by both Brown and the gold company. T.H. White, acting for the company, dammed the creek with rocks, mud, and tree boughs and excavated three terraces on a hillside for the foundation of a quartz mill above Brown's land. The dam was supposed to contain the tailings, but Brown contended that after the ore was pulverized for a just short period, the dam failed to block the debris that was carried down the creek and onto his land. His irrigation ditch was filled, and sediment was deposited over four acres of his alfalfa. Brown also complained that he was forced to drive his cattle elsewhere in search of water. After much testimony on both sides, one person stating that mill tailings "when discharged into the running streams, have no greater tendency to deteriorate the quality of the water than the material washed from the natural banks," the judge felt otherwise and found for Brown.[27]

A number of cases revolved around priority water rights. In the most frequent instances, water, already authorized by an earlier permit, was appropriated by another. E.W. Borman, owner of a placer mine in Quartz Gulch of Baker County, found his water flow dried up after Gertrude Blackmon excavated a ditch above his placer grounds. Once the court determined that Borman held the oldest water right, dating back to the 1880s, it ordered the restoration of his stream.[28]

Approaching the end of the nineteenth century, nearly all the territory of eastern Oregon was claimed. "The land is all settled up with homesteaders around here now. I don't see what those people live on, there is absolutely nothing to stay there for – there is neither wood nor water." [29] The high hopes for growing diversified crops of fruits and vegetables were doomed to disappointment in the face of drought and the climate. Many unsuccessful farmers turned to other means of earning an income or sold to out and moved elsewhere. Those who remained, fenced and divided up the open range, forcing ranchers to depend on federally owned pasturage and water. Not until the development of big irrigation and water diversion projects did the desert come close to fulfilling the anticipations of the first Euro-Americans, who had arrived fifty years earlier.

By 1900, the process of civilizing the Northwest was under way with isolated farms and towns now connected by a network of roads. Surveys by the Corps of Topographical Engineers were instrumental in placement of the rail line across the continent to reach the Pacific Ocean. Mapping by the General Land Office and U.S. Geological Survey was making headway in furthering knowledge of the topography, but there were still many gaps and vast regions merely labelled, "Land gently rolling, soil good," or "Rough mountains unfit for settlement and unsurveyed." Rivers were sometimes charted incorrectly, their headwaters off by miles. Cooperation between the Oregon State Engineer and federal surveyors was instrumental in collecting information. Flow measurements on major rivers had started as had gathering and maintaining weather data, although efforts at record keeping were sporadic.

At that time Oregon had no comprehensive regulations or agencies dealing directly with its waters, but within fifty years the stewardship of this resource was entrusted to the State Land Board, the State Water Board, and the State Sanitary Authority. With frequently overlapping responsibilities and conflicting goals, these bureaus were charged by the legislature with protecting state-owned wetlands and navigable waterways, with overseeing water allocations, and with controlling water pollution and protecting public health. Other departments such as forestry, fish and wildlife, geology, and agriculture were all involved with water to varying degrees. The U.S. Army Corps of Engineers was responsible for projects and maintenance that would enhance navigation along rivers and harbors, while the Bureau of Reclamation developed large-scale dams for agricultural water storage. Yet one other entity took a hand in the regulation of water. Whenever a dispute or question arose over the actions and decisions of any public functionary or body, as well as between private parties, the ultimate recourse was frequently found in the court system.

Once surveys, measurements, and calculations had begun, Oregon's waters were increasingly governed by the passage of laws and by the establishment and expansion of both state and federal bureaucracies. All of these procedures combined to meet the challenge for development presented by the vast resources of the west.

Human settlement inevitably alters the landscape, and those pioneers, who sought land in the west, toiled to tame the Garden of Eden. Their accomplishments were touted as unequalled in the world as the state grew into "The Land that Kept its Promise." [30] Histories of Oregon speak glowingly of development, growth, and manufacturing, but, except in a general way, the ultimate cost to the water resources was never added up. The ensuing years saw water altered for navigation, power, supply, and irrigation, as laws and legal decisions directed its development.

ENDNOTES: OREGON, THE END OF THE GREAT MEDICINE ROAD

[1] Wallis Nash, *The Farm, Ranch and Range in Oregon* (Salem, The Lewis and Clark Centennial Exposition, Commission for the State of Oregon, 1905), [1].

[2] H. O. Lang, ed., *History of the Willamette Valley* (Portland, Geo. Himes Publ., 1885), 520.

[3] Samuel Lancaster, *The Columbia; America's Great Highway* (Portland, Lancaster Publ., 1915), 41-42.

[4] Dow Beckham, "Lonely Outpost: The Army's Fort Umpqua," *Oregon Historical Quarterly*, v.70, 1959, 245.

[5] Gustavas Hines, *Wild Life in Oregon* (New York, Worthington, 1887), 139.

[6] *Oregon State Journal*, September 10, 1881, 5.

[7] *Oregon State Journal*, February 14, 1890, 3.

[8] John Minto, "From Youth to Age as an American," *Oregon Historical Quarterly*, v.91, no.2, 1908, 153.

[9] Frances Fuller Victor, *All Over Oregon and Washington* (San Francisco, J.H. Carmany, 1872).

[10] Hines, 1887, 101.

[11] *Corvallis Gazette*, May 4, 1877.

[12] Hubert H. Bancroft, *History of Oregon* (San Francisco, History Company, 1886), v.1, 3.

[13] Ibid, 401.

[14] Gerard Steckler, "The Founding of Mount Angel Abbey," *Oregon Historical Quarterly*, v.70, 1969, 323-324.

[15] Shirley Ewart, *et al.*, *A Long and Wearisome Journey: The Eakin Family Diaries – 1866* (Bend, Maverick, 1991), 156.

[16] U.S. General Land Office, *Regulations under Timber and Stone Law* (Washing-

ton, D.C., General Printing Office, 1908), 3.

[17] French Live Stock Company, v. Springer, 35 Or. 312, 1899, 315.

[18] Christopher Raven and Robert Elston, eds., *Land and Life at Malheur Lake* (Portland, U.S. Fish and Wildlife Service, 1992), 29.

[19] Minnie McCaffery, "Central Oregon as I First Knew It," *Yesteryear, Deschutes Country*, Deschutes County Historical Society, 1986, v.1, 13.

[20] Many Hands, *Jefferson County Reminiscences* (Portland, Binfords & Mort, 1998), 247.

[21] C. Aubrey Angelo, *Sketches of Travel in Oregon and Idaho* (Fairfield, Washington, Ye Galleon Press, 1988), 64.

[22] Edward Gray, *William "Bill" W. Brown, 1855-1941* (Eugene, Gray Publ., 1993), 34.

[23] Alvin Cyrus, "The Double Winter," *Yesteryear, Deschutes Country,* Deschutes County Historical Society, 1986, v.1, 10.

[24] William H. McNeal, *History of Wasco County, Oregon,* (The Dalles?, 1952?), 178.

[25] Robert Dawson and Gray Brechin, *Farewell, Promised Land* (Berkeley, University of California Press, 1999), 47

[26] Isaac Hiatt, *Thirty-one Years in Baker County* (Baker City, Baker County Historical Society, 1997?), 25.

[27] Brown v. Gold Coin Mining Co., 86, Pac. 277, 1906, 287.

[28] Borman v. Blackmon, 60 Or. 304, 1911, 304.

[29] Helen G. Rees, *Shaniko; from Wool Capital to Ghost Town* (Portland, Binfords & Mort, 1982), 12.

[30] Marjorie H. Hayes, *The Land that Kept Its Promise* (Newport, Lincoln County Historical Society, 1976), title page.

CHAPTER 3

WATER HIGHWAYS FOR NAVIGATION AND COMMERCE

All navigable waters in this state shall be deemed public highways ... and the improvement of such streams, sloughs, and waters shall be deemed and declared a public use and benefit.[1]

Oregon settlers needed water for their farms and homes and to drive their waterwheels, but they also required the advantages that rivers offered for transportation. Streams were lifelines to the outside, and without easy access to water courses towns lagged behind in trade, often to vanish from maps. For a land rich in surface water, navigation along its streams and rivers was an obvious means for pioneers to move people and goods. Travel by boat gave frontier families a way to keep in touch with friends and relatives. Mary Elder, writing from her home in March, 1850, explained, "We have passed through one winter in Oregon. We have a great deal of rain ... and some snow ... We live ... right on the bank of the river. I have never been any place except to Milwaukie. We have no way of going but by the river and mama is so uneasy when we go that way ... I have been there once to meeting, once to singing school, once to a party and once to temperance ... There have been as many as five vessels at Milwaukie at once this winter. I went aboard two of them."[2]

The years from 1850 onward were exciting times of growth, and Oregon anticipated supplying the world with its excesses of wheat, salmon, and lumber. In the absence of roadways or rail lines, river transport was the answer to moving goods. Individual canoes or French-Canadian bateaux, each with six Indian rowers and about five tons of merchandise, plied the Columbia and Willamette rivers, loading and unloading at towns along their banks. The first landing upriver on the Willamette was at St. Johns dock, where the night was spent. The second night was passed at Milwaukie, and on the third day Oregon City was reached.

From the outset, Willamette Falls became the focal point of trade. Oregon City and Canemah were situated on the east side, while Linn City and Multnomah lay on the west. The first to navigate the river to within a few miles of the falls was the Boston-owned *Owyhee* in 1829, which was followed by the Hudson's Bay Company supply steamer *Beaver*. Other craft ventured to several other upriver ports, some reached as far as shoals at the

The steamship *Beaver*, built in England, was one of the first ships to carry on trade along the lower Willamette and Columbia rivers for Hudson's Bay Company.

mouth of the Clackamas River, where their cargo was transferred to flatboats for continuing up to the falls.

Portland soon surpassed Oregon City in growth and commerce. Lying between the Willamette and Columbia rivers, Portland was favored by a deepwater port and by a lack of cascades or falls between itself and the ocean. As more and more vessels anchored at its docks, Portland's population swelled, and it prospered. Surveyed as a town site in 1844, the city was incorporated in 1851. Milwaukie briefly rivaled Portland, but a shallowing in the river there hindered ship passage.

In 1844 an enterprising Englishman, Aaron Cook, felt he could profit by offering a steady service between the Willamette and Columbia rivers, replacing the irregularly timed canoes and rafts. Building the *Callapooiah*, a thirty-five ton scowlike schooner, Cook launched it in August, heading toward Astoria from Oregon City. The trip was accomplished in four days, and thereafter Cook made the run on a regular schedule. He began to lose revenue when numerous other flatboats began to carry cargo to points along the river. Cook's competition came from the *Mogul* and *Ben Franklin*, which followed a regular route twice a week between Oregon City and the Champoeg trading center at present day Champoeg State Park. The eighteen-mile distance took the flatboats from seven to ten hours when powered by Indians. The *Oregon Spectator* of April 30, 1846, advertised that the *Mogul* and *Franklin* were "well caulk'd, gumm'd, and greas'd ... passengers can board with the Captain, by finding their own provisions ... Punctuality to the hour of departure is earnestly requested. As time waits for no man, the boats will do the same."

Paddles and sails were soon replaced by steam power. The first steamboat built in Oregon was the *Columbia*, a clumsy double-ended side-wheeler. Constructed in Astoria of machinery sent from San Francisco, the *Columbia* had her maiden voyage to Oregon City in 1850, taking twenty-six hours for the journey. In that same year a second steamboat, the *Lot Whitcomb*, built at Milwaukie, was launched on a sunny Christmas afternoon to the "Star Spangled Banner" and "Hail, Columbia," played by the military band from Ft. Vancouver. Speeches were given and cannon shot, one exploding and killing the captain of a nearby schooner, marring the event. One hundred and sixty-feet-long, with an eighteen-foot-diameter side wheel, and a six-foot draft, the *Lot Whitcomb* carried goods and passengers from Milwaukie to Astoria twice a week, charging $25 a ton for freight. Competition between the *Columbia* and *Lot Whitcomb* eventually brought prices down to $15 then to $12. When the owner of the *Lot Whitcomb* refused to stop at the Portland docks, favoring instead the commercial development of Milwaukie, the ship proved too expensive to operate and was sold in California.

Towns upriver, such as Albany, Corvallis, Harrisburg, and Eugene, which had easy access to the river, gained commercial advantages. Placed near a large pool created where the Calapooya River enters the Willamette, Albany boasted a gristmill by 1851 that was serviced by steamers the following year. At the confluence of Marys River with the Willamette, Corvallis grew to a population of 1,000 with hotels, a planing mill, a tannery, and enough business to keep its docks busy moving people and goods. At the southern end of the valley, Harrisburg and Eugene depended on steamboats and sidewheelers to export a rapidly expanding agricultural output. During dry intervals, people were unable to travel, and goods couldn't reach tidewater. On January 16, 1869, at Eugene, "A boat was up to this place on Wednesday, and returned on Thursday loaded with hogs." But 14 days later residents reported, "The river has been so low that we have had no boat at this place for several weeks." [3]

By the mid-1800s, steamers began to ply the Willamette and its tributaries in ever-greater numbers. At least fourteen steamboats competed for trade along these ready made highways. Since the falls at Oregon City necessitated that separate boats operate on the upper and lower sections of the river, for navigational purposes, they became the geographic dividing point. Circumventing them by ship was, at best, a challenge and, at worst, impossible before alterations were made to the channel.

Settlers took advantage of river transport by organizing their own shipping businesses, then purchasing and placing their own boats into the waterways. In a short time companies such as the Yamhill Steamboat Company, the Tualatin River Navigation and Manufacturing Company, and the Long Tom Transportation Company were scattered throughout the Willamette Basin.

The Yamhill Steamboat Company hauled passengers and merchandise on regularly scheduled runs between Portland and Dayton, the end point. The all-day trip provided lunch on the boats. The company financed its own steamer *Elk,* but the boiler on the ill-fated ship exploded near the mouth of the river, removing the cabin, the stack, and much of the deck, blowing the captain into the top of a tree on shore. Another of its small boats, the *St. Claire,* deemed unfit for upper river traffic, was ridden over the falls of the Willamette by Captain George Taylor in what must have been a wild trip. Although Taylor took advantage of high flood waters, his was the only steamboat ever to accomplish this feat.

Willamette Falls was the dividing point for steamship transport. One fleet operated above and one below the falls. The Oregon City Transportation Company's steamer *Pomona* at the falls. (The Irwin-Hudson Company, Portland, 1902)

On the Santiam River, little steamers easily chugged upriver but had to back down because turning around was impossible. The Tualatin River Navigation and Manufacturing Company employed the diminutive *Onward* for a trip from Forest Grove and Hillsboro to Lake Oswego, at which point travellers boarded the *Minnehaha* to cross the lake to the Willamette River, then down to Portland, a total of sixty miles. Eventually selling grain locally in Washington County proved cheaper than carrying it on the meandering Tualatin to docks elsewhere.

Despite the fact that the Long Tom River channel presented even more of a challenge to shipping, the Long Tom Transportation Company in Lane County didn't hesitate to operate. A company of grain farmers purchased the *Ann*, which had begun her career inauspiciously on a Saturday night in April, 1869, by quietly sinking near the dock at Harrisburg. The sleeping crew were only aroused when they felt the "Wallamet dew" in their bunks. Most of the cargo was salvaged when the craft was raised, but the following month it was sold by the sheriff for $3,000 because of bad debts. In June the *Ann* was seized by U.S. Marshalls for violations of federal law, after which the boat was purchased by the farmers to begin a successful career on the Long Tom River.[4]

Within a short time, however, these small companies were unable to compete with the powerful Oregon Steam Navigation Company or its challenger, the Peoples Transportation Company. Both gained monopolistic control of shipping throughout the Pacific Northwest. With a fleet of fast powerful steamboats, the Peoples Transportation Company dominated the Willamette above Portland, while the Oregon Steam and Navigation Company held sway on the Columbia. The companies flourished during the Golden Age of river transportation between 1860 and the coming of the railroad in the 1880s. Eleven boats belonging to the Oregon Steam Navigation Company regularly tied up at Celilo. Visiting Californian Aubrey Angelo found, "These boats … are popular with the travelling community."[5]

Steamboat traffic on the Columbia and Snake rivers was stimulated by discovery of gold in central Idaho during the 1860s. Gold not only brought miners, but it also meant money could be made transporting freight and passengers to the Boise area. Ships had no trouble operating on the lower section near Portland, but the cascades and rapids at The Dalles presented special navigational problems that were solved temporarily by having different boats on the separate stretches of the river. The *James Flint*, a side-wheel steamer, was hauled over the cascades to run between that point and The Dalles. While carrying goods and passengers, it struck a rock and sank but was raised and repaired. At the cascades the cargo was transferred to several steamers operating on the lower stretch to Portland. Built above The Dalles, the *Colonel Wright* covered the route between Celilo Falls to Fort Walla Walla, and then up the Snake River, dispersing baggage as well as miners wanting to reach the gold districts. The ship negotiated the Snake to attain the mouth of the Clearwater River before an especially strong eddy forced it to turn back. Even with the passengers themselves assisting the boat's crew, it failed to overcome the rapids.

Of all the boats on the Snake, the *Shoshone* left behind the most colorful legend. To capture inland trade, officials of the Oregon Steam Navigation Company schemed to establish a route from Olds Ferry, at present day Huntington, to Owyhee Ferry near Adrian. The company contracted to have the *Shoshone* built at Ft. Boise with machinery hauled in from Portland. There were great hopes for opening the route. "Steamer on the Upper Snake … The first link in the chain of steam communication, to be made continuous at no distant day between Salt Lake and the Columbia river was welded to-day." [6] When the owners failed to take into account the lack of wood for fueling the boilers in this sagebrush country, the *Shoshone* made a run as far as Owyhee Ferry southwest of old Fort Boise, where it remained tied up for three years. At that point the Oregon Steam Navigation Company realized it was cheaper to haul goods overland from Boise to Olds Ferry than to move them by boat. Then, in a feat to rival that of fur trader Donald Mackenzie, the navigation company sent Sebastian Miller with a crew of three to ride the steamer down through the notorious Box and Hells canyons on the Snake River to the Columbia. Used for a short time on the Willamette, the *Shoshone* struck a rock and sank near Salem. When spring rains sent parts of its frame downriver, they were salvaged and modified by a farmer into a chicken coop. In another attempt at shipping on this desert plateau, the Snake River Transportation Company built the *Norma* near Huntington, but, after a distance of only ten miles, it hit rocks and was taken out of operation.

Navigators along Oregon's coastal shores faced a variety of challenges. Winter storms and fog frequently had the waves breaking against submerged rocks, on stony headlands, or over sandy spits. Even in the face of repeated disasters and costly delays, shippers continued to ply the shoreline seeking out its timber resources, which could be sold for considerable profit in California.

Not only did ships provide the main commercial transportation up and down the coastline, they frequently were the only connection between isolated families or communities on the banks of the inland rivers. Typically villages and farms began with a trading post or cabin and boat landing, where flatboats and steamers picked up passengers or distributed mail and farm produce. Empty milk cans along the Coos River were exchanged for full ones from passing steamers. Twice a day shoppers could travel the few miles around Coos Bay from Empire to Marshfield and back. Anyone lingering in town would be alerted by the boat's whistle – three blasts meant thirty minutes remaining before the boat left, two blasts warned of fifteen minutes, and one blast meant only five minutes.

Along the perilous shoreline, some ports proved to be more dangerous than others. Of all the estuaries, the fluctuating sands across the mouth of the Umpqua River were among the most contentious. Between 1850 and 1855, the sandbar was responsible for six wrecks, which carried cargo that amounted to one-fourth of the total tonnage into the harbor during those years. Well after the lighthouse began operation in 1857, ships still negotiated the shifting bar at their own risk. The U.S. Coastal Survey reported that the steamer *Columbia* was unable to leave the safety of the bay for ten days when, upon examination, "it was found that the channel across the bar had moved about three-quarters of a mile to the northward of its former position." [7] Depending on vague instructions from such publications as the *Pacific Coast Pilot*, captains followed confusing directions to steer for an opening in the breakers, then pass around the southern point at the north end of the waves. In the face of mounting losses, steam tugboats were hired to guide or tow lumber-carrying vessels to safety.

Reliance on navigation became the mode along the state's waterways as rivers came alive with all kinds of vessels. Stacks of wood waited to fuel steamships, whose whistles mingled with shouts from men aboard or on shore. By following tributaries inland, bateaux, canoes, flatboats, sailing vessels, and steamships provided transportation to and from every region where water flowed. River navigation made the settlement and early economic development of the state possible. It was the key to Oregon's early success.

Alterations for Commerce

No matter how seemingly attractive or accommodating Oregon's rivers and coastal estuaries were for transport, entrepreneurs quickly realized that changes were needed. Something had to be done to improve access and to manage the flow of water in order for the state's full economic potential to be realized. The concepts of "improvements" or "management," when applied to nature or the earth, essentially mean how resources can be modified and controlled for profit or to benefit humankind. "A free people should have a free river. Can the chains with which nature has seen fit to bind its waters be broken? Can the lock which controls its usefulness, which only lets it fret and fume away its life between rock-ribbed walls [of The Dalles] be opened? It can, and the people hold the key." Joseph N. Teal, a lawyer and member of the Open River Transportation Company, expressed the "visionary" standpoint, which was popular in 1866.[8]

During the nineteenth century community leaders had no hesitation in proposing sweeping solutions to roadblocks thrown up by nature to retard navigation. Smaller streams needed clear pathways into the larger rivers, and the large rivers themselves needed altering. On Oregon's two main waterways, the Columbia and Willamette, a variety of projects were undertaken to open the way for commercial shipping. "Clearing, snagging, damming, scraping and blasting operations" came into their own, forever altering the flow of Oregon's waters.[9]

Ten years after the changes had begun, the 1874 Oregon Legislature formally authorized channel altering by enacting, *Improvement of Rivers:* "Deepening channel, removing bars, snags, etc. ... It shall be lawful for any person, association, or corporation ... to make such improvement of the same by clearing out or deepening the channel thereof, constructing wing dams, blasting and removing rocks or ledges, removing sand bars, gravel bars, snags, and all obstructions to navigation." [10] This broadly written regulation pretty much opened the way for the elimination of any naturally occurring impediments to river highways.

From modest beginnings before 1900, projects to open the rivers in order to gain access to every location and for everyone became larger and grander as the century progressed. Once the state government and U.S. Army Corps of Engineers took over, ditches became concrete-lined canals, streamside vegetation was stripped away, and mile-after-mile of stone bulwarks controlled meanders or blocked floodplains. Changing economic patterns and the enactment of environmental regulations by the 1960s have failed to halt such "improvements."

LOWER COLUMBIA AND WILLAMETTE RIVERS

Since commercial shipping was concentrated along the stretch from Portland to the Pacific Ocean, this region came in for an inordinate amount of diking, fill, jetty construction, rip-rap, and dredging. Throughout the early years, maintaining the shipping lane for the Portland-to-the-Sea Program proceeded by fits and starts beginning with the sandy obstruction across the mouth of the Columbia River. By the 1840s, the bar at the river's entrance had acquired the reputation as a bugbear, when more ships became casualties crossing through from the Pacific Ocean. Guides, who initially directed vessels into the deepwater channel, were replaced by ship captains, who were more familiar with the tides, winds, and currents. A slow steady approach with constant soundings was the only safe method of by-passing the bar to reach the quieter estuary. Covered only by a few feet of water, and exposed at low tide, the shifting sands produced a narrow passageway that was worrisome and frequently disastrous to ships. In 1841 the *Peacock* of the U.S. Exploring Expedition failed to navigate the sand barricade and wrecked at the entrance. "But there is one difficulty that will ever exist in passing over the bar ... I allude to the cross-tides, which are changing every half hour. These tides are at times so rapid, that it is impossible to steer a ship by her compass or maintain her position." [11]

The "dreadful bar" was feared by missionary Gustavas Hines, reaching the West Coast from Hawaii one year later. Hines sought divine help to achieve a successful crossing, however, his more practical ship captain took on board an experienced man to pilot the boat through. Going aloft, the man directed their passage. Hines still felt, "All was anxiety on ship board" as the pilot called out five and one-half fathoms, "for then we knew that we were passing over the fearful bar, and that very soon we should experience the fate of a number of vessels, which ... rush to inevitable destruction." Contrary to his worries, their boat made it safely into Fort Vancouver. [12]

In 1846 the Oregon Provisional Legislature passed an act to license pilots on the bar and river. Under this regulation S.C. Reeves began work, but he lost his permit two years later after he failed to steer the *Vancouver* successfully through the surf. Although Reeves was later exonerated of deliberately wrecking the *Vancouver* for the sake of plunder, as had been rumored, he moved on to California. No guides were available at all in 1848, and in May of that year a ship with a valuable cargo, destined for the fort at Vancouver, was lost at the entrance. Dry goods and agricultural implements, cast up on the beaches, were quickly salvaged by the natives, who preened in English silks before the disgruntled settlers. Following arrival of the licensed and experienced pilots J.G. Hustler and Cornelius White from New York in 1849, commerce resumed on the Columbia River.

Twenty years later, California traveller Aubrey Angelo wrote happily that steam tugs were not only towing vessels up and down the river but over the bar as well. "At present, the principal dangers in attending the crossing of the bar are removed in consequence of some enterprising men having always cruizing [*sic*] about the dangerous locality a secure steam-tug, called the *Rabboni*, a boat well worthy of the Queen of Sheba's beautiful aphorism."[13]

In actuality, shallows along the entire channel from Portland to Astoria still presented continual hazards to shipping. Portland officials realized that the conditions needed improving, petitioning the federal government for assistance. From 1866 onward, modifications directed by the Army Corps of Engineers took on vast new dimensions. Acting under congressional authorization from the 1878 River and Harbor Act and its subsequent amendments, Corps engineers have planned and managed massive projects that are widespread across Oregon. Once the Port of Portland was created by the state legislature in 1891, the same year that the Corps opened an office there, both agencies worked together to enhance the state's economic future.

Trouble sites first tackled by the engineers were the silts and sands that blocked the Columbia shipping lane at a variety of locations downriver from Portland. Such obstacles develop when the river current slows around a bend or when one stream enters another. In the Columbia, water shoaled dangerously over sandy deposits where the river curved between Rainier and St. Helens and where the flow carried sediments into the Columbia from both the Willamette River and Multnomah Channel. In an effort to increase water depths along this stretch, Walker, Martin, and St. Helens islands were diked. Near St. Helens, at the entrance to the Multnomah Channel, a tug was hired to drag a heavy iron rake across the bar. Next the engineers built dams across three sloughs at the mouth of the Willamette River, filling behind them, thereby funnelling the current into a single pathway north of Percy Island and scouring out the debris. Its third project involved blowing up roughly 100 feet of Warrior Rock, which jutted out at the northern tip of Sauvie Island, and placing a pile dike across from the shore. Such barriers are rows of heavy poles, driven into the riverbottom, which extend from both sides to the center of a river in order to concentrate the current. Some were erected during the late 1880s, but most of the system was put into place from 1917 to 1923 and between 1933 to 1939.

The accumulation of sand in the Willamette channel at Portland was also seen as a hindrance to the city's future as a profitable harbor. In Angelo's view, "A great drawback to the future of Portland is the gradual filling up of the Wahlamette river below Portland. During certain periods of the year the ocean steamers are compelled to discharge their freight at the mouth of the river, thus entailing additional expenses ... a dredging machine has been put into active operation, which will probably lead to favorable results." [14] Portland's small bucket dredges toiled away to remove the obstacles, but the deepening efforts were only temporary, as seasonal freshlets rebuilt the sandbars almost as soon as they were excavated.

In 1868 federal funds were allocated to remove silt near the head of Swan Island. Using Portland's dredge, Corps engineers took several months to scrape away 18,184 cubic yards of debris from around the island, clearing snags and sandy deposits. Pile dikes were installed to close off side channels, and dredging was continuous, but neither proved successful. Eventually, in 1927 the Corps permanently blocked the northeast passage, filling in Guilds Lake (now Northwest Industrial Portland) and Mocks Bottom (the University of Portland and St. Johns Junction), thereby shutting off the small network of tributaries and attaching the island to the riverbank. The southwest channel was deepened at the same time to accommodate new moorings as the shipping business grew considerably.

Some thirty years after Angelo's prediction that ships were successfully negotiating the bar at the mouth of the Columbia River, it still remained troublesome. His optimism was supported by that of the Army Corps, which felt that the entrance had an "undeservedly bad reputation." [15] Its belief was reinforced by subsequent surveys demonstrating that modifications would be too costly and that the tides would sweep away any hindrances. Not until 1882, after businesses in Astoria complained of financial loss, did the Corps Engineers draw up a plan for a four-and-one-half-mile-long jetty to project out from Ft. Stevens.

Engineers calculated that the construction of jetties at the entrance to the Columbia would clear away the hazardous deposits and deepen the water. The reasoning was that the Columbia's waters would scour out their own channel if directed by rock sea walls. Putting their ideas to work, the energetic engineers dumped an enormous rock barricade, but it was immediately destroyed by winter storms. Continually stymied by the force of the waves, they turned to quarrying larger boulders upstream, carrying them by barge to the jetty site. In their enthusiasm, the Corps even drilled holes into the spectacularly scenic columnar basalt of Beacon Rock upriver near

Skamania, Washington, in order to blow it up for use, until a private investor purchased the landmark.

As the jetty building crept along, District Engineer Solomon Roessler concluded, "It is no exaggeration to say that there is no work in progress in the United States to-day at all comparable with this one in the difficulties, uncertainties, and dangers that arise at every stage of its construction."[16] The south jetty was completed in 1903 and the north in 1917. Composed of nine million tons of stone, these seven-mile-long structures are the largest in the world. The massive projections disintegrated continuously up to 1941 when huge concrete blocks were poured at the seaward ends, partially halting the erosion. In unplanned consequences, water over the western and northern portions of the outer bar deepened, no longer protecting the channel, while Clatsop Spit advanced into the entrance, adding to the danger for ships. After 1941, shoaling decreased the depth to forty-four feet, and by 1951 it was reduced to forty-two feet. In an attempt to regain the forty-eight-foot channel, a spur was extended from Cape Disappointment inside the north jetty, and mechanical dredging was begun, but it wasn't until some years later that this depth was achieved after pile dikes were built at Sand Island near the entrance. The continued dredging of four million cubic yards of material annually helps to limit the build-up of the bar, as does rehabilitating the jetties and dikes.

In July 17, 1966, the *Oregonian* newspaper announced "River Channel Program 100 Years Old," and in 2003 the same newspaper informed readers that "Ports Ready Bid for Funds for Dredging."[17] After almost 140 years of efforts at control, the Columbia has not been humbled by technology.

The Army Corps and Port of Portland undertook a major renovation of the entire 115-mile navigation route along the lower Willamette and Columbia from Portland to the Pacific Ocean in 1964, but the project took over ten years to complete. The amended 1962 River and Harbor Act authorized a forty-foot-deep, 600-foot-wide channel and called for a combination of diking, dredging, riprap, and rock removal. According to the plan, twenty-nine new pile dikes extending 19,600 feet were to supplement over 159 dikes totaling 148,400 linear feet, which were already in place. Additionally, four rock "obstructions" were tagged for removal or alterations. Downriver from Portland, underwater blasting broke Warrior Rock, at the end of Sauvie Island, and Stella-Fisher Bar west of Crims Island. Finally, hundreds of deposits in the channel were periodically excavated, totalling 11 million cubic yards of material, by the time the project was completed.

Objections to the environmental impact of this undertaking delayed completion until an assessment could be put together and approved. The blight caused by dumped spoils, the effects of dikes on fish migration routes, the omission and errors in the report, and the loss to wildlife and fisheries were acknowledged by the Corps as the "temporary, local disruption and removal of river bottom habitat and organisms, re-suspension of bottom materials; temporary increases of turbidity; improved hydraulic characteristics; smothering of aquatic and terrestrial habitats and organisms ... [and the] filling of wetlands and submerged lands." Before the final statement was released in 1975, the contract had already been awarded.[18]

Works to improve the length of the Columbia shipping lane were formalized by Oregon law in 1997 under the title *Columbia River Channel Deepening Project*. This agreement between the states of Oregon and Washington and the federal government stressed the economic importance of a deep channel, which would allow northwest businesses to compete in the world market. Lottery money for projects was set aside each fiscal quarter.[19]

At the present time the Port of Portland and the Army Corps are aiming for a forty-three-foot depth between Astoria and Portland. This project has been in the planning stages for ten years, stalled over a final environmental impact statement that filled two thick volumes. Dredging was to have begun during the summer of 2004 and completed in two years. Dissenting environmental groups, biologists, and Clatsop County officials protested a Corps proposal to dump 1.2 million truckloads of spoils, enough to fill 152 Rose Gardens, inside the Columbia River estuary. The Corps claims the fill would result in producing a wetlands, but opponents argue that this action would destroy fishing grounds and cause more harm than benefits to the environment. The Oregon Department of Fish and Wildlife contends, "The Corps' restoration projects are less than ideal." [20] Omitted from the federal budget in 2003, money for dredging has been promised for 2005 through the efforts of Oregon Senator Gordon Smith. "I'll use all the tools available to me. And in this case, I think there is a fortunate eclipse of a good policy and political timing." [21] Perhaps it is Senator Smith who has been eclipsed. One month later Northwest Environmental Advocates filed a lawsuit saying the government was failing to protect salmon and steelhead. In September, 2004,

President George Bush promised an initial $15 million for the beginning stages, and in the following month ecosystem restoration at Lord and Walker islands near Longview, Washington, was finished.

UPPER WILLAMETTE RIVER

Although ship navigation throughout the upper Columbia and Willamette river basins has not been not as financially lucrative as that near Portland, streams provided settlers with their only means of transportation when faced with muddy rutted roads and no rail line. Once the mainstem of the Willamette River became the center of population and industrial growth, alterations to segments of the channel commenced in the 1800s. Upstream from Portland, the first restriction to be tackled was the shoal at the mouth of the Clackamas River where it enters the Willamette. Over $30,000 was spent to clear these rapids, although this deepening effort was not wholly successful.

Without doubt, the falls at Oregon City presented the greatest impediment to shipping on the Willamette. Numerous imaginative and ambitious projects were initiated on both the east and west banks of the river, as well as above and below the falls, to circumvent the rocky ledge These enterprises took their toll on the natural features of the cascading water, which had once inspired wonder to Indians, explorers, and pioneers. In 1853 the Rockville Canal and Transportation Company was incorporated to construct a basin or breakwater and canal around the falls on the west side. Although the finished product was said to increase the comfort of travel greatly by avoiding the portage, the "improved" method sounds similarly difficult. "The hoisting works were made with ropes, wheels, and cages, in which passengers and goods were lifted up," thereby avoiding a wagon trip of a mile or more.[22] The contraption subsequently caught fire and burned, after which similar works were begun on the opposite (east) side of the river. During the same year, but below the falls and on the west side at Linn City, the Willamette Falls Canal, Milling, and Transportation Company constructed a gristmill, a sawmill, a warehouse, wharves, and a breakwater. The basin created by the barrier allowed boats to tie up. Freight was then carried around and above the falls to a similar basin and dock. The project cost the company close to $100,000, and all of the buildings were destroyed in the flood of 1861.

At the same location, the Willamette Falls Canal and Locks Company was promised $150,000 in gold coin by the Oregon Legislature once a by-pass system was satisfactorily completed. This amount proved insufficient, and several years later the legislature pledged an additional $200,000. For the opening on January 1, 1873, the only vessel available to test the locks was the little steamer *Marie Wilkins*. A stiff wind kept the boat from reaching the falls until, at the last moment, it shifted, and the steamer cleared the entrance. The lock system brought freight prices down by fifty percent and made the earlier basins and canals linking the upper and lower sections of the river obsolete. Around 1890, the crest of falls was covered by a five-foot-thickness of concrete, a resurfacing thought to be necessary in order to replace rock that had worn away naturally.

Passing through several owners, the locks were purchased on May 6, 1915, by the federal government. Over the years the U.S. Army Corps of Engineers made several improvements to the original design, which, today, is listed on the National Register of Historic Places. The locks were officially enrolled as part of the natural setting in September, 2002, when a flotilla of boats, representing the Willamette Falls Cultural Heritage Committee, rallied to save them after the Corps engineers announced there was no money forthcoming for maintenance or repairs. The gathering was attended by county commissioners and city councilors, as well as by

The annual fall closing of the locks at Willamette Falls in 2004. Obtaining federal money for the upkeep of the facility is becoming increasingly difficult. (Courtesy Jean Mooney)

federal Congresswoman Darlene Hooley, who vowed to fight for the installation. Citing the current use by privately owned pleasure craft, the handling
of the unwieldy transport of Howard Hughes' airplane, the Spruce Goose,
along with the temporarily assistance provided for passengers when the
Wheatland ferry wasn't operating, the attending politicians encouraged the
cheering crowd. Two years later the locks were kept open on a part-time
basis but still operating under threat of closure.

Other smaller tributaries in the Willamette basin were altered just as drastically to open them for transportation. In 1900, the bed of the Yamhill River
was cleared to McMinnville for $3,000 of state money, while Congress paid
$72,000 for the Army Corps to build a lock around the rapids at Lafayette in
Yamhill County. A single lock handled the eighteen-foot-drop in the Yamhill,
but its opening came in the waning days of river traffic. Rivers as transportation routes ceased for all practical purposes by 1903 to be replaced by the
railroads then by roadways. During the wet season of 1930, "The [Yamhill]
locks are opened once every ten days, just to shake the rust out and to show
that all is well." [23] The locks proved useful once again during the 1940s and
1950s, when log rafts came downriver, before trucks took to hauling the
lumber. Since that time Yamhill County acquired the lock and dam system,
incorporating it into a park as a curiosity viewed by tourists.

The heavily populated Tualatin basin was another region where moving
farm goods depended almost exclusively on waterways. Draining the hills
west of Portland, the winding Tualatin River with its gentle gradient was
frequently blocked by "rock heaps, logs and drift." [24] In 1856 the Tualatin
River Navigation and Manufacturing Company was incorporated by an act
of the territorial government and commissioned to keep the river clear.
Under contract, James Miller hired a crew and started upriver in October,
1858, with the *Hoosier* steamship, cutting through jams as far as Hillsboro.
Miller and his men lasted until December, when they quit.

Approximately fifteen years afterward, a canal between the Tualatin River
and Lake Oswego was excavated by Chinese laborers, permitting ship passage from one water body to the other. The Tualatin River Navigation and
Manufacturing Company was "authorized and empowered to take and divert from the said Tualatin river … so much of the waters … as may be
necessary … for the purposes of constructing, maintaining, and operating a

canal and locks [for] navigation by all vessels."[25] The canal went through an interval of neglect until 1939, when increased widening was proposed to enhance lakeside homes rather than for navigation. After narrow gauge railroad tracks extended into the Tualatin basin, much of the reliance on ships was eliminated. Surrounded by housing, the grass-filled canal, with areas of standing water can still be seen.

Commercial traffic on the main Willamette and its branches decreased considerably after the appearance of the railroad and the building of a highway system. By the 1970s the Army Corps had scaled down its maintenance. Dredging was

Today the Tualatin Canal is filled with grass and weeds, but at one time it was a necessary link between navigation on the Tualatin River, Lake Oswego, and the Willamette River.

confined to the heaviest deposits of sediment, and even in these shoals the amount of debris removed was drastically reduced. Snagging and excavation were no longer performed annually but carried out every several years. Repair on the stretch from Newberg to Corvallis became minimal, and in the fifty miles from the Ross Island Bridge in Portland upriver to Newberg the depth was to provide for small craft and barges only, as the emphasis switched to recreational boating.

UPPER COLUMBIA RIVER

Over the years the upper stretches of the Columbia were modified as well.

In 1867 Corps attention was directed to three small obstructions, Umatilla, Homly, and John Day rapids. Today the rocky shallows of the Umatilla River are covered by the concrete of McNary Dam, those of Homly lie beneath the waters of the McNary pool, and rapids of the John Day are under waters of The Dalles Dam. Before dam construction, however, only the most experienced navigators negotiated these shoals, and in making a case for eliminating them, John Ainsworth, President of the Oregon Steam Navigation Company, emphasized the vital relationship between agriculture and transportation. "Cheap freight is one of the first importance to an agricultural country. To secure this ... it is absolutely necessary that the navigation be so improved." [26]

William Heuer of the Corps set to work surveying, blasting, and moving rock, hampered by conditions that were extremely hazardous. In order to reach rock projections, the men worked from platforms attached to scows, drilling and placing dynamite with six-minute fuses. On the upper Umatilla a disastrous explosion during one such operation killed thirteen men, wounded another, and destroyed the construction already completed. In the John Day River channel, work parties used "a boat to place a torpedo with a 200-pound charge of blasting powder on the rock. 'It proved anything but successful'." Other "engineering challenges" on the Columbia River all the way to the Snake were similarly dealt with.[27]

The two imposing upriver restraints to continuous navigation that remained were Cascade Rapids some forty-five miles downriver from The Dalles and Celilo Falls upriver about fifteen miles. When finished, the locks and canals at both locations enabled ships to make their way from the Pacific Ocean to Lewiston, Idaho. Before construction of the by-passes, small locomotives ran around the cascades as well as on a ten-mile section of track from The Dalles to a point above Celilo Falls. Originally pulled by mules, the portage railroads were converted to steam engines, which transported the increasing amounts of wheat grown east of the Cascade Mountains.

The Great Chute or Cascade Rapids were famous among travellers as a barrier to downriver stretches. Here the current tumbled over rocky landslide rubble in a channel 450 yards wide "through which the whole mass of water pours with great impetuosity." [28] At Celilo Falls, the river looped south then north in an elbow, compressing itself into a narrow passageway 300 feet wide and half a mile long between perpendicular walls of basalt. When the water was high, it coursed through four or five other small side channels. A traditional Indian fishing site, the falls was the first of several rapids where the river was confined in a deep steep-sided gorge past Big Eddy and Three-Mile rapids. "The Falls are formed by ledges of rocks, over which the river pours its mighty volume ... with such a roaring sound as almost to confuse the senses... At one season may here be seen Cascades of twenty feet in height, while at another the current swells itself into little more than a rapid."[29]

The site where The Dalles Dam was constructed on the Columbia River.
(The Irwin-Hudson Company, Portland, 1902)

As early as 1870 Congress authorized the U.S. Army Corps of Engineers to assess the possibility of building both systems of locks and canals. Work on the Cascade canal and locks began eight years later at a cost of $90,000, but it was two decades before the facility was opened after engineers surmounted incredible difficulties, changes in plans, dangerous complications, and loss of workers. On November 5, 1896, hundreds of sightseers aboard steamships toured through the 3,000-foot-long canal with much fanfare as cannon were shot off. Today the locks are submerged by waters of Bonneville Dam.

Resembling the engineering feat at Cascade Locks, Celilo Canal near The Dalles was delayed until 1905. The Corps spent nearly twelve years blasting and drilling away at the rock ledges and steep walls to create a sixty-five-foot-wide, eight-mile-long chute with turnouts for passing vessels. Following its completion, businessmen of the Open River Association, the Open River Transportation Company, and the Portland Chamber of Commerce attained their goal of an unencumbered water route into the interior.

"An open river does not mean merely the completion of the Celilo Canal, blowing out a few rocks at the rapids, scraping the gravel off a few shoals. It means a 40-foot channel across the Columbia river bar, a 30-foot channel from Astoria to Portland … It means canals and locks around Priest Rapids, Rock Island Rapids and Kettle Falls [Idaho]. It means dams with locks on the Snake and other rivers to submerge the rapids, reefs and bars, and it means that … the water that now flows useless by our thirsty plains will be raised to give them life. The verdant field, the orchard and the vineyard will soon replace the cactus thorns and sagebrush. The busy hum of factory wheels will wake the echoes of our rock-ribbed canyons. Cities will grow beside the rapid streams. … May it be as spoken!" These were the words and thoughts of Captain W.P. Gray, President of the Columbia and Snake Rivers Waterways Association in 1908.[30]

A week of celebration in 1915 marked the opening of the Celilo Canal, when the first steamer, *Undine*, made the journey from Portland to Lewiston in a matter of three days. Arriving in Idaho on the morning of May 3, the *Undine* was greeted by a festive crowd of governors, congressmen, citizens, and businessmen. The changes wrought on the rapids and falls along with further engineering exploits by the Army Corps were all covered in 1957 by waters of The Dalles Dam.

PACIFIC COAST

Once they reached a safe harbor, shippers plying the Pacific Coast were able to load lumber and agricultural products directly onto their ocean-going vessels. However to attain the calm inner bays, ships had to deal with fluctuating bars and unpredictable tides. Deposited by both north and south longshore currents, sandy deposits shift with the seasons and block river entrances. In the absence of good maps, lighthouses, or a knowledge of ocean conditions, many ships were lost at river entrances as they maneuvered in and out of the treacherous estuaries. Well before its Portland office opened in 1891, the Army Corps had embarked on a program of eliminating such impediments.

Jetty construction and dredging were the most frequent solutions. Because of a lack of understanding and knowledge of the complexities of marine sedimentation, currents, and ecology, many engineering projects had the exact opposite effect of that desired. So-called solutions were notoriously optimistic. Jetties projecting out into the ocean were supposed to protect ships by deepening the water over the bar, by reducing the sand deposit, and by blocking the force of the waves. Because engineers were unable to predict accurately the vagaries of nature, however, sand piled up against the breakwater, was eroded from the beach, or was carried out to sea. With fluctuating ocean currents or stormy weather, ships wrecked on the jetties themselves as the piers failed to live up to the purpose of their design. Maintenance was never ending, and frequent dredging became an ongoing event.

Modifications to coastal estuaries from the Chetco River north to Tillamook Bay, and especially to the Columbia, brought "navigational improvements … essential to the economic development of the region." [31] All of Oregon's main river entrances – the Columbia, Nehalem, Tillamook, Depoe Bay, Yaquina, Siuslaw, Umpqua, Coos, Coquille, Rogue, and Chetco – have been altered significantly by Army Corps' jetties, levees, riprap, and dredging. Excluding the Columbia, construction, maintenance, and rehabilitation through 1980 for the Coos Bay harbor were the most costly at nearly $30 million. Tillamook Bay followed at $22.5 million, Yaquina Bay was close to $20 million, and on the Umpqua $18 million was spent. Overall, $99 million was put into construction and $90 million into upkeep. Maintenance and rehabilitation have been necessary every ten years in the busier ports and every twenty years in the less used ones.

Along both the east and west coast of the United States, approximately 62 million tons of debris, most of which came from Army Corps' dredging operations, was deposited in the oceans before the 1960s. Since then, such activity has been curtailed somewhat by environmental restrictions.

On the Oregon coast, the efforts of Army engineers were hampered by winter storms and shifting sands, as well as compounded by technical difficulties. The remoteness of the locations meant supplies such as picks, chains, crowbars, and especially lumber had to be shipped down from Portland or up from San Francisco. In trying to make the Umpqua River navigable for 120 miles inland from Scottsburg to Roseburg, the Corps spent over $18,000

carrying away nearly 2,000 cubic yards of rock. After their work was finished in 1871, the supervising engineers concluded that the swift current
would hinder shipping, an opinion shared by the company, which had requested the job. To the disgust of Major Robert of the Corps, the steamboat company refused to use the modified channel. "The channel is made,
but it will not pay anyone to navigate the river."[32] A jetty on the north side
of the entrance to the Umpqua harbor was authorized in 1922, and a south
one in 1933 was extended five years later. This construction was accompanied by dredging. Meanwhile, the jetties were rehabilitated in 1942 and 1963,
a third projection was placed parallel to the entrance in 1951, while a new
sixteen-foot-wide, ten-foot-deep, 4,300-foot-long boat channel was carved
out in 1984.

One of the "less expensive" harbors on the Coquille River underwent
similar modifications. Extolling the commercial advantages to be obtained
and resources utilized, residents of Bandon passed around a petition at the
1876 Oregon convention seeking money from Congress to eliminate river
snags. John Wilson, from the Portland office of the Army Corps urged,
"The timber, minerals, and agricultural abundance …justified improvement
of the Coquille entrance."[33] Work, begun in 1880, involved placing a breakwater on the south side of the harbor by blasting boulders from Tupper
Rock, a monolith, now demolished, which once graced the mouth of the
river. Ten years later a north jetty was authorized, the south one extended,
and both have been rehabilitated. In practice, however, the narrow channel
and bar still proved hazardous to boats, and in November, 1953, the freighter
Oliver Olson, entering the harbor for a cargo of lumber, was thrown into the
pier by strong winds and currents. The crew was rescued, but the ship was a
total loss and could only be salvaged.

A protective 308-foot-long breakwater was erected in 1985 for a small
commercial boat basin within the Bandon harbor. Requested by the Port of
Bandon, the purpose was additional commercial moorage. Dredging at the
entrance and access channels accompanied construction by the Army Corps.
The physical impacts included submergence of two acres of wetlands, elimination of the clams, snails, and other invertebrate population as well as the
fish, which were identified as "common and some were extremely abundant." Following destruction of the nesting and feeding area for many birds,

Dramatic changes in sand deposition near the entrance of Winchester Bay on the Umpqua River can be seen after the one small jetty was replaced by two, then both extended some distance into the ocean. (Oregon Department of Transportation)

the plants would be reestablished "over a period of time thus restoring suitable avian habitat." [34] The philosophy seems to have been that, although the birds left, the vegetation was restored.

The qualities of the estuary and early timber and fish reserves made Coos Bay into the busiest harbors between Portland and San Francisco, the second largest in Oregon, and one of the most extensively modified. "Since 1951, the Portland District of the Army Corps of Engineers has been engaged in a maintenance dredging program at Coos Bay designed to assure depths suitable for ocean-going vessels carrying primarily timber and petroleum products." [35]

Settlement around Coos Bay began in 1853 with the community of Marshfield, which consisted of a log cabin, a store, and a dock. A sawmill and shipyard were added ten years later, after which its name was change to Coos Bay. From the moment pioneers cast their eyes upon the natural riches of the area, they viewed the 200-foot-wide entrance, with a mere ten feet of water atop the sandbar, as the only hindrance to navigation and subsequent development. At the opening to the harbor, a single reef of partially submerged rock was one-fourth-mile-long and fifteen-feet-wide.

Local residents and governments were confident that dredging was the answer, agreeing with an editorial in the *Coos Bay Sun* in November, 1891, that such action was badly needed, "the hanging up of a steamer [on the bar] once a week on an average reminding us of the fact." At low tide, the bar was not deep enough to accommodate the bigger ships necessary for the flourishing lumber mills.

Wrecking on the Coos Bay bar was something of an annual event, and often times several freighters were lost during the same season, taking tolls on life and merchandise. Confidently advertising a weekly trip between Coos Bay and San Francisco in 1906, the *S.S. Czarina* wrecked less than four years later. Loaded with coal and lumber, the *Czarina* was destroyed by the high surf in the channel on January 12, 1910. After its boilers had been extinguished by waves washing over the ship, it was carried northward along the shoreline until grounded. The twenty-five people aboard clung to the rigging in the hope of rescue, but by the following day only two remained. They also fell into the sea, and just one of the men reached the beach alive.

Although the ship *Oregon* had been assigned to clear the bay earlier in the century, a formal sediment removal program actually began in 1914, when the dredge *Colonel P.S. Michie* arrived. Working until 1921 the *Michie* removed around six million cubic yards of debris from four main shoals, placing the spoils as fill on wetlands or dumping it randomly out in the ocean. Deepening also took place along the mainstem of the Coos River to its confluence with the Millicoma and South Fork.

Congressman Binger Hermann, "to realize his father's dream of commercial development in the Coos Bay region," garnered $725,000 in federal money for jetty construction under direction of the Army Corps.[36] In the late 1880s a jetty was extended southwest from Fossil Point, but this structure was later abandoned in favor of two new ones, projecting into the ocean from North Spit and Coos Head. Virtually destroyed by winter storms in the 1890s, the north jetty had to be restored and reinforced with an astonishing 200,000 tons of stone, before the second parallel south jetty was completed by 1929 to a length of 3,900 feet. Both projections were reconstructed in 1940 and rehabilitated in 1942, 1962, 1963, and 1989, with major repairs in 1970.

Today Corps programs at Coos Bay continue. In 1985 their engineers created a turning basin at Charleston at the request of the Port of Coos Bay, and at roughly ten-year intervals it continues to remove over two million cubic yards of sand and rock to deepen the Coos-Millicoma channel. Much of the material is deposited behind dikes.

The north coast has accounted for so many shipwrecks that its geographic features have received names such as Terrible Tillamook, the isolated rock island, or Graveyard of the Pacific, the entrance to the Columbia River. Known for its heavy surf, the entrance to Tillamook Bay is equally dangerous and the scene of boating accidents that took place almost annually. Costly jetties, completed by the Army Corps in 1917, failed to halt ship casualties, when the *Phoenix* capsized in rough seas four years later while attempting to enter the bay. Lifesaving crews were alongside in only twenty minutes, and, hearing a noise inside the ship and thinking it was a signal, they chopped a hole in the bottom. The sound proved to be clanking gear, moving as the ship rolled, and none of the four aboard were found alive. Major jetty restoration and extension have been performed roughly every ten to fifteen years. However, on June 15, 2003, the Tillamook harbor claimed the lives of nine people when their boat was hit broadside by a wave and capsized in the choppy water.

What have been the consequences of jetty placement on the Oregon coast? One of the negative physical results is that the northward and southward drift of sand along the shore has been altered significantly. "In almost all cases the jetty acts like a dam …[sand] accretes on the updrift side while erosion occurs on the downdrift side." [37] Sand, carried from one region of the coast, undermines housing and property in that area, while the deposition elsewhere creates "new" land as the beach migrates outward. Planners and builders move in with condos and restaurants that are, themselves, particularly vulnerable to winter storms.

A 5,400-foot-long north jetty, constructed from 1914 to 1917 at the entrance to Tillamook Bay, provides a classic case. The jetty eroded sand from Bayocean Spit, depositing it in a wide shoal at the mouth of the bay. With rehabilitation and extension of the jetty, the ocean side of the spit began to erode rapidly during the 1930s and 1940s, sending the touted resort developed there into the ocean. A breach in the spit, following the storm of 1952, was diked by the Army Corps, thereby reconnecting the sandy island to the mainland. To the south at Coos Bay, the original configuration was altered when sand piled against the jetty to create Bastendorff Beach; while in 1980 the lengthening of a third jetty in Umpqua Bay, parallel to the entrance of the river, unexpectedly caused waves to reach further up the estuary, damaging facilities lining the shore. To remedy this, engineers armored the shore with riprap in 1995.

Meanwhile, the Corps still strives to improve commercial shipping, attempting to solve unexpected difficulties that might arise. One of its projected solutions to the unforeseen sand build-up and alterations to ocean currents is the placement of small spur jetties projecting at an angle from the main structures. Focusing on the cost and navigation benefits of spur jetties on the Siuslaw River in Lane County, engineers concluded that, "Overall, the 1985 jetty improvements are a success." Navigability improved, the extension was less costly, and dredging requirements were reduced. Jetty spurs redirected sediments further offshore or back into the longshore current. "Long-term effects to the shoreline appear to be benign." [38] Only a lack of data – meaning an understanding of ocean sedimentation patterns - prevented confirmation of future outcomes or changes. Oceanographer Paul Komar's perception is different. "We once believed that jetties could be safely constructed on coasts that have no net longshore sand movements. The erosion of Bayocean Spit demonstrated otherwise." [39]

Alterations to river and stream channels for navigation commenced as soon as pioneers began to utilize Oregon's watercourses. From modest beginnings with channel clearing and deepening, improvements were enlarged and formalized under government agencies and regulations. By the beginning of the nineteenth century, Oregon was set to expand its markets and economy. "While Oregon stands first in her forest possessions, is rich in her mines of coal and precious metals, with great open waterways with fish roads from the ocean and inland waters teeming with millions and her valleys and hillsides heavily laden with all of the products that the soil of a temperate and semi-tropic zone is capable of producing," only the clearing away of obstacles to shipping transport stood in the way of a successful "open" river system, on which to move the merchandise.[40]

Reshaping the land year-after-year in search of economic gain, advocates of changes demonstrated little awareness of the notion that the setting itself might be of aesthetic, cultural, or financial benefit and that at some future period navigation alone might no longer be of prime importance. Fishing, logging, and farming remain viable, but "Today the most important 'commodity' for the Northwest coast economy is the vacation visitor." [41]

ENDNOTES: WATER HIGHWAYS FOR NAVIGATION AND COMMERCE

[1] *Oregon Compiled Laws*, 1940, Chapter 455, Section 113-1405.

[2] Howard McKinley Corning, *Willamette Landings,* (Portland, Oregon Historical Society, 3rd edition, 2004), 26–27.

[3] *Oregon State Journal*, January 16, 1869.

[4] *Daily Oregonian*, April 21, 1869.

[5] C. Aubrey Angelo, *Sketches of Travel in Oregon and Idaho* (Fairfield, Washington, Ye Galleon Press, 1988), 36.

[6] *Walla Walla Statesman* May 25, 1866.

[7] James A. Gibbs, *Sentinels of the North Pacific* (Portland, Binfords & Mort, 1955), 73.

[8] Marshall N. Dana, "The Celilo Canal – Its Origin – Its building and Meaning," *Oregon Historical Quarterly*, 1915, v.16, no.2, 113.

[9] William F. Willingham, *Army Engineers and the Development of Oregon* (Washington, D.C., General Printing Office, 1983), 55.

[10] *Oregon General and Special Laws*, 1874, 86.

[11] Charles Wilkes, *Narrative of the United States Exploring Expedition* (London, Ingram, Cooke, & Co, 1852), v.2, 191.

[12] Gustavas Hines, *Wild Life in Oregon* (New York, Worthington, 1887), 86.

[13] Angelo, 1988, 11.

[14] Ibid., 17.

[15] Willingham, 1983, 40.

[16] Ibid., 64.

[17] *Oregonian*, March 4, 2003, C1.

[18] U.S. Army Corps of Engineers, *Columbia and Lower Willamette River Environmental Statement* (Portland, 1975), i.

[19] *Oregon Revised Statutes*, 777.277, et seq., 2001.

[20] *Oregonian*, April 26, 2003, D3.

[21] *Oregonian*, February 3, 2004, 1A.

[22] *Statesman*, February 26, 1853.

[23] Ruth Rydell, "Tributaries of the Willamette: Yamhill, Santiam, Calapooya," *Oregon Historical Quarterly*, 1943, v.44, 151.

[24] James D. Miller, "Early Oregon Scenes," *Oregon Historical Quarterly*, 1930, v. 31, 175.

[25] *Acts and Resolutions of the Legislative Assembly ... Oregon*, 1870, 172.

[26] U.S. Army Corps of Engineers, *Annual Report of the Chief of Engineers* (Washington, D.C., 1867), 511.

[27] U.S. Army Corps of Engineers, *Annual Report of the Chief of Engineers* (Washington, D.C., 1868), 880.

[28] J. Quinn Thornton, *Oregon and California in 1848* (New York, Arno, 1973), v.1, 277.

[29] Ibid., 274.

[30] Dana, 1915,122.

[31] Willingham, 1983, 148.

[32] U.S. Army Corps of Engineers, *Annual Report of the Chief of Engineers* (Washington, D.C., 1872), 990.

[33] U.S. Army Corps of Engineers, *Annual Report of the Chief of Engineers* (Washington, D.C., 1879), 1807.

[34] U.S. Army Corps of Engineers, Portland District, *Breakwater and Entrance Channel for the Proposed Bandon Small Boat Basin, Coquille River, Oregon* (Portland, 1980), 4.

[35] U.S. Army Corps of Engineers, Portland District, *Draft Environmental Impact Statement, Operation and Maintenance Dredging Coos Bay and Coos and Millicoma Rivers Navigation Project, Oregon* (Portland, 1976), x.

[36] Nathan Douthit, *The Coos Bay Region, 1890-1944; Life on a Coastal Frontier* (Coos Bay, River West Books, 1982), 22.

[37] Paul Komar, *The Pacific Northwest Coast* (Durham, Duke University Press, 2000), 86.

[38] Cheryl E. Pollock, *et al.*, *Effectiveness of Spur Jetties at Siuslaw River, Oregon.* (Portland, Prepared for U.S. Army Corps of Engineers, 1995), 97- 98.

[39] Komar, 2000, 92.

[40] *Oregon Blue Book,* (Salem, 1911), 9.

[41] Paul Komar, "Ocean Processes and Hazards along the Oregon Coast. *Oregon Geology*, 1992, v.54, no.1, 3.

CHAPTER 4
WATER FOR POWER

As nature never could have formed such an abundant water privileges as are afforded by the Falls of the Willamette, without some purpose, it is but just to conclude that man must improve them.[1]

Bringing with them their eastern skills and knowledge, pioneer businessmen reaching the Northwest were carried on a wave of industrial enthusiasm. Once they applied their talents to Oregon's abundance of resources, these adroit managers turned sheep's wool into cloth, trees to lumber, wheat to flour, and animal hides into leather, but water was the crucial element for them to make a profit on the bounty. Before the development of turbines, steam engines, and electricity, the earliest commercial applications of water for power in Oregon were to drive mill wheels. After the erection of the first water-powered mills on both sides of Willamette Falls, hundreds similarly materialized on virtually every stream and river throughout the state. In an amazingly short time every small community had its water wheel on a Mill Creek or a Mill Street. Mills for grain, lumber, paper, and wool became Oregon's initial streamside industries, churning out commodities that were sent to wharves and placed on waiting ships for overseas markets.

Establishing their businesses along waterways, entrepreneurs set to work exploring the possibilities of harnessing Oregon's swift streams, and the cascades tumbling over the basalt at Willamette Falls were immediately perceived as an obvious source of unlimited power. One of the first to view the location with an eye toward potential economic benefit was J. Quinn Thornton, future Chief Justice of the Provisional Government for Oregon. Although he found Willamette Falls lovely, at the same time he expounded on its future as a resource. "In the heart of the chasm is a varied and beautiful assemblage of a thousand forms of running water." As the water gathers strength and velocity, it falls, "with a single and hurrying leap, over a precipice into the foaming and boiling pool twenty-five feet below, where the curves and cavities … cause the clear waters to assume a thousand varied forms; and when the sun shines, a beautiful rainbow, that changes its position every moment, is formed in the cloud of ascending spray. Although this tremendous cataract now forms an impassable barrier to vessels, yet nature has left two natural locks, which need very little more than the gates to admit of steamboats … These falls afford, also, an almost inexhaustible water power." [2]

The utilization of water for power at Willamette Falls triggered one of the earliest conflicts in Oregon over stream ownership and rights to the flow between Director John McLoughlin of Hudson's Bay Company and Methodist missionaries at Salem. Water-powered wheels were needed to develop industry, and in 1829 McLoughlin was told to establish a station on the eastern shore of the Willamette River at the falls. He erected three log houses, planted a field of potatoes, and "had the same foresight and had blasted out a millrace" by removing enough rock from the fringe of the falls to create a trench for a wheel. [3] McLoughlin laid a private claim to a signifi-cant amount of property from the "upper end of the falls across to the Clackamas River, and down where the Clackamas falls into the Wallamette, including the whole point of land, and the small island [now Abernethy Island] in the falls on which portage was made." [4] Angry at the infringement into their traditional salmon-gathering territory, Indians burned the cabins. Rebuilt by McLoughlin in 1842, a sawmill on the riverbank was soon up and running, the first to harness the power of the falls.

Methodist missionaries near Salem took issue with Hudson's Bay's claim. Seeing the advantages of being situated at the falls themselves, they orga-nized the Oregon Milling Company on the island being claimed by McLoughlin. A sawmill was to be followed by one for flour, and a wooden footbridge was to connect the island to the mainland. As the basis for their ownership, the missionaries pointed out that a small stream separated the island from the riverbank, thereby creating two separate parcels of prop-erty. McLoughlin countered that the stream was "not more than forty feet wide in summer," meaning it was too small to be used as a dividing line to cut his property in two.[5] To forestall the missionaries, who were now asserting ownership to part of his land along the bank as well, McLoughlin had it surveyed and lots laid out, which he sold or gave away to newly arriving settlers. Disagreements over ownership between McLoughlin and his adversaries dragged on for years, but because of legal as well as political maneuverings, McLoughlin eventually lost most of his holdings during his lifetime, even though after his death they were restored to his heirs.

Water ownership at the falls became increasingly complex as industries developed and rights were passed from hand to hand when properties were sold. In 1863 McLoughlin's daughter Eloise and her husband Daniel Harvey deeded land on the east shore to George LeRoque, with perpetual water rights "to drive six run of stones and the necessary machinery connected therein." With this land and available water, LeRoque constructed the Imperial Mill for grain. One year later the Harveys sold property nearby to the Oregon City Manufacturing Company, a woolen mill, along with enough rights to furnish power to run the machinery equal to "the maximum to seven hundred inches of water." In 1864 John Moore, George Marshall, Samuel Stevens, and Joseph Sweitzer gained the right to "three hundred inches of water under an average head of eight feet," and five years later businessman Ben Holliday acquired the "right to create at all time, forever, fifty horsepower with a twelve foot heat." When Hawley Pulp and Paper Company bought the old Imperial Mill property just after the turn of the century, it acquired the attached rights. The U.S. Government gained water rights with the canal and locks system, as did the state of Oregon for the fish ladder. The Willamette Electric Company, reorganized as Portland General Electric, owns the remaining rights.[6]

Settlers took advantage of natural falls or rapids where the flow dropped enough to turn wheels, but canals, flumes, or dams could be arranged to direct the current and increase the force. Brownsville in Linn County was typical of communities maximizing water resources. Here companies harnessed the Calapooia River to furnish power for a saw, flour, and woolen mills. "A dam has been built which turns almost the entire river into a race conducting the water to the mills in an inexhaustible supply."[7] Canals routinely diverted water from the Yamhill, while ditches, some twelve-miles-long, supplied Albany, Lebanon, Jefferson, and Stayton from the Santiam River. Union Mills in Clackamas County, established by Gabriel Trullinger, similarly combined a grist, a woolen, and a sawmill on the banks of Milk

Creek. Damming the creek, digging a canal, and installing a headgate, Trullinger was able to use water power for all three until he purchased a steam boiler in 1886.

A flouring mill at Salem utilized water to power a wheel for grinding, water for cleaning, and for water transport to markets (1860s). (Courtesy Salem Public Library)

WATER WHEEL POWER

Water power was essential for processing Oregon's agricultural output, as farming became the backbone of the state's economy. John McLoughlin correctly saw that the Willamette Valley would become great wheat-raising country, and, in just a short time after the first farmers plowed and harvested their fields, the basin became famous for the quality of its produce. An 1843 letter to the *Iowa Gazette* from M. M. McCarver, living on the Tualatin Plains, glowingly stated, "The soil of this valley and in many other portions of the territory is equal to that of Iowa ... and its productions in many articles are far superior, particularly in regard to wheat, potatoes, beets, and turnips. The grain of wheat here is more than one-third larger than any I have seen in the States."[8] By the middle 1800s, access to a gristmill was essential to a community's stability. Hudson's Bay Company operated one at Fort Vancouver and at Willamette Falls. Methodist missionaries ran a one at Salem and at the falls as well. Others were scattered throughout the valley at French Prairie, Rickreall, Milwaukie, Brownsville, and Eugene.

In Eugene, a cut-off meander of the Willamette River, modified in 1850 by Hilyard Shaw, became the source of water power. Prior to alteration, the race was marshy during rainy periods, when water would back up into the meander, forming ponds. Shaw recognized that by connecting the flowing Willamette to the dry slough with a ditch the meander could be put to use. Scraping out a deep channel about five blocks long, Shaw sent enough water through the race to power both a sawmill and gristmill. His property deeds allowed him "the right to dig the present raceway as deep and wide as may be necessary and bank the dirt and stone on either side ... also the right to take water out of the dam for other mill purposes by increasing the flow to the extent of the amount so taken out."[9]

Well before Shaw's mills fell into disuse, the race developed as the center of Eugene businesses. During the late 1800s a small privately built steamboat carried people through town on the waterway, but by 1949 the "millrace [was] merely an ugly old ditch." Today students at the nearby University of Oregon, along with city residents, canoe on the water recreationally.[10]

Coos County was the site of the first gristmill on the coast, the engine, boilers, and burrs brought all the way from Baltimore. Across the Cascades, Prineville had the only flour mill before Baker City and Burns each acquired one with outputs around fifty barrels a day. These, along with a small mill at the mouth of Canyon Creek powered by water from the John Day River, sold flour to miners for a good profit. At The Dalles, Robert Pentland's flour mill was converted to processing wool, then resold and retrofitted for grinding wheat – all by 1867. Rye, wheat, and barley were grown successfully in the Klamath region by the pioneer Applegate family, but the planting of these crops was not taken seriously until the late 1800s. Even then, Thomas Martin, who set up a flour mill, had to pass around free seed in order to interest the farmers.

Flour mills were easily combined with or redesigned as sawmills, providing a steady supply of wood, and by the mid 1800s lumber manufacturing went hand-in-hand with the grinding of wheat in the "flouring, chopping and lumbering business."[11] In no time, "The Pacific Northwest took on the aura of an investor's frontier as capitalists from far points of the continent sought to tap the region's abundant resources."[12] Trees immediately bordering rivers were the first to be cut, and whenever possible they were toppled directly into the water. As the clearing operation moved uphill, the logs were rolled or dragged down to streamside.

Hudson's Bay Company began producing lumber in 1827, and ten years later it was exporting 3,000 board feet daily. Western Oregon became sawmill country as demands for lumber skyrocketed with the discovery of gold in California and extension of the railroad across the continent. For a time railroad ties accounted for half of Oregon's output. Before the turn of the century, when large commercial lumber enterprises came on the scene, small sawmills operated independently, and in 1870 there were 173 throughout the state.

With its easy accessibility to the shipping facilities at Portland, the Willamette Basin was particularly attractive to loggers, and in a short time sawmills materialized beside every tributary. When the current was low, splash dams, water-filled flumes, troughs, or canals were constructed to keep the mill operating. Water, ponded up behind a temporary dam, was released during a freshlet, when the obstruction was pulled open, allowing a surge to carry its load to the mill. Most companies followed the same policy as that of Jones Lumber in the Tualatin Valley, which installed a small wheel below a natural thirty-two-foot waterfall on Mill Creek, operating for nearly fifty years until "the timber supply was exhausted."[13]

The coast was equally accommodating to commercial navigation, enticing lumber barons to its timber riches. By the early 1900s several lumber companies added fleets of ships to their inventory, bringing fabulous sums of money to their owners. In Coos and Curry counties the first building materials were shipped up from San Francisco shortly before a mill opened at Port Orford in 1854. Turning out 5,000 board-feet a day, the company sent local cedar back down the coast. Two other lumber operations were established close by, while in Coos County an undershot waterwheel provided power to mill timber at the mouth of the Coquille River. On the north coast in Clatsop County, the first venture on Mill Creek at Cathlamet Head in 1844 could run night and day, turning out 10,000 board-feet in twenty-four hours. In coastal estuaries, if a slough were inaccessible, a channel could be blasted through to open up the waterway. An energetic mill owner in Clatsop County dug a three-mile-long, twenty-foot-wide, ten-foot-deep canal from Seaside to Warrenton for floating logs to tidewater.

Even eastern Oregon, with its seeming dearth of flowing water, was not immune from the logging enterprise. By 1862 a mill on Big Pine Creek in the John Day Valley was furnishing just over 1,000 board feet per day. At Mill Creek along the Crooked River, Ike Schwartz cut timber for houses and barns, as did Albert Robie, whose portable mill was brought from Boise, Idaho. On the other hand, the Mailing Mill on upper Willow Creek east of Madras was transformed from modest beginnings to a commercial operation when the owners acquired extensive stands of pine on the western slopes of the Ochoco Mountains. Boards from this mill went into many cabins around the area as well as for construction of the first bridge over the Crooked River. In Baker County, a water-powered mill was set up at Auburn, and in 1891 the Oregon Lumber Company opened near Baker City producing boxes and molding, while shipping the lumber to Ogden, Utah.

Mill Creek, entering the Columbia River at The Dalles, was the site of several sawmills, the first run by the military to provide material for constructing Fort Dalles. About sixteen miles up the creek, The Dalles Lumber and Manufacturing Company was owned by the brothers Sam and Thomas Johns, who erected a flume to carry the logs. From there, the processed lumber was floated to The Dalles. Just after the turn of the century, the company was forced to shut when the U.S. government purchased the area that was to become the Mt. Hood National Forest, prohibiting further timber harvesting.

As elsewhere in Oregon before the coming of the railroad by the 1900s, almost all of the sawmills in the Klamath region were located near a water body. Lumbering began when the federal government set up two mills on the Klamath Agency, one for the Indians and another to assist in the construction of a military fort. Powered by water, the circular blade here could cut "10 planks in four minutes" from an eighteen-foot-long, ten-inch-diameter log, having an output of approximately 3,000 board feet per day.[14] Of the private mills, the most successful was owned by William Moore on the west side of Link River near Upper Klamath Lake. Moore's canal, carrying water from the lake, was ideally situated for floating logs and for powering his saw. Thomas Martin also utilized water from Moore's ditch for his gristmill.

The manufacture of paper from wood pulp evolved automatically in a region so rich in timber, however, the first producers in 1866 used cotton rags or straw before adapting to wood fibre. The early facilities were located at Willamette Falls, although the Lebanon Paper Mill took its power from the South Santiam River, and another one located at Bridal Veil Falls was thought to have distinct advantages because of easy access to the Columbia River. Begun in what had been a flour mill, the Lebanon company made butcher and grocer paper from wheat straw, while at Bridal Veil Falls the poorly-equipped operation utilized straw and rags for just a short time in 1891 before shutting down.

The falls of the Willamette River have been the center of pulp and paper production since the beginning days of settlement. On the east bank, a two-story brick building (still standing but enclosed by warehouses) contained the variously named Pioneer Paper Manufacturing Company or the Oregon City Paper Manufacturing Company. Its prospects seemed poor after the machinery failed during a grand opening banquet and dance in 1867, when the owners were hoping to sell stock. However, the temperamental equipment was soon running with two water wheels that furnished power, turning out brown straw wrapping paper, which sold for $1.50 a ream. Operating for just under one year, the company was shut down by a sheriff's foreclosure notice on a debt of $10,000 owed to the Bank of British Columbia.

Even before Pioneer Paper closed its doors, the Clackamas Paper Manufacturing Company was established two miles north at Park Place on the site of a defunct sawmill. Pulp grinders were run by four water wheels on the Clackamas River, turning out fine quality paper. When they quit after seventeen years, the machinery from their small plant was incorporated into the larger one at Camas, Washington.

During the late 1880s two processors, the Willamette Pulp and Paper Company and Crown Paper Company, both opened on the west bank at the falls only to be destroyed soon afterward by the flood of 1890. Repairs were begun immediately on the Willamette mill, which started up again that same summer. Leaving his job at Crown Paper, William Hawley began his own operation in the old electric power plant on the rocky outcrop at the falls in 1908, prior to setting up in the abandoned flour mill on the east side. Over the next hundred years the facilities were expanded and the companies merged.

The Crown and Willamette Pulp and Paper mills consolidated with the Zellerbach Corporation to become Crown Zellerbach. In 1986 the James River Corporation acquired the mill, in 1990 it became Simpson Paper Company, and finally in 1997 Belgravia purchased the facility, opening as the West Linn Paper Company. Hawley Pulp and Paper on the west side became Publishers Paper, then Smurfit Newsprint Corporation, which was sold to Blue Heron Paper Company in 2000. Today the Blue Heron and West Linn dominate both sides of the falls. The buildings, steam chimneys, pipes, and walkways of the Blue Heron plant spread over most of historic Oregon City, where much of the beginnings of the state took place.

Oregon's first woolen establishment opened in 1851 atop the workings of an older defunct milling facility. Methodist missionaries erected a flour and sawmill on Mill Creek at Salem in 1840, but finding that the wheels only operated intermittently during periods of high water, they sold to John Force after just a few years. Attempting to increase the creek's flow, Force hired a team of laborers and started a six-mile-long ditch to connect Mill Creek

Today paper mills dominate Willamette Falls, where the original beauty, admired by Indians, explorers, and pioneers, is obscured by the unlovely warehouses, concrete platforms, and even waste treatment facilities.

with the North Santiam River. Although he had obtained a water right for his diversion, Force realized that property owners along the way weren't pleased with his canal, and their vehement protests were enough to make him abandon the project. Force continued to grind wheat until selling his mill and rights to both the creek and the unfinished ditch to James Watt.

The wool business began with Joseph Watt, who brought purebred merino sheep as well as the necessary equipment, when he reached Salem. Organizing the Willamette Woolen Manufacturing Company, he solved the low water flow problem by obtaining the right to 254 cubic feet per second from the North Santiam and completing the Salem Ditch one year later. The community celebrated what was the beginning of their new industrial prosperity. "Whiskey was passed, a cannon boomed, and nearly every pioneer felt a little richer."[15] Two water turbines in Mill Creek powered the factory, which employed 100 people for the next twenty years, while a small upstream dam produced enough of a drop to give an additional boost to the water wheel.

At Willamette Falls, the Oregon City Woolen Manufacturing Company benefitted from the natural advantages of water power. Organized in 1862, the company contracted with landowner Daniel Harvey to purchase a site near the falls along with a sufficient quantity of water to drive the machinery. After some negotiating over the sale price, both parties agreed that Harvey would provide water through a canal crossing his property.

When water for The Dalles Woolen Mill became scarce in June, 1869, manufacturing was suspended until the flow in Mill Creek was supplemented through a ditch from Hood River. A flume extended from the creek to a reservoir on a high bluff and from there a wooden pipe completed the water's journey. In later years the mill was used briefly for grinding flour before burning down. Fire seemed to be the fate suffered by many woolen mills. On February 18, 1904, the Sellwood mill at Portland was destroyed by fire, even though Johnson Creek was full to its banks with winter rains. Help from a 1,500-foot-long wooden flume, which carried water from the creek to the mill, was not enough, and pressure in the Sellwood fire department mains was too low to put out the flames.

ELECTRIC POWER

Water to produce electricity followed on the heels of its use to turn mill wheels. It wasn't uncommon for mills to string lines and install incandescent lamps around their yards, running them from the company to city streets where lights were hung. Throughout the state similar small operations utilized water power from mills to provide municipal lighting. The first recorded water turbine wheel in 1850 near Silverton in Marion County generated sixty horsepower from Silver Creek.

Long distance transmission of electricity was introduced to Oregon in 1889, the beginning of such deliveries in America. Viewing the falls as "an enormous engine of economic growth," much the same outlook as held by Judge J. Quinn Thornton earlier, "elite" businessmen from Portland and Oregon City organized the Willamette Falls Electric Company.[16] Putting up one million dollars, an immense amount of money at that time, the men gained control of water rights, intending to manage the falls and bring lights to both cities. The company placed a two-story building, fifty feet by sixty feet, on the rock ledge above the falls toward the east side, sending an electric line from its generators the fourteen miles to light Portland, "a service that is not available today in any city in the United States."[17] A new powerhouse on the west side of the river was completed in 1895, before the station became obsolete and was shut down just eight years after opening. By the turn of the century the facility was consolidated with other local utilities under the umbrella of Portland General Electric Company.

Ultimately all Oregon cities were looking to light up their own streets with electric power. Independent companies, each with its own water-powered generator, provided regional municipalities and customers with service. In the western part of the state, small electricity providers at Salem, Silverton, Woodburn, Albany, Corvallis, and Eugene were typical of the spreading phenomena. In Clackamas County, the Oregon Iron and Steel Company at Lake Oswego filed a water right on Sucker (Oswego) Creek appropriating 750 cubic feet per second to construct a dam and generate electricity for local residents.

Across the Cascade Mountains, the generation of electricity fell into the hands of a variety of companies competing for water rights on the Deschutes River. When the Interior Development Company filed on the lower river for rights to 10,000 cubic inches per second, intending to convey water through a flume, which enabled it to generate and sell electricity, those holding water permits near Bend geared up to go to court. One such was the

Owned and operated by Portland General Electric Company since 1911, River Mill Dam on the Clackamas River was the first large structure in Oregon to produce electricity.

Cline Falls Power Company, which had gained control of all the Deschutes water at a point west of Redmond as early as 1892. Taking advantage of the forty-foot-high falls, the company proposed to generate 40,000 horsepower. In addition, it secured 2,500 acres on both banks of the river at Cline Falls, platted a town site, and offered lots for sale to the public, advertising the limitless pure water, electric lights, and cheap power to attract buyers.

Most plans were not as grandiose, and towns such as Heppner in Morrow County were provided with services by the Heppner Light and Water Company. At The Dalles, the Electric Telephone and Power Company operated from two turbine water wheels behind a dam on White River. Wires were strung to houses for a thirty-day free trial, and subsequent charges were $1.50 a month for bulbs not greater than 100 watts. Electricity was shut off during the daytime because using it then would be a "waste."[18]

Early electrical facilities were small and located close to cities, where installation and conveyance costs remained low, but massive federal and private power-generating projects altered this picture completely. President

Theodore Roosevelt's call for vast developments in water power was seconded by President Woodrow Wilson's Federal Water Power Act in 1920. This act encouraged private companies, such as Portland General Electric and California-Oregon Power, to enter into the hydroelectric business, generating and marketing unprecedented amounts of excess energy. On the Clackamas River, Portland General Electric operated the River Mill hydroelectric dam by 1911, the Oak Grove in 1924, as well as the Bull Run facility on the Sandy River in 1912. The California-Oregon Power completed its structure on Link River in Klamath County in 1925.

Directed by Congress to manage both hydroelectric and flood control projects, the U.S. Army Corps of Engineers initiated an era of federal works in the Columbia watershed. The Bonneville Dam was completed in 1937, followed by the McNary in 1953, one at The Dalles in 1957, and another on the John Day in 1968. In Washington state, the Grand Coulee was competed in 1942 by the Bureau of Reclamation, and the Chief Joseph in 1961 by the Army Corps. Four massive hydroelectric edifices were erected and managed by the Corps on the lower Snake, along with eight multipurpose dams on the Willamette River. The largest by size is the privately controlled Brownlee hydroelectric facility on the Snake River, impounding 1,426,700-acre-feet, whereas the John Day and The Dalles dams have the greatest generating capacity.

The goals of the U.S. Army Corps of Engineers were pretty straight forward. "In over forty years since work started at Bonneville, the Columbia has been transformed from an untamed and, at times, destructive river to a slackwater navigation stream and a major producer of hydroelectricity."[19] With eleven massive concrete barricades blocking its flow from the headwaters in the Rocky Mountains to the Pacific Ocean, the Columbia River has indeed fulfilled the expectations and hopes of the Corps. Instead of a freely flowing force, the Columbia has become a chain of tepid pools, restrained behind dams. But at what cost? Fish are unable to negotiate the concrete dam walls or fail to cross the stagnant lake waters. Ponded water behind reservoirs covers the homes and memories, where families had lived for decades.

While engineers viewed dams as interesting design challenges, as generating units, as powerhouses, or as electrical load, their calculations failed woefully when it came to adding up the cost to the human and natural environment. With the building of the dam at Cottage Grove in 1940, Marie Greer reflected, "The dam destroyed something in the valley that never returned. A few homes were moved back into the foothills. Others were destroyed. Our old neighbor, George Taylor ... His father and mother had come to that home site as bride and groom, so many years earlier. Now the big old trees were cut; and the old house torn down."[20] The Corps moved cemeteries and excavated graves at Lowell in order to construct the Lookout Point Dam on the Willamette River in Lane County. For the Winishut family, which had lived and fished at traditional Indian places along the Columbia River, losing their home to waters behind the Bonneville Dam in 1937 "was worse than terrible." [21] The Winishuts, as others, knew that the government rolled forward over all objections. Reginald Winishut expressed his fears. "At the time the dam was built, the tribal fishermen recognized 'we were in a pickle' because the dominant culture could and would go ahead with its projects regardless of the price to the area's original inhabitants." [22]

For the government, on the other hand, emplacement of Bonneville Dam during the late 1930s was a success story. Bonneville was part of a

The massive complex of Bonneville Dam on the Columbia River, constructed by the U.S. Army Corps of Engineers, was dedicated by President Franklin Roosevelt in 1937. (Spence Air Photos, 1938)

much larger scheme to produce electricity authorized under President Franklin D. Roosevelt's New Deal program. In the Corps opinion, the construction was justified because "Oregonians had been urging the construction of Bonneville Dam … for navigation and flood control as well as for power generation."[23] When the power was turned on by President Franklin Roosevelt on September 28, 1937, cheers went up.

Those not cheering were the long-time streamside residents whose story was not fully told. Despite the fact that the rising waters of Bonneville Lake ended their way of life, this wasn't the first, nor was it to be the last time, that they were displaced. In 1896 the Indians were relocated when the Corps of Engineers built a canal around the cascades, and in 1957, twenty years after Bonneville, they were again uprooted with erection of The Dalles Dam.

The planning process clearly didn't proceed as outlined when the government attempted to disenfranchise the tribes as well as their claims for reimbursement by failing to invite them to conferences between Corps engineers and agents for the Bureau of Indian Affairs. The high-handed tone of John Herrick from the bureau was evident when he wrote, "Later, of course, it will be necessary to bring representatives of the Indian tribes involved into the discussion."[24] In anticipation of the filling of Bonneville Lake, an attorney for the U.S. Bureau of Indian Affairs took photographs of Indian fishing locations several months earlier. These photographs, along with sworn statements by individuals stressing the importance of salmon to their culture and livelihood, were presented. New sites and facilities were promised by federal agents, however, fifty years passed before the Indians gained just five replacement spots, one-tenth of that guaranteed.

Concerns about the effects of placement of the Bonneville dam on fish runs were expressed by both the Indians and John Collier, the U.S. Commissioner of Indian Affairs. The early design omitted fish ladders, but three long stairs with wide pools were eventually added to help fish move upriver, and by-pass channels were placed to aid fingerlings making their way down. Although supporting information was lacking, the ladders were touted as exceedingly successful. "The [Corps] engineers have the utmost confidence in the fish ladders, up which salmon and trout may progress."[25] Many years would pass with more dams and development along the Columbia before the irreparable damage to salmon was acknowledged. As recently as 1976 the aesthetics, not the effectiveness, were praised: "The fish ladders at Bonneville, in a beautiful park-like setting, attract more visitors."[26]

The controversy about whether water should be used for fish survival or for selling electricity "to keep California air conditioning on" has never been resolved, and it emerges periodically. In 2004 the Bonneville Power Administration announced it was not going to release spills over the dam in order to "save $77 million by using the water to generate electricity … only a handful of salmon would be affected." A coalition of conservation groups and Native American tribes joined in a lawsuit contending that thousands of fish would be killed by the action.[27]

A letter written in 1934 by Jobe Charley expressed the feelings of his displaced Yakima tribal members. "The Columbia river is like a big vein in your body. When they cut your main vein, what will happen? What will happen when they shut the river? The Bonneville dam will hurt the people worse than the depression."[28]

President Roosevelt failed to address power rates at the Bonneville opening, but he promised control would be handled through regional commissions rather by than by federal agencies. In 1940 the Bonneville Power Administration was created as a bureau within the U.S. Department of Interior to set rate schedules, to establish marketing, and to plan additional facilities. Coordination and management of the Columbia basin system, which covers seven states as well as a good portion of western Canada, fall to the Reservoir Control Center housed in Portland.

Cheap federal electricity encouraged the expansion of private utilities and attracted industries to the Northwest. New arrivals such as aluminum companies consumed prodigious amounts, equalled or surpassed only by agricultural demands, whose gigantic sprinklers, operating with electric pumps, would water eastern Oregon crops. Just after World War II, the words of Paul Raver, Bonneville administrator, expressed his belief that, "The Pacific Northwest at the present time is power hungry."[29] Such uncurbed habits of energy consumption carried over into the present day when the three percent of the nation's inhabitants, living in the Northwest, use fifty percent of the national hydroelectric output.

Public versus private power ownership has long been controversial, but, with soaring demands for cheap electricity, both types of utilities accelerated their output, explored for new sites, erected their own facilities, and purchased federal energy. From the 1940s to the 1970s, the thirty peak years of dam construction in Oregon, the state's largest private company Portland General Electric planned two new dams on the Deschutes River and one on the Clackamas. In 1948 the company filed plans with the Oregon Hydroelectric Commission to build the Pelton Dam and in 1958 the Round Butte Dam, both on the Deschutes. Along the Clackamas, the North Fork project was completed in 1958 and the Faraday in 1965.

Through considerable opposition and subsequent legal battles to their impoundments, Portland General Electric has prevailed. Resistance to the Round Butte and the Pelton on the Deschutes was especially vigorous. The first setback to the Pelton application came when the Oregon Fish Commission denied PGE's permit. The commission and other "antidevelopment forces" attempted to block "exploitation of the Deschutes and Metolius rivers for the purpose of power generation."[30] In court the issue between fish rights and dam construction degenerated into one dealing with state's rights versus federal authority. Although the Federal Power Commission had granted PGE's permit, the state of Oregon objected. Ultimately reaching the U.S. Supreme Court, the case revolved around who controlled water on federal lands, which had been "reserved for power purposes," since the east bank of the Deschutes, where one abutment was to be placed, was "reserved" land.[31] Rights to the west bank, belonging to the Warm Springs tribe, were signed away by Charles Jackson, Chairman for the Tribal Council. Strong dissenting opinions were expressed by several of the federal Supreme Court judges, as well as by many Indians, but PGE won the day. Afterward the company "proceeded with a program designed to repair its relations with the public, which focused on promoting conservation … parks … and recreation facilities at many of its project sites."[32]

Testimony as to the effects of Pelton Dam on the fish populations in the Deschutes River was given at subsequent hearings on PGE's Round Butte application. A letter from the Oregon Game and Fish commissioners urged the state Water Resources Board to revise its minimum downstream flow data on the Deschutes because preliminary studies found that, "Only about half the migrant steelhead expected went through the skimmer [at Pelton Dam] and of 20,000 blueback salmon fingerlings released, none showed up." George Eicher, an aquatic biologist for PGE, responded with the remarkable notion that river fluctuations were detrimental to fish spawning and that more stable flows would provide "better reproduction, less scouring of eggs and larval life, and ... We can expect to see enhancement in fishing."[33]

Not until its licenses for dams from the Federal Energy Regulatory Commission expired was PGE constrained to look at ways to improve fish passages. Fish ladders at its four structures on the Clackamas were upgraded in 2002, but, instead of relicensing its ninety-year-old Bull Run Hydroelectric Project, PGE decided to take down the forty-seven-foot-high Marmot and the sixteen-foot-high Sandy dams in the Sandy River basin. This included removal of tunnels, canals, and a 15,000-foot-long wooden flume. After two years of negotiations, an agreement between PGE and the Confederated Tribes of the Warm Springs Reservation was signed in July, 2004, to improve fish passage and habitat at the Pelton-Round Butte hydroelectric complex. The proposal is to erect a massive 270-foot tower rising from the bottom, through which enough water will be pumped to guide fish toward an intake tunnel. Here they will be collected, trucked, and released below the impoundments.

A scheme by Amos Black to generate power from beautiful Waldo Lake east of Oakridge in Lane County came to naught. In conjunction with engineer Simon Klovdahl, Black laid claim to 100,000-acre-feet of water in the early 1900s, planning to supply irrigation and electricity to the Willamette Valley by installing four power plants and increasing the size of the lake with a dam. The additional storage of winter rainfall was to be released during the dry summer months and carried through ditches to farms in the valley. With fading enthusiasm for the project, Black sold to promoter Frederick Ray of Helena, Montana, who created the Waldo Lake Irrigation and Power Company to attract wealthy backers. By 1909 a headgate was in place on the western shore of the lake, and work had begun on a roadway and tunnel, blasted through 500 feet of volcanic rock. The ditch system was abandoned in favor of a tunnel, which opened into Black and Salmon creeks, tributaries of the Middle Fork of the Willamette River. Because of poor financial decisions, a lack of an irrigation and power market, as well as political vicissitudes, the system was never completed. In spite of interest in valley irrigation projects by influential officials from the Oregon Department of Agriculture, there was opposition from Eugene citizens, who formed the Anti-Bonding Irrigation and Drainage League.

In 1933 the Federal Power Commission refused an application that would have allowed the Waldo Lake Irrigation and Power Company to install the power plants and miles of canals, and in 1934 the Forest Service terminated the company's special-use permit. By 1987 the tunnel was leaking so badly – at the rate of 300 gallons per minute – that the Forest Service sealed it with concrete. Today the headgate and tunnel are a "tangible reminder that the beautiful Waldo Lake ... could have been rendered a highly modified ecosystem if the unfolding of history had taken a slightly different course." [34]

Harnessing water for power was essential for Oregon's emerging businesses, enabling settlers to market their commodities effectively and profitably. Mill wheels of all kinds, which grew quickly along many streams, supplied the ever-expanding needs, but it wasn't long before they were converted to small generating systems. Cheap electricity, which was produced through private and public projects, encouraged excessive consumption and the erection of more dams. Even with today's knowledge of impoundments and their effects on stream habitat and water quality, changes in power policies and outlook are rarely voluntary and are generally accomplished through regulations and court decisions.

ENDNOTES: WATER FOR POWER

[1] *Oregonian,* June 28, 1864, 3.

[2] J. Quinn Thornton, *Oregon and California in 1848.* (New York, Arno, 1983), v.1, 287.

[3] Vera M. Lynch, *Free Land for Free Men* (Artline Printer, 1973), 449.

[4] Hubert H. Bancroft, *History of Oregon* (San Francisco, History Company, 1886), v.1, 204.

[5] Robert C. Johnson, *John McLoughlin, Father of Oregon* (Portland, Binfords & Mort, 1958), 178.

[6] Lynch, 1973, 107.

[7] Edward G. Jones, *The Oregonian's Handbook of the Pacific Northwest* (Portland, Oregon Newspaper), 185.

[8] *Iowa Gazette,* November 6, 1843.

[9] Bob Tweedell, *Old Millrace; How it was Born* (Eugene, Register Guard, @1949), 6.

[10] Ibid., 46.

[11] Penny Cass and J. Ronald Miner, *The Historical Tualatin River Basin* (Corvallis, Oregon State University, Oregon Water Resources Research Institute, 1993), 29.

[12] William G. Robbins, *Hard Times in Paradise, Coos Bay Oregon, 1850-1986* (Seattle, University of Washington Press, 1988), 7.

[13] Hazel Young, "Cedar Mill History" *Land of Tuality,* 1978, v. III, 47.

[14] Samuel Dicken and Emily Dicken, *The Legacy of Ancient Lake Modoc; A Historical Geography of the Klamath Basin Oregon and California.* (Eugene, University of Oregon Bookstore, 1985), 3-20.

[15] Frank Mauldin, *Sweet Mountain Water* (Salem, Oak Savanna , 2004), 16.

[16] Craig Wollner, *Electrifying Eden* (Portland, Oregon Historical Society Press, 1990), 38.

[17] *Oregonian*, January 1, 1895, 14.

[18] William H. McNeal, *History of Wasco County, Oregon* (The Dalles?, 195?), 103.

[19] William F. Willingham, *Army Engineers and the Development of Oregon* (Washington, D.C., General Printing Office, 1983), 163.

[20] U.S. Army Corps of Engineers, Portland District*., Historic Use of Six Reservoir Areas in the Upper Willamette Valley, Lane County, Oregon* (Eugene, Heritage Research Institute, 1982), 145.

[21] Roberta Ulrich*,* "Empty Promises, Empty Nets" *Oregon Historical Quarterly,* 1999, v.100, no.2, 136.

[22] Ibid., 135.

[23] Ellis L. Armstrong, ed., *History of Public Works in the United States, 1776-1976* (Chicago, American Public Works Assn., 1976), 357.

[24] Ulrich, 1999, 141-142.

[25] *Oregonian*, September 5, 1937, Magazine Section, 10, col.1-8.

[26] Armstrong, 1976, 358.

[27] *Oregonian*, April 21, 2004, B4.

[28] *Oregonian*, January 27, 1935, Magazine Section, 5.

[29] *Oregonian*, September 28, 1947, Magazine Section, 5, col.1-7.

[30] Wollner, 1990, 236.

[31] Federal Power Commission v. Oregon et al., *U.S. Supreme Court, Reports*, 1954, v.349, 439.

[32] Wollner, 1990, 241.

[33] George Eicher, *The Effects of Round Butte Dam on the Deschutes River Downstream.* (Portland?, Portland General Electric?), 1959, 5-6.

[34] Paul Claeyssens, *Private Enterprise and Early Twentieth Century Water Resource Development on Oregon's Second Largest Lake* (Eugene, Willamette National Forest, 1987),11.

CHAPTER 5

CONTROLLING WATER: DAMS, DITCHES, AND FILL

It is the relatively rare flooding event, however, that causes the greatest damage. Predicting such floods is necessarily an imprecise art; to a large extent, the irregularities of weather remain a perplexing mystery to us.[1]

In the natural design of the landscape, floodplains, wetlands, and estuaries are closely related. All rivers periodically expand beyond their channels and spread across valleys depositing sediments to create a flat plain interspersed with low-lying bogs. These continuous level stretches or floodplains are imminently attractive for settlement, and historically communities, farms, and industries have clustered here. First drainage "made available [lands] that otherwise would have been of little value except for wildlife," and after people and towns began to take over fertile river bottomlands, the need to control flooding from storms and snowmelt became more urgent.[2]

By characterizing natural water phenomena with such weighted words as "destructive," a "menace," or "adverse," the government set about the long process of control. "With population and commerce continually expanding, it became clear that flooding rivers could not be allowed to spread destruction whenever adverse weather occurred."[3] Dams, canals, revetments, levees, and extensive works from the headwaters to the mouth of a stream became the order of the day.

A considerable amount of effort, energy, and money has gone into dominating the flow of water. Water management historically involved removing or controlling the excess rather than searching for a supply. Prairies of the Willamette Valley were waterlogged, the numerous winding channels of the Columbia River flooded periodically, and the marshy coastal estuaries from Clatsop to Curry counties were unfit for settlement, and eastern Oregon was plagued with flash floods. Pioneers did their best to confine rivers to their channels or to drain swampy floodplains, reclaiming the rich soils, but, when rivers overcame these modest efforts, much of their streamside and lowland development was damaged or destroyed.

In order to make wetlands and floodplains suitable for cultivation and habitation, and then subsequently to protect them from inundation, the Oregon Division of State Lands and the U.S. Army Corps of Engineers entered water resource planning. Planning became synonymous with the construction of levees and ditches to dry up swamps, with the filling in of marshes, and with the erection of dams to eliminate floods.

The first agency to exercise control over Oregon's wetlands was the State Land Board that derived its powers from the Oregon Constitution. Rather than being composed of individuals hired to serve specifically on the board, its members are the governor, the state treasurer, and the secretary of state, whose decisions are inherently susceptible to political influences. With statehood in 1859, the admission act designated approximately six percent of the territory as under public ownership. The board was charged with managing and marketing this property for school funding and for supporting its own agency. This land was attained from the 16th and 36th sections of each township and amounted to 3.4 million acres, of which just about one-fifth or 773,000 acres remain today. In addition, the state gained ownership over the submerged and submersible banks and beds beneath all navigable rivers, as well as over lakes, tidelands, and swamps.

Once this assortment of property was placed into its hands, the State Land Board was authorized to sell or contract the wetlands and swamps out for filling or draining. "Early state officials did their best to reduce the administrative responsibilities … riparian owners along the Coos, Coquille, Umpqua and Willamette rivers were granted title down to the ordinary low water line, the state disposing of thousands of acres of fertile flood plain land." Entire estuaries were granted to the railroads, while other tidal areas sold for $1 to $5 per acre.[4] Today the Land Board and its administrative arm, the Division of State Lands, oversee 600,000 acres of rangeland in

Approximately 2,000 acres of "new land" on Sauvie Island, (in the foreground) were formerly lake beds which were drained and diked. (Sauvie Island Soil Conservation District, 1947)

eastern Oregon, 132,000 acres of forest lands, 800,000 offshore submerged acres, and the beds and banks of all navigable lakes and rivers

At the federal level, Congress passed the Flood Control Act in 1936, designating the U.S. Army Corps of Engineers as the agency to construct and oversee flood control projects. Of the fourteen flood control dams under the Army Corps, eleven are in the Willamette Valley, two are in the southern part of the state, and one is in eastern Oregon. The Bureau of Reclamation has funded thirty-two projects across the state, of which eleven have flood control as a secondary or tertiary motive after irrigation.

Taking a project-by-project, piecemeal approach to water control, the U.S. Army Corps and Bureau of Reclamation, the Oregon Division of State Lands and Water Resources Department, along with other agencies overseeing water issues, avoid comparing the impact of any new project to that of the many others already built. If one dam degrades the waterway, what will three or four do? How much of a stream's original character has already been lost to prior restraints, or how does removing wetlands impact the character of a watershed?

WETLANDS – WILLAMETTE VALLEY

Drainage began early in the nineteenth century when it was estimated that 350,000 acres of low-lying bogs in western Oregon, at least half of which were in the Willamette Basin, could be turned into production. Ira Williams, a geologist with the Oregon Bureau of Mines and Geology, concluded in 1914: Once winter rains began in the Willamette Valley, the so-called "white lands" or depressions became "filled with standing water. Every furrow stands full, many planted fields are partially or entirely inundated; all of the evidences of insufficient drainage are present. Thorough drainage is, therefore, the next essential step in the development of this magnificent agricultural country." [5] As a testimonial to the diligence and success of human endeavors, calculations in 1990 showed that that a mere 7,221 acres of Willamette Valley swampland remained.

Before the imprint of settlers altered the flat-lying Willamette Basin, the floor of the valley was dotted with swamps and bogs left over from the Ice Ages when river tributaries were overwhelmed by glacial debris carried out of the Cascades. The Pudding, Molalla, Tualatin, and Yamhill river systems, as well as the Willamette itself, were formerly characterized by such wetlands. Peter Burnett, who purchased a claim on the Tualatin Plains, described the swales as "peculiar winter drains," which were dry in summer when "their flat bottoms become almost as hard a brick." [6]

Early attempts at drying up swamps in both the Willamette Valley and coastal estuaries were rudimentary and generally ineffectual. Moving the water off marshes could be accomplished through ditches and dikes or by burying tiles and perforated pipe at various depths. Open ditches had the disadvantage of having to be cleaned out periodically since they filled quickly with plants and sediment. While ditches and conduits led water away from lowlands, levees narrowed the pathway of a stream, keeping the water from its natural course.

Some of the first efforts at drainage in the Willamette Valley occurred in the watershed of the meandering Tualatin River. Floodplains of the slow-moving Tualatin were dominated by standing water interspersed with bogs.

Open Drains
1,578,720 Lineal Feet

A trench, which was cut through wet Willamette Valley farming land during the 1960s, quickly filled with water. (Courtesy Oregon State Archives)

In Washington County, peat at dry Ice Age Carlton, Wapato and Lousignont lakes, and on Onion Flat denotes old river channels where ponded water fostered layers of decomposing vegetable matter. Trapper John Work characterized the soil as "composed of a thick strata of dark vegetable mould perhaps not over 6 or 8 inches deep." [7] Twenty-to-thirty-foot-thick silt, sand, and clay often covered the peat deposits, which yielded unsatisfactory farm crops because of the high acidity of the soil.

Around the turn of the century, ditches dug by private property owners in the Tualatin Basin directed water away from these ancient lake beds. Some 1,000 acres of bogs, making up Lake Lousignont at the head of Daisy Creek, were initially drained by a hand-dug trench, but a number of years later a steam-powered shovel opened up and deepened the channel. Since then it has been maintained by members of the Washington County Drainage District, organized in 1912. Ditches and levees similarly emptied the bed of

Lake Wapato near Gaston, however, a pump allowed the local drainage district to control the water flow as a means of gaining maximum benefit for crop irrigation.

One of the largest wetlands to be drained was Pleistocene Lake Labish trending northeastward from Salem in Marion County. Originally over ten miles long and one-half mile at its widest, the lake contained enough water to permit travel by boat. Under terms of the Swamp Lands Act, the federal government turned the Labish wetlands over to the Oregon Land Board, which sold it for $1.00 an acre to private claimants. Roughly forty-three acres were reserved to teach the Chemewa Indians agriculture.

The channel of the Little Pudding River kept water flowing steadily out of the Labish wetlands before human alteration, but when a dam was constructed across the mainstem river near Parkersville, water backed up for some six miles into a lake. Belonging to William Parker, water stored behind the dam ran his grist and sawmill. Local residents, distressed by Parker's reservoir and the continual flooding it brought to Labish farmland, gained political clout by organizing as the Lake Labish Drainage District in the early 1900s. They decided to "reclaim" the swamp. At one point the district obtained a court order for removal of the impoundment, but when this was ignored, a disgruntled member decided to take action, dynamiting the offending obstruction on a Sunday in 1906. Before the damage could be repaired, the district was granted an injunction against rebuilding the dam, but, after five years in court, the members lost.

Meeting in December, 1911, the Lake Labish Drainage District reconsidered its reclamation plans for the lake, "now entirely worthless through the overflow of water. The area thus lost to cultivation covers from twelve to eighteen hundred acres of surface ... If this [reclamation] could be accomplished it would mean development and happy homes to a deserted swamp, which is now the habitation of beavers and muskrats and the deathtrap of head of cattle." [8] Within a short time, Madison Jones, a landowner on the west end, dug the first drainage ditch several miles toward the lake's center. The Jones ditch was later extended about six or seven miles. When two wealthy Californians acquired the swampland property in 1913, they immediately saw the agricultural potential if the excess water were removed. Establishing the Hayes Labish Farms, they organized with surrounding landowners to buy out the water rights for the Parker dam. By dredging, they

To create farmland within the Lake Labish wetlands, a twenty-foot-wide trench drains one section, while a ditcher works at adding new channels. (Oregon Bureau of Mines and Geology, 1914)

significantly altered the wetlands through a system of ditches and tiles, moving water down the middle of the bog and into the Little Pudding River.

A 1958 ruling found the courts setting policy on Lake Labish. Anne Garbarino, who had forty-three acres there, brought suit against upland property owners after they installed tile drains to remove excess water from their land. Garbarino claimed that water from their drains submerged and damaged her land during the winter of 1953 to 1954. The court found against Garbarino, concluding that the law permitted the owner of a higher tract of land to install pipes, which directed the surface flow to pass "through the natural channels upon or over the lower or survient estate." The court went on to allow placement of drains and ditches for agricultural improvement as long as the modifications carried the water in the natural channel. The key word here is "natural." With Lake Labish drained and farmed for close to 100 years, the judge must have been omniscient to be able to base his decision on the "natural" flow.[9]

In 1959 the Water Resources Department authorized a pumping plant, floodgates, channel work, and elevation of an existing dike. Because of "principal problems - floodwater to agricultural lands" the modifications were promoted by local soil conservation districts as well as by the Lake Labish Water Control District.[10] Today the rich soil produces record crops of onions, celery, mint, and lettuce. The irony is that once drained and turned into cultivated fields, the "reclaimed" swamps must be irrigated, and the water removed a second time.

In 2002 the Marion County Public Works and Parks Department began efforts to "restore critical wetlands" of Lake Labish. The lake was part of the county's Overall Ecosystem Restoration Master Plan, and the department called for protection of 120 acres of the swampland and for reestablishing the historic peat bog ecosystem. Marion County Commissioner Randy Franke, Keizer Mayor Lore Christopher, and Oregon Senator Gordon Smith took a favorable stand on what looked to be a non-controversial environmental cause. Even though the project was advertised as a "community-based effort," property owners in the Lake Labish district had never been consulted and were predictably very angry, instantly quenching political enthusiasm for the undertaking. Two small voluntary restoration projects on private property remain.[11]

Irregardless of mitigation attempts and the preservation goals of the Division of State Lands, over 500 acres of wetlands in the Willamette Valley are still lost annually, the continuation of a pattern that began with the first white settlers. By requiring some mitigation features, few of the roughly 800 annual fill and removal applications, which come into the division, are denied. With the changes in political administrations, estuary and boggy ecosystems face even greater dangers. In 2004 Governor Ted Kulongoski, along with members from the Department of Land Conservation and Development, the Department of Agriculture, the Division of State Lands, business services, and others, travelled around the state searching for "developable land." Prospective industrial parks include the wetlands along Mill Creek and those near Aumsville in Marion County. "Research indicates that the highest and best use (and opportunity for highest financial return to citizens of Oregon) is an industrial and employment center" near Mill Creek.[12] At Aumsville close to two and one-half acres of wetlands are similarly proposed for commercial zoning, as development across the state continues to eat away at the remaining low-lying acres.

WETLANDS – COLUMBIA RIVER

Transformation of the once extensive wetlands stretching along the Columbia westward from the Sandy River to the Pacific Ocean began during the pioneer days. Created over the centuries where the river channels curved and waters slowed, the island habitat varied with the amount of rainfall or snowmelt. The shape and number of the low-lying marshy islands were cut away by a surging Columbia, but a slow sluggish river would add debris to build them up. Today, as the result of diking and fill, these habitats have been completely converted to industry, urban dwellings, and agriculture. Almost all of the islands and boggy areas are surrounded by dikes, which direct the river's flow away from the development. "One of the greatest assets of the lower Columbia region is its 30,000 to 40,000 acres of fertile dyked land just now in the process of being placed under cultivation." [13]

Near Portland, the Columbia Slough, a meandering stream immediately south and parallel to the Columbia River, was particularly hard-hit. Only about one percent of the original swamplands remain. A flowing current through the slough once cut an eighteen-mile-long channel from Fairview Lake westward to empty into the Willamette River near Kelley Point as it wandered through and around hundreds of small islands, ponds, and low-lands. Formerly inhabited by abundant birds, game, and fish, this region "would not survive the early twentieth century intact. The city of St. Johns would see to that." [14]

The slough and surrounding landscape of the peninsula were altered during the early 1900s when St. Johns actively sought to expand businesses. Situated close to the junction between the Columbia and Willamette rivers, the city gained a commercial boost, and by 1910 officials bragged of their lumber and cotton mills, of their iron works, stockyard, and slaughterhouse. The Chicago-based Swift & Company meat packing plant filled a bog along the north side of the slough, then cut a mile-long canal through it. As part of a plan to improve shipping, the canal connected the slough with Mud and Force lakes, but, when silt collected in the channel, constant dredging was required to keep it open. The spoils were dumped onto other marshy areas. As sedimentation continued to block the waterway, interest waned, and canal was abandoned by 1925. The closure failed to hamper other businesses, which grew prodigiously as the lowlands were filled in anticipation of more development.

Several years later the city of Portland diked both sides of the slough, installed a pumping station, and completed yet another canal to the Columbia River. It was hoped that the City Canal would carry fresh water from the river into the now heavily-polluted slough and flush sewage away into the Willamette. When silting closed its canal as well, the city placed a dam and culverts across the river opening, but this modification failed too, and the opening and pipes were permanently sealed in 1956. Today remnants of the canal can still be seen along the Riverside and Columbia Edgewater golf and country clubs, where the filled regions are occupied by the airport, businesses, golf courses, and residences.

The Multnomah County Drainage District No.1 regulates the flow of water through the slough by a system of artificial canals and levees. Organized in 1917, the district manages over 8,000 acres from Fairview Lake to Kelley Point, operating with contracts from two Peninsula Districts and one Sandy District. This area is completely enclosed by levees built by the U.S. Army Corps of Engineers but maintained by the district. The dikes keep river water away from the lowland, while rain and storm runoff are removed

A map of the Columbia Slough wetlands, islands, and canals.

through pumps and canals. Although the district has water rights, they are unused, and individual members are charged by how much water has to be pumped from their property.

The six miles of islands and wetlands along the Willamette River from the southern tip of Sauvie Island to Swan Island, making up the Portland harbor today, were also subject to substantial change. During the 1920s Guilds Lake on the west bank, as well as the flat plain where the river formerly lapped up against Willamette Heights, was filled in. Similarly, sections of the east bank were closed off, connecting Swan Island to the mainland and, in the process, eliminating adjacent Mocks Bottom wetlands. "To turn submerged lowlands of the East Side, between Madison and Burnside streets, into high and dry building sites, and make of them one of the most thriving business districts of the city, plans are proposed for filling in the low places with sand and gravel from the bottom of the Willamette River, by means of the dredges of the Port of Portland." Sponsors of the filling project were the East Side Improvement Association, the Portland City Council and Executive Board, and the Port of Portland.[15]

Today this heavily industrialized segment of the river has been placed on the Environmental Protection Agency's Superfund list, which targets areas of high chemical contamination. The Columbia American Plating Company at Guilds Lake has dozens of violations going back to the 1980s for storing thousands of gallons of hazardous waste and contaminating the groundwater. Near the University of Portland, the McCormick & Baxter site is also scheduled for cleanup. Wood preservatives with creosote, pentachlorophenol, and metals were dumped directly into the Willamette by the company for almost fifty years before it declared bankruptcy in 1991.

Immediately northwest of the junction between the Willamette and Columbia rivers, Sauvie Island lies within the same wetland habitat. Now extensively drained, the island's previous 30,000 acres of swamps and lakes provided the Indians with a rich source of the root of the wappato plant. Although recognizing the difficulties inherent in establishing their homes on the low-lying island, settlers weren't deterred, adapting to the natural ebb and flow of the water. Residents often had to move their household goods and animals during spring flooding or in times of warm winter snowmelt, while livestock was transported back and forth during low river cycles. They knew the benefits brought by floodwaters that left fertile topsoil as well as thousands of tiny fish in small puddles, which could be harvested and shipped out to supply lakes elsewhere.

Management of seasonal flooding began when a majority of Sauvie Island residents organized the Columbia Drainage District and voted to construct a twenty-one-mile-long dike enclosing 1,600 acres on the eastern side of the island. The dike protected farms and homes from the annual river floods for over a decade, until exceptionally high water in 1933 surged through a seventy-five-foot-wide break After a similar event five years later, property owners agreed to the placement of Big Dike,

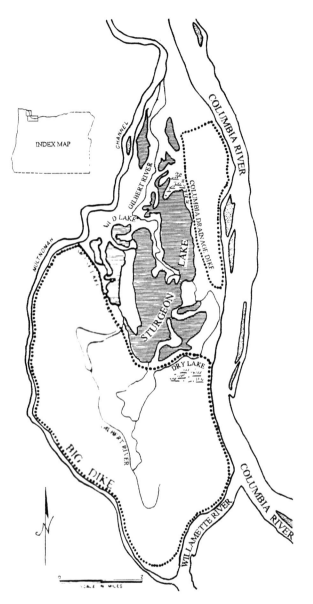

The Sauvie Island habitat includes lakes, bogs, farmland, and a wildlife refuge.

enclosing the entire the southern tip of the island and providing another 12,000 acres for cultivation.

Organizing in 1938, the Sauvie Island Drainage District was able to obtain around $1.5 million in federal money for the diking project. Heavy earth-moving equipment dug a canal to redirect the Gilbert River to a pumping station, and nineteen miles of a rock embankment cut off water from the river, which fed Little Sturgeon, Mouse, and Marquam lakes. As the lake beds dried out, they reverted to ownership under the State Land Board, which subsequently sold the areas for farming. Except for the flood of 1948, Big Dike has kept the river away from agricultural lands, homes, and roadways. Together both districts control water flow over 13,577 that are protected by more than one hundred miles of canals.

During the early 1950s the Oregon Wildlife Commission purchased 13,000 acres at the northern end of Sauvie Island to be set aside as a refuge for birds. Some farming and limited hunting would be permitted as well. Omar Spencer, President of the Oregon Historical Society, reflected the current mood in 1950: "In the first place, it is a short-sighted policy which would permit public money to be spent for the purpose of putting on the shelf fertile land which should continue to produce food." [16]

WETLANDS – COAST

Where rivers enter the ocean, swamps, sedimentation, and meanders are part of the natural cycle of the estuary. Here a mingling of fresh stream and salty ocean waters supports a complex web of plant and animal life enhanced by frequent flooding during high tide or spring inundation. Boggy areas develop naturally when sediments are carried downriver. The Coos and Millicoma rivers bring 72,000 tons of sediment into Coos Bay annually, the Coquille River discharges 100,000 tons, and the Umpqua 565,000 tons. The consequences of dikes, tidegates, and fill have been to alter the estuarine habitats by changing the water circulation and by drying up some wetlands while developing swampy ground elsewhere.

Although such lowlands are especially hazardous for the placement of communities, farms, and industries, local drainage and diking districts have worked continuously with the Army Corps of Engineers to restrict the coastal ebb and flow away from development in these areas. Authorized by the Flood Control acts, the Army Corps built levees and revetments from Astoria to Coos Bay and Bandon. No project that met the "economically justified" criteria was denied, and it wasn't until the 1980s that the coastal ecology was given even passing consideration as a sensitive and valuable environment.

By that time almost seventy percent of the tidal wetland habitat in Oregon had been lost.

Most coastal drainage districts were formed in Clatsop, Tillamook, and Coos counties, and all except one diking district in Clatsop County. Initially residents built levees with soft wet clays dredged from the nearby bays and riverbeds, but once federal assistance became available, undertakings were improved and enlarged, after which the local districts kept them maintained. Of the coast rivers, those entering Youngs and Tillamook bays on the north coast and the Umpqua and Coos to the south have been the most heavily controlled by levees.

In Youngs Bay at Astoria, the height of the original levees was raised and tideboxes improved by the Corps in 1938 at the request of Clatsop County Diking District members. This system hemmed in the river for a distance of nearly five miles, allowing agricultural, residential, and commercial interests to move onto the reclaimed floodplain. Wood-stave pipes carried water from the tideboxes, through the levee, and into the river. After years of such modifications, ninety percent of the Youngs River marshlands had been converted to pasture. In order to justify a 1986 upgrade of the dikes, which were no longer adequate to protect farms, the Corps proposed planting vegetation on a new interior levee slope as a mitigation measure instead of setting aside land to replace the habitat destroyed by their activity. Existing large trees, where bald eagles and other raptors wintered over, were to be "eliminated by the project," since Corps "policy forbids large trees on levees." [17] Perch poles were installed.

To aid industry and related development, Army engineers initiated a channelization program at Tillamook Bay during the late 1800s that included placement of dikes to redirect waters in Hoquarten Slough and along the Trask, Wilson, and Kilchis rivers. Fill was to be spread over 100 acres of state-owned submerged and submersible lands in the estuary. Expansion was continuing in 1972 when the Corps, in conjunction with local businessmen, concluded that the protection offered by the antiquated dike system wasn't sufficient. Tillamook County and the ports of Bay City and Tillamook Bay were looking at a "testing program to determine the practicability of restoring and enlarging the pike dike system." Local financing was to be provided if the Corps performed the work, and the feeling was that the additional costs for improved boat facilities were "necessary modifications" to develop the inner harbor.[18]

This activity came immediately after Governor Tom McCall issued an executive order directing "all state agencies involved in construction or construction-related activities on the coast [to] stop planning or implementing any project that would modify the natural environment of the coast." In spite of McCall's order and vehement declarations by Tillamook officials that, "The public will no longer tolerate imbalance in use of natural resources," an environmental assessment for the work on the dikes was essentially meaningless.[19] The only evaluation of impact to the fish and wildlife was taken from an old "limited study" with little "tangible information." A checklist of species was provided, but there was no complete inventory.[20]

On the south coast in the Coquille watershed, Fat Elk, Fish Trap, and Beaver Slough drainage districts, organized in the beginning 1900s, removed water by ditches from over 6,000 acres to improve farming prospects. "Where the land had formerly been covered with four to eight feet of water for several months of the winter rainy season and seemed fit only for ducks and beaver, its rich soil grew grass and grain crops." [21] The main ditch in Beaver Slough was thirty-six feet wide, with twenty-seven-foot-wide laterals. Near Coquille an additional 1,800 acres of low-lying bogs were diked, drained, and sold in small lots when the local agricultural agent encouraged the practice of growing silage crops on bottomland. " 'Cow Heaven' is a good name for the country," he intoned.[22]

In conjunction with levees and ditches, the filling of wetlands with debris was yet another method employed to bring unusable land into production. Under Oregon's fill and removal law, the Division of State Lands also has authority over gravel mining or fill operations in excess of fifty cubic yards of material. In spite of the regulations enacted in 1971, which set four criteria for evaluating such proposals to ensure that they didn't interfere with the division's aims of preserving waters for navigation, public health, use, and safety, it was able to process and approve 800 to 1,000 wetlands fill-and-removal permits annually well into the 1980s. Few were denied each year.

In 1973, the Marine Advisory Program at Oregon State University found that the increasing and disastrous effect of "industrialization, development, and filling in Oregon's tidal bays" in order to create land for malls, parking lots, and disposal of dredge spoils was "poisoning ... clam and oyster beds, fish and waterfowl feeding and spawning areas, and sport and commercial fishing … scenic resources, and recreation." Regardless of the Marine Board's criticism, the Division of State Lands permitted Bohemia Lumber Company to fill one and one-half acres of tidelands in the Umpqua estuary at Reedsport. For this proposal in 1972, the hearings officer found that, "The project facilities will increase the ability of the Reedsport area to conduct timber processing activities without any demonstrated detriment to tourism," concluding that, "The prospective loss of public historical rights of navigation, fishery or recreation … will be more than compensated by the public benefit … from the development of a project capable of providing primary jobs and payroll benefits."

Levees and fill along the Coos Bay estuary have claimed 3,500 acres of wetlands, beginning in the early part of the 1900s with organization of the Englewood Diking District and the Libby Slough, the Catching Inlet, the Larson Slough, and the Haynes Slough drainage districts. All the way around the bay from Pony Slough, beneath the airport and mall at North Bend, to Eastside, land has been fabricated from what was once a boggy habitat. At Eastside alone, roughly 270 diked acres were eventually covered and raised over twenty-feet in height, while in the main part of Coos Bay buildings and planks on Front Street were slowly elevated above the marsh. Filling what seemed to be bottomless holes, frustrated residents of Marshfield – to become Coos Bay – remarked, "Efforts are still being made to fill up that big hole on the corner of Front and A Streets. The amount of debris that has gone into that cavity is past computation. Parts of Australia, and a large fragment of the South Sea Islands have been pitched into it without visible effect. Last fall a large hill … was dumped into its hungry jaws, and still it is not full." [24]

Between 1910 and 1920, dredge spoils were continuously unloaded along Front Street, Mill Slough, and most of the swamp to the south of town. When a dam was placed across Mill Slough the opinion expressed was, "That stream is a thing of the past." [25] Unfortunately planners miscalculated. The following winter rains turned the slough into "ponds of stagnant water" costing the Port of Coos Bay $7500 to correct. "That the drain is a fizzle is now being realized by those who gave it the O.K. before … Boating on Central avenue will be good." [26]

A few years later the city council ordered that material from a harbor improvement project be employed to produce "usable land." As the harbor was built-up, many houses were moved to higher ground to accommodate the new elevation; but because the fill debris was poorly compacted the streets were continually cracking and had to be redone. "The pavement on Front street at the corner of Market is being repaired today where it has sunken." [27]

At the urging of the Coos Bay business community, the U.S. Army Corps of Engineers, planned the filling of extensive wetlands in 1976. The feeling was, "Channel improvements at the Port of Coos Bay are essential to the economic well-being of the Bay area." [28] Environmental interests opposed such actions, fearing long-term ramifications to the ecosystem. The Corps, on the other hand, considered the three disposal islands, already built from spoils opposite the city of Coos Bay, as no longer adequate. Weyerhaeuser Timber Company was urging that its 125 acres of diked swamplands north of the mouth of the Coos River be used for what was estimated to be 5.5 million cubic yards of debris. In addition, the Eastside disposal site could be "topped off" with about 500,000 cubic yards of sand, creating "fast land" and providing space for expansion of commercial, residential, and municipal structures. The work was justified by the argument that the marsh had already been partially drained and that the dikes, constructed of inferior material, had a "tendency to break and spew out the spoils." At that time, breaching the existing dikes and restoring the bog was still an option. Jerry Rudy, a professor at the University of Oregon, Institute of Marine Biology, saw fill as permanent destruction of an estuary. What is lost "can never be recovered. Many other forms of pollution can be cleaned up." [29]

One of the most pristine areas of Coos Bay, the inlet of South Slough became the first National Estuarine Sanctuary on June 27, 1974. Through several years of political maneuvering and hard work, efforts of personnel from the office of Coastal Zone Management and from the Coos Bay Port Commission, along with local officials, property owners, and businesses, brought about the preservation of this 4,400 acre tract. The sanctuary is home to a variety of trees, birds, clams, and crustaceans living in its tidal flats and salt marshes, offering a valuable source for research, education, and recreation. Not everyone was pleased with the preserve. Local resident

Eastside, 1939

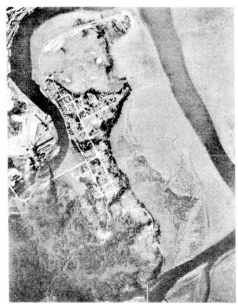

Eastside, 1944

Eastside, 1959

Eastside, 1975

A series of U.S. Army Corps of Engineers photographs dramatically demonstrate the amount of fill at Eastside from 1939 to 1975.

Stella Whittick remarked, "My dad cleared all this land and now it's really a shame to watch it grow back over like it is." [30]

What happened to Governor's McCall's order to safeguard coastal wetlands? Just seven years later a 1978 report on the water and land resources found that the north coastal region alone would *require* 466,000 feet of streamside improvements to halt loss of farmland. An additional 16,000,000 feet of subsurface drains, 2,000,000 feet of drainage laterals, 175 tidegates, and fifty water control pumping plants would be necessary to create more land for agriculture. Findings on the middle and south coasts concluded, "Loss of farmlands exists due to streambank erosion and resultant downstream sedimentation ... Some agricultural lands suffer from drainage problems" that could be solved by levees, drains, tidegates, and pumps. The environmental impact of such actions on fish and wildlife was rated as either "unknown – study needed" or "generally positive." [31] Paradoxically the same report gives habitat destruction as the most serious coastal problem.

This warning failed to halt the loss of wetlands. The momentum for development continued on for twenty more years until the most heavily modified estuaries had become so badly damaged that they were in need of repair. In 1992 Governor Barbara Roberts and Fred Hansen, Director of the Oregon Department of Environmental Quality, petitioned the U.S. Environmental Protection Agency to include Tillamook Bay in the National Estuary Program, dedicated to managing environmental problems. Sedimentation, pollution by dairy wastes, and habitat degradation in the estuary had reached the point of impairing the local economy, causing Governor Roberts' concern. "Tillamook Bay has suffered commercial shellfish harvesting closures ... loss of salmonid spawning and rearing habitat." [32]

The Environmental Protection Agency accepted the bay as a project. A Comprehensive Conservation Management Plan was drawn up, and the resulting water quality monitoring between the years 1997 to 2002 identified a number of pollutants. Even though ecosystem restoration was to be the goal, reluctance on the part of some local residents hindered the outcome. An assessment pointed out that there had been no changes in land use practices over the past five years and concluded, "It will be necessary to affect a substantial amount of on-the-ground improvement in watershed conditions and management practices." [33]

Similar problems were encountered in an evaluation of Beaver Creek, a tributary of the Tillamook River. "Dairy farmers in the Tillamook Basin (and elsewhere) [*sic*] feel threatened by the prospect of additional ... pollution regulatory actions and remain unconvinced that management activities ... make any appreciable difference for water quality." [34] However, on those agricultural areas where "fencing, riparian planting, hydrological modifications, and manure-spreading setbacks" were carried out, a substantial reduction in fecal bacterial counts and sedimentation occurred in the creek.

Between 1870 and 1970, the 30,000 acres of diked or filled wetlands in the Columbia estuary constitute the highest loss. Swampland destruction here was followed by that in the Coquille estuary (4,600 acres), at Coos Bay (3,360 acres), at Tillamook Bay (3,274 acres), and in Nestucca Bay (2,160 acres). [35]

FLOODWATERS – WILLAMETTE VALLEY

While a network of ditches and pipes removed water from poorly drained Willamette Valley lands, allowing development, continued flooding would

In 1953, a car makes its way through a flooded road along the Tualatin River near Forest Grove. (Courtesy Oregon State Archives)

undermine those efforts. Reservoirs, designed to manage floodwaters, were the solution. Augmented by waters of its numerous tributaries flowing in from both the Coast Range and Cascade Mountains, the Willamette River flooded on the average of every five years. Throughout its 180-mile-length from Eugene to Portland, the basin experienced one catastrophic event in 1861, followed by similar ones in 1881, 1890, 1894, 1901, and so on. Eighteen flood control dams were projected by the Corps of Engineers for the Willamette Valley, and thirteen were ultimately constructed. The five begun during the 1940s are in the southern part of the valley near Cottage Grove and Eugene, whereas the other eight facilities for both flood and hydro-power stretch the length of the valley. The final one was placed across Blue River in Lane County in 1968.

The well-known House Document 308 directed the Army Corps to survey both the Willamette and Columbia rivers for navigation and not for flood control. Completed in 1931, the report downplayed flooding, and Major Oscar Kuentz of the Portland District stated, "There is no flood problem on the Willamette of sufficient magnitude to necessitate formulation of a general plan for flood control." [36] Not satisfied with this unfavorable review, Congress directed the Portland district office to take another look at flooding in the valley. In an accounting issued four years later, engineers emphasized multipurpose planning, which entailed flood control, navigation, stream purification, and irrigation. This second document concluded that flooding in the Willamette watershed would be catastrophic, resulting in extensive property damage. Overnight the basin went from a region of minimum flooding to one where "the seriousness of the flood menace" had to be reduced.[37]

To reach this entirely opposite conclusion, Colonel Thomas Robins of the Portland District "interpreted the stream flow data for the Willamette River differently" than Major Kuentz. Robins based his conclusions on weather records, showing that a thirty-year drought had just ended with a return to the wet cycle.[38] He immediately called for seven dams to be placed across streams throughout the basin. Like other administrators, Robins viewed such barricades as a way to eliminate flood conditions and to smooth out "destructive fluctuations" in the downstream flow.

In response to this report, the state initiated the Willamette River Basin

Project in 1935. The entire length of the river came under scrutiny of the Willamette River Basin Commission, a three-member board appointed by the governor to direct progress. Its purpose was "the greater utilization of the natural resources of this watershed for the economic and social betterment of its inhabitants and of newcomers who may settle here." [39] The extensive and unrealistic goals of the plan not only called for flood control, but for the maintenance and deepening of the navigation channel, for purifying the river water, for protecting the bank from erosion, for "making" cultivatable land, for providing irrigation, and for protecting forests as well. These aims were all to be remedied through dams.

Dams were seen as solving all of the water woes already emerging in the increasingly populous western Oregon, although little or no research had been done on the effects of reservoirs on fish migration or on the benefits derived from flowing water and flooding. While directors for the Willamette River Basin Project took into consideration measures recommended by the Oregon Fish and Game commissions, the outcome of blocking stream flow was unknown. "Where the occurrence or extent of adverse project effects cannot be defined at this time, the project estimates include necessary funds for further study and liberal construction allowances for facilities considered likely to be required." [40] In other words, even though the impacts of dam placement were not certain, construction was not to be held up. The mantra that enough money, technology, and science could solve any problems was never clearer.

Receiving a travelling budget of $18,000, the Willamette River Basin Commission financed annual junkets of politicians and citizens to project sites. After administering the river for sixteen years the commission was abolished, during which time the development and expansion of industry and business had been the primary focus. Under its stewardship the river evolved into one of the most heavily polluted streams in the Northwest and one of the dirtiest in North America.

The construction of large dams in the Willamette Valley slowed considerably after the 1960s when the river flow appeared to be under control, and since then Army Corps time is spent operating and maintaining the various aspects of the lengthy Willamette system. The season-by-season regulation of flooding and storage has been combined with the construction and upkeep of works, all designed to protect the banks from erosion and to keep water away from agricultural fields, roadways, or houses. Authorized by the Flood Control acts and known as the Willamette River Basin Bank Protection Project, a program of riprap, stretching along 100 miles of the bank, was begun in the 1930s and scheduled for completion in 1979. Annual maintenance of the stone barriers, intended to "inhibit the natural tendency of streams to wander over a broad 'meander belt'," was necessary as the banks were frequently damaged by swift currents or floating logs.[41] Streamside trees and vegetation, which might harm the riprap or hinder inspection, were cleared. Aerial spraying of herbicides by helicopter has been replaced by hand application in recent years. The revetments remain intact even though wildlife biologists have testified that they reduce habitat, prevent a natural eroding process, and impair the scenic value of the waterway.

Along the Middle Fork of the Willamette River near Natron in Lane County, the placement of riprap successfully removed any meanders from the bank. (Courtesy Oregon State Archives)

One major result of the Corps flood control projects has been to encourage utilization of land that had once been part of a floodplain. Businesses, housing, golf courses, gravel pits, sewage treatment facilities, and landfills have spread out onto areas formerly considered hazardous. "The demand for land caused by population expansion, combined with the advantages (flat land and low construction costs) of flood plain sites, made some flood plain development inevitable." [42] In other words, because of population pressures, construction on wetlands would have occurred anyway. By pointing out that a city like Salem, much of which was build on a low-lying riverbottom, would be under water regularly without flood control programs, the Corps can justify the effectiveness of their dams and revetments in preventing costly damage. Following this logic, dam construction, which permits the expansion of development into the river pathway, allows the Corps to base its calculations on how much damage *would have* occurred to the development without the impoundments. A more reasonable calculation would be the cost-damage ratio had there been no structures built there in the first place.

FLOODWATERS – SOUTHERN AND EASTERN OREGON

Whereas flooding elsewhere in Oregon was not considered the "menace" it was in the western part of the state, recurring floods in the Rogue River basin caught the attention of the Army Corps during the 1950s. Here it planned a program that was to control the flow on Lost Creek, the Applegate River, and Elk Creek in Douglas County. Senate Committee hearings produced heated arguments by farmers and Soil Conservation Service employees who declared their project shouldn't be stopped by what few fish could be found in the Rogue drainage. Minimizing the value of the Rogue salmon, Walter Kasworm, a local berry grower "declared that figuring time at $1 per hour, it costs about $100 to get one salmon. He said that to catch a salmon on the Rogue, a person has to be 'extremely shiftless and lazy'." [43]

Objections to the Lost Creek project, finished in 1976 for $157 million, and the Applegate, completed in 1980 for $95 million, culminated in the Milltown Dam across Elk Creek. Begun in 1971, it was to cost an estimated $174 million but was halted in 1987 by a U.S. District Court injunction sought by the Oregon Natural Resources Council. The 186-foot-high concrete edifice lacked a fish ladder, a legal requirement in the state. When the

Oregon Fish and Wildlife Commission was adamant that one was needed, the prohibitive cost permanently stopped work on the partially completed structure. Setting the fish issue aside, the General Accounting Office had already concluded the dam would never pay for itself, and that the Douglas County taxpayers would have to cover the deficit. Even the U.S. Army Corps doubted the wisdom of going ahead. In a February, 1990, memo a Corps engineer stated, "It is now apparent that operation of the project as formulated and authorized may not be advisable. … I suspect I would recommend not resumption, but termination in a 'mothball' state." [44] As the existing concrete footings block passage of coho salmon and steelhead, the Corps has been trapping and trucking the fish around the barricade. The promised "notching" of the unfinished dam awaits congressional funding.

About the same time that it was planning flood control projects for Douglas County, the Corps also was seeking to control flashfloods in Willow Creek Canyon on the east side of the Cascade Range. Its proposal was to erect a 161-foot-high dam above the city of Heppner in Morrow County. Historically Heppner has been subject to periodic flooding, and, as expressed in the words of former mayor Cliff Green, the dam "issue has been on the burner since 1903, when we had the big flood through here." [45]

Heppner citizens, opposing construction of the Willow Creek Dam, would have been happy with a simple inexpensive warning system or an improved channel through the city. The necessity, design, and cost of the dam had been contested for years before the Corps pushed ahead with its project after a 1971 flood revived the idea. According to Green, "Most of us on the council opposed it and tried to fight the regulations other ways. It finally reached the point that the dam seemed to be the only thing that would save the downtown core area. Basically we built the dam to save Main Street from government regulations, not from water." [46]

To reduce costs, a revolutionary new roller-compacted method was used, in which successive layers of concrete and fill were laid down and each one rolled with heavy equipment. The Willow Creek Dam was the first in North America to use this technique, and Corps design engineer Ernest Schrader hosted an international set of interested visitors. Schrader saw in "rollcrete … a new era of economic construction where structural integrity is not compromised, but where standards are within prudent limits not laced with quality overkill." [47] Unexpectedly, however, the layers within this structure failed to seal, and leaking quickly became a serious problem. At one point, the face of this impoundment was covered with a luxuriant growth of green moss and algae nourished by the percolating water. Eventually the dam began to disintegrate from within as a mixture of hydrogen sulfide and carbonic acid, resulting from the polluted lake waters, ate away at the concrete. By 1983 nearly 3,000 gallons per minute were pouring in torrents through cracks and off the face. Although aware of the seriousness of the problem, the Army Corps was not prompted to warn the residents of Heppner, fearing negative publicity would jeopardize the pending roller-compacted dam on Elk Creek in Douglas County.

Attempting to control the leakage in 1988, the Corps raised the water level, but this only made matters worse. Studies to mitigate the problem, costing close to $1 million, would eventually lead to subsequent repairs by drilling and inserting grout, thereby reducing the leak. This later work ate into much of the $3 million "saved" by the revolutionary method.

The surface of the Willow Creek Dam leaked so badly that it was covered with a luxuriant growth of vegetation. (Courtesy Oregon Water Resources Department)

A similar rolled-concrete structure at Galesville, erected by Douglas County for flood control on a tributary of the South Umpqua River, developed serious leaks as soon as it was filled in 1987. A membrane lining on the upstream surface wasn't effective against leakage because it was unable to span the shrink-swell cracks. Citing facts and figures, officials exuded confidence in their plans, and John Youngquist, water resources coordinator for the county, remarked that the cracks "were very easy to repair … the leakage is now in the neighborhood of 120 gallons per minute." [48] Despite several studies, including one by the publicly owned Eugene Water and Electric Board demonstrating that retrofitting a dam for power is not cost-effective in today's energy market, Galesville was subsequently adapted to hydropower. Since construction, the structure has been consistently subsidized from the county budget.

PRESENT-DAY

Since the 1960s, the Division of State Lands has operated with programs for habitat protection, but when faced with pressures from proponents of growth and development, it fails to follow its own conservation policies. As recently as 1973 a report by the Oregon Student Public Interest and Research Group (OSPIRG) found within the Division of State Lands, "A lack of concrete jurisdictional, operational, and definitional standards, combined with division confusion over the complex set of legal doctrines on which the fill and removal law is based, tend to make improper waterway use decisions … particularly when powerful economic interests are involved." [49]

The division had no overarching strategy well into the 1990s, and without comprehensive management directives, it dealt piecemeal with separate applications as they were received. The scrutiny of individual projects could not provide long-term broad views of what was actually happening to swamplands or tidelands throughout the state. Decisions of government agencies often turn on political fortunes, and under conservationist Governor John Kitzhaber the division formulated extensive goals in 1995. Its plan was to assess the current financial picture, to classify lands under state ownership, to suggest strategies for improvement, and to review its policies every five years.

Although identification and preservation of wetlands were given priority, a 2001 "Report Card" from the division showed that throughout the state an estimated thirty-eight percent of its original wetlands had been lost. In the Willamette Basin over half was gone, while in the Klamath region three-fourths had been drained "primarily due to government-sponsored conversion to agricultural production." [50] On the coast, where most marshlands have been significantly altered by diking and draining, the tidal wetland loss between 1870 and 1970 was close to seventy percent; the total estuary destruction amounted to twenty-five percent or roughly 50,500 acres. [51]

Attempting to reverse this trend, the division initiated a Wetland Reserve Program, under which a former marshy area can be restored, a new wetland created in an upland, or a degraded swamp enhanced. The success ratio for producing new wetlands in non-lowland areas is less than fifty percent, while restoration of a prior swamp habitat has a much better rate of success. Kicked off with much publicity and fanfare, many such projects floundered in a bureaucratic maze. Livestock farmers Dan and Kathy Ridgeway in the Sprague Valley of southern Oregon, walked "in two very different worlds and develop both environmental and agricultural eyes." [52] Placing 259 of their total 273-acre property into the mitigation program, they researched, built fences, and planted vegetation, but an unexpected consequence was hostility from the neighbors and lack of direction from government agencies, regulations, and criteria. "Throughout this process we have often felt lost, not knowing if we were at the beginning, midway through, or just about done and ready to construct." Organic dairy farmers Doug and Sharon Sinko at Myrtle Point on the Coquille River encountered the same "setbacks, delays and red tape." [53] The Sinkos cut their herd from 300 to 150, reduced their pasturage, secured thirteen permits, and "haggled" with the Farm Service Agency before beginning riverbank and pasture restoration.

In spite of current moves toward arresting wetland loss and dismantling dams, contaminated runoff, invasive plant and animal species, dredging, and channelizing, as well as additional construction, are still taking their toll. Most restoration efforts by groups such as the Wetlands Conservancy, the Oregon Wetlands Joint Venture, and the Audubon Society, in conjunction with Native Americans and the U.S. Fish and Wildlife and Forest services, are occurring along the coast where all of the major estuaries are the scene of a variety of activities. Throughout the state, wetland prop-erty is being purchased for rehabilitation, but most of the work is taking place on private lands. By contrast, no large flood control impoundments, and indeed few dams of any size, have been dismantled. The Army Corps is suggesting that some dams along the Snake River could be eliminated, although elsewhere dams are being upgraded and increased in size.

ENDNOTES: CONTROLLING WATER

[1] Stanley Chernicoff and Haydn Fox, *Essentials of Geology* (Boston, Houghton-Mifflin, 2000), 250.

[2] Ellis Armstrong, ed., *History of Public Works in the United States, 1776-1976* (Chicago, American Public Works Association., 1976), 292.

[3] William F. Willingham, *Army Engineers and the Development of Oregon* (Washington, D.C., General Printing Office, 1983), 106.

[4] Robert E. Stacey, *The State Land Board: A Study in Administrative Negligence* (Eugene, OSPIRG, 1973), 1.

[5] Ira A. Williams, "The Drainage of Farm Lands in the Willamette and Tributary Valleys of Oregon," in: *The Mineral Resources of Oregon,* 1914, v.1, no.4, 8.

[6] Peter H. Burnett, "Recollections of an Old Pioneer," *Oregon Historical Quarterly*, 1904, v.5, 90.

[7] Leslie M. Scott, "John Work's Journey from Fort Vancouver to Umpqua River, 1834," *Oregon Historical Quarterly*, 1923, v. 24, 241.

[8] *Gervais Weekly Star*, December 29, 1911.

[9] Garbarino v. Van Cleave, et al., 214 Or. 554, 1958, 559.

[10] Chris Wheeler, *Twenty-nineth Biennial Report of the State Engineer to the Governor of Oregon, 1960-62* (Salem, 1962), 55.

[11] Marion County Public Works Department, *Lake Labish Wetlands Restoration Project*, leaflet, 2002.

[12] Salem, Oregon. Community Development Department, Mill Creek Implementation Strategy, 2003, leaflet, [1].

[13] Oregon Department of Agriculture?, *Oregon,* pamphlet (Salem?, 1930?), 21.

[14] Ellen Stroud, *A Slough of Troubles: an Environmental and Social History of the Columbia Slough* (Eugene, Masters, University of Oregon, 1995), 16.

[15] *Oregonian*, November 22, 1905,10.

[16] Omar C. Spencer, *The Story of Sauvies Island* (Portland, Binfords & Mort for the Oregon Historical Society, 1950), 84.

[17] U.S. Army Corps of Engineers, Portland District, *Clatsop County, Oregon, Diking & Improvement District No.9,* (Portland, 1986), 4.

[18] Tillamook County, Port of Bay City, Port of Tillamook Bay, *Development Program for Tillamook Bay, Oregon* (Portland, Thomas J. Murray & Associates, Portland, 1972), 65.

[19] Ibid., 14.

[18] Tillamook County, Port of Bay City, Port of Tillamook Bay, *Development Program for Tillamook Bay, Oregon* (Portland, Thomas J. Murray & Associates, Portland, 1972), 65.

[19] Ibid., 14.

[20] Ibid., 27.

[21] *Coos Bay Harbor*, April 6, 1911.

[22] *Coos Bay Times*, October 16, 1915, 7.

[23] Stacey, 1973, 15; 23-24.

[24] *Coos Bay News*, January 14, 1885.

[25] *Marshfield Sun*, February 12, 1919, 3.

[26] *Marshfield Sun*, October 13, 1914, 3.

[27] *Coos Bay Times*, December 15, 1921, 4.

[28] U.S. Army Corps of Engineers, Portland District, *Draft Environmental Impact Statement; Operation and Maintenance Dredging, Coos Bay and Coos and Millicoma Rivers Navigation Project, Oregon* (Portland, 1976), 4-12.

[29] *Oregon Journal*, June 3, 1970, J5.

[30] Nathan Douthit, *A Guide to Oregon South Coast History* (Coos Bay, River West Books, 1986), 75.

[31] Pacific Northwest River Basins Commission, *The Oregon Coast, an Informational Report on Water & Related Land Resources* (Corvallis, Oregon State Study Team, 1978), 62-73; 88.

[32] Oregon Governor Barbara Roberts, Letter to William K. Reilly, Environmental Protection Agency, Washington, D.C., April 17, 1992.

[33] E&S Environmental Chemistry, Inc., *Results of Storm-Based Monitoring of Water Quality in the ... Tillamook Basin Oregon from 1996 to 2002* (Corvallis, 2002), 47.

[34] Tillamook County Performance Partnership, *Remediation of Agricultural Contributions of Fecal Coliform Bacteria, Sediment, and Heat in the Tillamook Basin* (Corvallis, E&S Environmental Restoration, Inc., 2002), 6, 9.

[35] A.B. Borde, et al., "Geospatial Habitat Change Analysis in Pacific Northwest Coastal estuaries," *Estuaries*, 2003, v.25

[36] U.S. Congress, House Doc. No. 263, 72nd Congress, 1st Session, 1931, 117.

[37] Cecil R. Moore, "The Willamette Basin Project," *Military Engineer*, v.31, 1939, 209.

[38] U.S. Congress, House, 1931, 81-90.

[39] Oregon State Planning Board, *Report to Gov. Charles H. Martin, The Willamette Valley Project* (Salem, 1935), 4.

[40] U.S. Army Corps of Engineers, North Pacific, *Water Resource Development of the Columbia River Basin* (Portland, 1958), v.1, 125.

[41] U.S. Army Corps of Engineers, Portland District, *Draft Environmental Statement, Corps of Engineers Actions Affecting Riverbanks and Channels in Willamette River Basin, Oregon* (Portland, 1974), 1-2.

[42] U.S. Army Corps of Engineers, Portland Office, *Final Environmental Impact Statement, Operations and Maintenance of the Willamette Reservoir System* (Portland, 1980), 2-10.

[43] *Oregonian*, October 21, 1956, 18.

[44] *Oregonian*, February 15, 1990, C6.

[45] *Eugene Register Guard*, September 18, 1988, A8.

[46] Ibid.

[47] Don and Inez Klopfenstein, "Rollcrete Dam – More Strength, Less Price" *Pacific Builder and Engineer*, July 5, 1982, 10.

[48] *Eugene Register Guard*, September 18, 1988, A1.

[49] Stacey, 1973, 22.

[50] Oregon Division of State Lands, *Wetlands Update*, 2001, v.12, no.1,4.

[51] Borde, 2003, 1104-1116.

[52] Esther Lev, *Heroic Tales of Wetland Restoration* (Tualatin, The Wetlands Conservancy, 2001), 34.

[53] Ibid, 17.

CHAPTER 6

THE GREENING OF OREGON; WATER FOR AGRICULTURE

The value of the irrigated sections of the state to, and the important part they play in our economy should not be forgotten.[1]

Expanding agriculture was seen as the key to western growth, and from the beginning the idea was to turn much of Oregon into a farming paradise by means of water. What wasn't taken into account by those determined to utilize the resource was that in the state there wasn't enough water to turn all of its dry eastern lands into production.

The idea of converting "wasteland" into a Garden of Eden was first articulated by geologist John Wesley Powell, who had explored much of the west for the U.S. Geological Survey. He advocated a regional plan, which was to develop water resources efficiently and systematically so that "these lands may eventually be rescued from their present worthless state."[2] Powell did not suggest that the federal or state administrations become involved but saw local farmers and ranchers organizing themselves into water districts based on topography, soil, volume of water, or other shared physical features.

Water hustling was the answer to maximizing land production. "The search [for a water source] resulted in a manner of moving more water from where it was to where the people were. That is how water hustling came to be the second oldest profession in the world."[3] The process of water hustling evolved from informal groups of individuals sharing, to corporations charging for water, holding regular meetings, electing boards of directors, and drawing definitive boundaries. In the early 1900s the Oregon Legislature authorized the formation of special purpose districts for irrigation, drainage, or control of water. As public and quasi-public bodies, they could undertake projects by assessing members or by incurring indebtedness through borrowing money. None of the districts were organized "to promote recreation, fish and wildlife management, or pollution abatement [although] there is every reason to believe they will be so used in the future." [4] In spite of the optimism expressed in 1967, districts have yet to temper their economic goals with environmental conditions.

Some districts were successful, some were bought out, or they themselves took over already established water works, but most eventually went defunct. Insufficient water or water that went in the wrong direction, prolonged and frequent litigation, lack of finances, or poorly designed and constructed projects plagued them throughout their histories. In eastern Oregon, over ninety percent of the private irrigation companies ultimately declared bankruptcy, and many came to rely on the government for financial assistance or to supply "federal water." At all levels, the necessity of hustling water proceeded unquestioned.

While the government in Washington, D.C., continued to encourage settlement in the "barren" wilderness, officials there soon reached the conclusion that the regional efforts were ineffectual and that direct federal participation would be necessary for success. By enacting the Swamp Lands Act in 1860, the Desert Land Act of 1877, and the Carey Act in 1894, Congress bolstered exploitation of the natural setting. Under the Swamp Lands and Desert Land acts private citizens could obtain wetlands or desert for a minimal cost provided it was improved by cultivation. With the Carey Act, up to one million acres of Oregon was granted to the state government, which in turn disposed of it to private property owners. State agencies were then directed to work with individuals putting together irrigation systems that sold water.

Stepping in to take charge of irrigation throughout the west, Congress created the Reclamation Service, later the Bureau of Reclamation, by passing the Reclamation Act in 1902. Once the federal bureaucracy began to intervene, western water projects were pushed into a whole new dimension. Temporary inexpensive dams and small makeshift ditches, operated by private enterprise, were replaced by massive concrete structures costing millions of dollars.

Through watering, the federal government encouraged the creation of new farmland from unproductive territory. A program of reclamation or reclaiming was based on the presumption that the current or naturally existing landscape needed to be changed for economic or utilitarian reasons to benefit people. Reclamation meant to reduce from a wild to a tamed state, to alter to a desired state by discipline, labor, or cultivation. The original act focused on "construction and maintenance of irrigation works for the storage, diversion, and development of waters for the reclamation of arid and semiarid lands." [5]

Forecast as a panacea, reclamation was intended to relieve population pressures on big cities by shifting people into rural areas. Additionally, water impounded behind dams would enhance the environment, and irrigated crops would be consumed locally and not sent to compete with farm surpluses elsewhere. Eventually, an enormous gap emerged between the artificially calculated predictions and the real consequences of these major changes. By prophesying a bright future with an unlimited water supply, the Reclamation Service actually encouraged the irrigation of substantially more acreage than could be accommodated through its storage projects. Populations never migrated east of the Cascades, and markets expanded out-of-state anyway. The lack of knowledge about hydrologic processes, the consequences of watering the desert, and the impacts of the alterations fostered ecological problems for the future.

After extensive fieldwork by professional consultants, each prospective reclamation plan was selected on the basis of such factors as water supply, size of the reservoir, and cost. Of the fourteen major reclamation projects in Oregon authorizing twenty-seven storage reservoirs, just a few were erected and are still operated by the Reclamation Bureau. Others were constructed or rehabilitated by the bureau but are operated by independent irrigation districts. Only the Warm Spring Reservoir, managed by the Vale Irrigation District, and the Upper Klamath Reservoir (Link River), handled by the Pacific Power and Light Company, were independently built and controlled. The Henry Hagg in Washington County, the McKay in Umatilla County, and the Lost River and Gerber in Klamath County are the only four dams operated solely by the bureau. The 2.6 million acre feet of stored water, owned by the federal government, was primarily designated for agriculture, even though secondary purposes included flood control, hydroelectric power, fish habitat, and municipal or recreational needs.

Initially the bureau directed its efforts east of the Cascade Range with the 1908 Cold Springs Reservoir in the Umatilla River watershed and the Lost River in the Klamath Basin in 1910. Malheur County, one of Oregon's most arid regions, was the scene of the bureau's most ambitious project with the Owyhee Reservoir in 1932. After the surge of dam-building during the 1930s, an interval of twenty to twenty-five years elapsed before another round of construction began in the 1950s to 1960s with thirteen additional impoundments. The last dam of any size was placed across Scoggins Creek in the Tualatin River watershed in 1975.

For most of the projects, the bureau bought out local private companies, which were already functioning. Of the 20,000 acres slated to be irrigated from the Cold Springs Reservoir via a canal from the Umatilla River, about 8,000 were already owned by the Maxwell Land and Irrigation Company. Contracting with the government for water from the proposed dam, the company agreed to relinquish its holdings, system of works, and water rights. Other interested landowners, which incorporated in 1921 as the Hermiston Irrigation District, currently operate the project.

EASTERN OREGON

The business of water hustling began in eastern and southern Oregon, where a settler's livelihood depended on finding a supply for irrigation and livestock. The first waves of land seekers selected the immediate streamsides for their farms, but with a steady influx of homesteaders all of the choice riparian areas were soon taken. Without direct access to the flow and with inadequate rainfall, it became obvious that some type of water diversion would be necessary to assure success. Initially farmers relied on modest ditches or temporary dams. Small low-cost developments along river bottoms were privately maintained or financed by the sale of stocks and bonds. When these systems were unable to keep up with demands, speculators and businessmen moved in, bringing machinery and money that were beyond the reach of individuals. Taking advantage of opportunities to acquire cheap or free land offered through the federal acts, irrigation companies could garner hundreds of thousands of acres throughout the drier regions of the state.

Under grand strategies to construct a system of works then sell watered land to settlers for a lucrative return, companies favored the words "development" or "improvement." Buyers were lured with promotional promises:

"Irrigation and free land in the State of Oregon form the magic combination that is now peopling Crook County and transforming it into a veritable bower of pleasant fields and thriving happy homes." The Deschutes Irrigation and Power Company and The Deschutes Improvement Company advertised thus in the early 1900s.[6]

Already sporadically settled by ranchers, the Deschutes River basin experienced a regular stampede of water appropriations during the early 1900s. Completion of the first railroad up the river brought a new wave of water speculators. Typical of the many people enticed to the Deschutes basin, Alexander Drake from St Paul, Minnesota, saw "that there was abundant water, and that ... the tract misnamed

During the early 1900s, the Deschutes Land Company's "muskrat" dredge works at trenching near La Pine in Deschutes County. (Courtesy Oregon State Archives)

the Oregon desert ... would, when irrigated from the rivers ... prove to invite home making by thousands of new settlers." [7] Forming the Pilot Butte Development Company, Drake ran a canal from the Deschutes River to reclaim 87,707 acres under the Carey Act. The Pilot Butte ditch provided water for the fledgling community of Bend. Drake's competitor was Charles Hutchinson, who obtained 56,000 acres on the Deschutes under the same act for his Oregon Irrigation Company. The two men argued over who had rights to the river, both ultimately selling in 1904 to the Deschutes Irrigation and Power Company.

The larger and more solvent Deschutes Irrigation and Power Company was able to command steam-powered machines and dump wagons to move up to 1,000 cubic yards of earth in just a few hours. Digging a 120-mile-long ditch with wooden laterals to service its 300,000 acre holdings near Bend and Prineville, the company dynamited and drilled through the hard basalt, moving ahead at the rate of 400 feet a day. By 1905, approximately fifty miles of completed canal furnished 50,000 acres with water.

With all its equipment, however, the Deschutes Irrigation and Power Company was unable to fulfill promises to its hundreds of landholders across Deschutes, Crook, and Jefferson counties, and, as with many speculators, it went through a process of merging and downsizing. Dissatisfaction surfaced when disgruntled homesteaders objected to several stipulations in the contracts, which they had signed in order to obtain watered land. Although farmers had been told the contracts were for "convenience only," they discovered otherwise when the Deschutes Irrigation and Power Company attempted to collect revenue prior to providing water, when it set high rates for the water, and when it demanded full cash payment. Similar tactics were unsuccessfully attempted by other speculators, but once the homesteaders formed the Deschutes Settlers Association and appealed to the State Land Board, the differences were resolved. The *Oregonian* newspaper reported, "The establishment of harmonious relations between the irrigation company, the State Land Board and the settlers means … the transformation of a desert waste into a garden of wealth and beauty." The newspaper went on to editorialize that the Deschutes Company yielded "many of its contentions," showing a "liberal spirit, which will be duly appreciated." [8]

Further discontent among stockholders in 1910 brought a complete reorganization of the Deschutes Company, whose assets were transferred to the Central Oregon Irrigation Company. However, as mandated by the Carey Act, which stipulated that reclamation water belonged to the purchasers, it had to turn the North and Pilot Butte canals, laterals, and ditches over to individual farmers, who formed their own district. Unhappy with having to give up its holdings to the water rights owners, the Central Oregon Irrigation Company resorted to the legal system, but the court ruled in favor of the farmers in a landmark decision known as the Dietrich Decree. Collecting assessments of $1.25 per acre to operate and maintain its system as well as to expand assets, the farmer-owned Central Oregon Irrigation District (not to be confused with the Central Oregon Irrigation Company) purchased the Cline Falls Power Company along with water rights in 1930. It also contracted for "federal water" from the Crane Prairie Dam constructed by the Bureau of Reclamation.

Federal water came to the Deschutes basin with the Crane Prairie Reservoir in 1940, whereas other bureau impoundments were built some ten to fifteen years later. The Wickiup (1949) and Haystack reservoirs (1957) are operated by the North Unit Irrigation District, the Ochoco (1950) and the Prineville (1961) by the Ochoco Irrigation District, and the Crescent Lake Dam (1956) is under control of the Tumalo Irrigation District. As with most early reclamation projects, "The local people … have shown a great deal of interest in securing additional irrigation water and protection from spring floods, and are favorable to a Federal project." [9]

By 1911, the State Engineer had granted a total of 183 rights to divert and use water from the Deschutes. Of these, sixteen were for power projects, seventeen for reservoirs, twenty-four for domestic users, and 126 for irrigation. These permits had been legitimately filed in Salem, whereas in the Crook County records at Bend, "unofficial" claims appropriated more than forty times the actual summer flow of the Deschutes itself. By 1960 the amount irrigated reached 265,470 acres, but during the following twenty years much of the land in the basin was divided into parcels of two-to-five-acre ranchettes. This breakup of farm land resulted in a dramatic increase in the number of water users. In the Tumalo Irrigation District near Bend, consumers rose 250 percent, although the number of water rights holders basically remained unchanged. Urban and rural subdivisions caused a drop in the amount of irrigated farm acreage to 126,700 acres in Crook, Jefferson, and Deschutes counties by 1992, while at the same time many new well applications were processed for golf courses and housing developments.

Since surface water in the Deschutes Basin has been closed to new appropriations for some years, residents and businesses came to rely on groundwater. Consequently the regional aquifers have been severely overpumped by the unusually high number of permitted wells. In spite of the fact that the Water Resources Department was considering a limitation on further groundwater users in 2002, it continues to process permits and to extend the completion time for those pending. Extensions ranging up to ten years on permits for seven wells to Avion Water Company would enable 620 families to water the lawns and gardens on their hobby farms. Even though the Ground Water Division of the Water Resources Department "advised that [two of the] wells … are hydraulically connected to the river," Water Resources concluded, "This can be shown on paper but could not be measured in the river." Consequently the permit stipulated, "Since the Deschutes River has been withdrawn from appropriation, any depletion of the river will require the wells to be shut down." [10] Initially approved in 1983, the application was given extensions through 2009. Such lengthy contracts are not unusual elsewhere, and in Lake County one well for irrigation of close to 300 acres for farms, golf courses, and ponds for aesthetics went to the Aspen Lakes Utility Company at Sisters in 1992 with extensions to 2015.[11]

Because of the close connection between surface and groundwater in the basin, Deschutes River protection laws required that each gallon pumped from an underground reservoir be replaced with an equal amount sent into a streambed. These rules were designated to mitigate the effects of withdrawal for new wells, but environmentalists argued in a lawsuit that under this plan the surface flow wasn't being adequately compensated for in water loss. In 2005, following efforts by Water Watch, the Appeals Court threw out the rules that permitted stream flow mitigation, but, unfortunately a short-sighted legislature undermined the decision by extending the pumping rules for another eight years.

Fresh from the disaster in the Klamath marshlands and faced with a vanishing water supply in the Deschutes, U.S. Interior Secretary Gale Norton granted $233,750 to establish basin-wide marketing and water banking measures. A coalition of seven irrigation districts, six cities, the Warm Springs Confederated Tribes, and the Deschutes Resources Conservancy are to head off any future water crisis with measures such as piping canal water and creating new groundwater rights by the purchase of surface rights. Environmentalists, among them Water Watch of Oregon, feel the overall effect may be to enhance one stretch of the river at the expense of another. Gary and Camille Harris, who farm in northern Jefferson County, don't think that cities should be allowed to purchase water rights from farmers. "Conservation measures rather than sale of individual water rights is [sic] critical to protection of farmland for the future." [12]

A present-day irrigation canal and pump furnish water to users in and around Bend. (Courtesy of Jean Mooney)

By the time the Deschutes River reaches Benham Falls near Bend approximately sixty percent of its annual flow has already been removed for irrigation. So much water has been withdrawn by late summer that the Deschutes is reduced to a placid stream as it moves through town. Because of wells, diversion canals, reservoirs, evaporation, pumping, and flood irrigation, the natural cycle of low summer and plentiful winter discharge has been completely reversed, with a higher summer supply provided for agricultural crops. One-half of all farms and more than one-third of all water rights lie along the middle Deschutes, where over 1,700 cubic feet per second is drained into canals leaving only 30 cfs remaining in the river bed. For success in managing what little water remains, farmers and the booming population throughout the basin may be forced to turn to cooperation and conservation, rather than to untried measures for "finding" water.

The lavish watering of the Deschutes basin has irrevocably altered the landscape. "A drive through the once arid, uninhabitable land at first light on a cool morning will show the mist rising like smoke from over 1,000 miles of canals running through green fields."[13]

Other areas across the Cascades weren't as lucrative for speculation by businessmen, and the Willow River Land and Irrigation Company, begun by Dennis Brogan, went bankrupt. Arriving in northeast Malheur County during the early 1900s, Brogan, who had already promoted development in Alaska and Washington, believed in "reclaiming, cultivating, and improving the earth which Divine Providence had given the white man."[14] Homesteaders here were struggling to make a living by raising fruit trees, when Brogan perceived that a dam across the headwaters of Willow Creek would enable them to expand their orchards, thereby sending up profits. Putting together a financial package from out-of-state financiers, bankers, and loan companies, Brogan purchased most of the water rights along Willow Creek, at the same time contracting for 10,000 acres of land to be irrigated. Dams on Pole and Bully creeks and another, along with the possibility of two on Willow Creek, were in the works by 1909, at which time Brogan had already sold 2,500 acres. Conditions of sale were that each homesteader could purchase not more than forty acres, which had to be "set out in high class fruit trees." Brogan busily platted a town, naming it after himself, all the while promoting the railroad to lay tracks in that direction. Pioneer Gladys Pugh expressed her feelings: "These were glorious years when the land and hills from the canyon to down below … were covered with beautiful apple, peach, and pear orchards. Many lovely homes were built."[15]

Like others with grandiose plans, Brogan frequently found himself in court defending his water rights. His primary opponent was the California-based entrepreneurial Eastern Oregon Land Company, which attempted unsuccessfully to keep the Willow River Land and Irrigation Company from constructing a dam and canals. On the witness stand, the Eastern Oregon Company's agent at Vale testified that its sole purpose was to block any water system proposed by Brogan. When asked the intended purpose of claiming options on lands along the creek, he replied, "It was desired to checkmate them." [16] One year later both corporations were in court over the same problem, the California company coming out the looser again. From the 1900s to 1930s the Eastern Oregon Land Company was involved in close to thirty lawsuits over water, many of which were appealed to the higher courts.

About 1920 nature doomed both Brogan and the Willow River project. Oregon experienced a drought, rivers dried up, irrigated acreage dropped, the fruit trees died, and the land returned to sagebrush. No orchards remain, and agricultural water from subsequent sources is used today for onions, potatoes, sugar beets, and alfalfa.

A few short years after Brogan's lack of success, the Bureau of Reclamation stepped into Malheur County to build the Owyhee reservoir that was able to store around 1.7 million acre-feet. Begun in 1928 for irrigation but retrofitted to produce power in 1985, the dam across the Owyhee River south of Nyssa was financed by the bureau but is operated by the North and South Boards of Control. This massive concrete edifice is the culmination of pioneering efforts that began with a small rock and sagebrush dam near Mitchell Butte. Every summer the farmers had to plug and patch the leaks to gain enough water to flood over into a ditch, the repairs being the users' way of payment. Eventually the ditch extended six miles, but when it failed to distribute water to all members along its length, the irrigators formed the Owyhee Ditch Company in 1888, constructing a higher dam and longer system to reach the city of Ontario.

As with most other water companies, the Owyhee Ditch organization wasn't immune from lawsuits. After the company enlarged and widened its canal, the overall water flow dropped so low that it failed to flood the fields of several users. Among them were W.G. Jenkins and J.C. McConnell, who sought permission from the court to construct a floodgate across the ditch in order to raise the level near their fields. Jenkins's request in 1912 was denied; however, when McConnell went ahead on his own and erected a small dam in 1923, the court upheld his action. [17]

By this time, outside members controlled the Owyhee Ditch Company's stock, and they began to increase fees. When a steady influx of homesteaders brought new water demands, the company realized a larger impoundment was needed. Reforming as the Owyhee Irrigation District in 1915, the members sent lobbyists to Congress to solicit federal assistance. In 1926 the Reclamation Bureau backed the Owyhee project in a report to President Calvin Coolidge stating, "Settlers on this project will begin the development of farms under the following favorable conditions: Increase in agricultural production in the Nation is not keeping pace with increase in population. They will realize at the outset that their farms must be intensively cultivated … Because of the urgent need for a larger and cheaper water supply by the settlers on 54,000 acres of this area, because the unimproved land is fertile, and because the development of this area is destined to greatly benefit the Nation, I recommend its approval." [18]

The Owyhee dam was completed in 1932, but the first flow wasn't sent through the extensive system of canals, tunnels, and laterals until three years later. This proved inadequate for all irrigation needs by the 1970s, at which time both the Malheur and Owyhee basins were essentially out of surface water. As expressed in the somewhat convoluted wording of the Water Resources Department, the basins have "no appreciable quantities of unappropriated (in-basin) surface water subject to the jurisdiction of the State Water Resources Board, although in some headwater streams, there still may exist limited possibilities for storage." [19] Put differently, in heavily utilized streams there was no unclaimed water, and only in the upper reaches, or where water had to remain in the channel legally to satisfy downstream water rights, would there be enough to support fish life or recreation. Streams with no reservoirs had "zero flow." During critical years the lake behind the Owyhee Dam was down seventy-five percent, in the Jordan Valley water shortages ran up to ninety-five percent, and they reached seventy-five percent near Vale. Many streams at the lower elevations of the basin had water in their beds only during spring or summer storms.

In spite of what could only be seen as a drastic lack of water, the Water Resources Department judged 291,000 acres as "potentially irrigable lands" in the Malheur region under artificial U.S. Department of Agriculture standards. It qualified this statement by adding that "significant irrigation water shortages" must be considered. The U.S. Geological Survey estimated that an additional 380,000 acre-feet of groundwater could be gained with improved pumping and drilling. These conclusions were reached after the department's assertion that if every drop of surface water were saved, "only about one-half the potential irrigation water requirements" would be satisfied.[20] The scarcity of water in the basin has never improved with at least seventeen registered irrigation districts, along with the government, controlling a complicated system of dams, canals, and laterals delivering water essential to maintain high agricultural productivity.

Water scarcity isn't Malheur County's only problem. Water pollution from agricultural practices is another. A two-year sampling program, begun

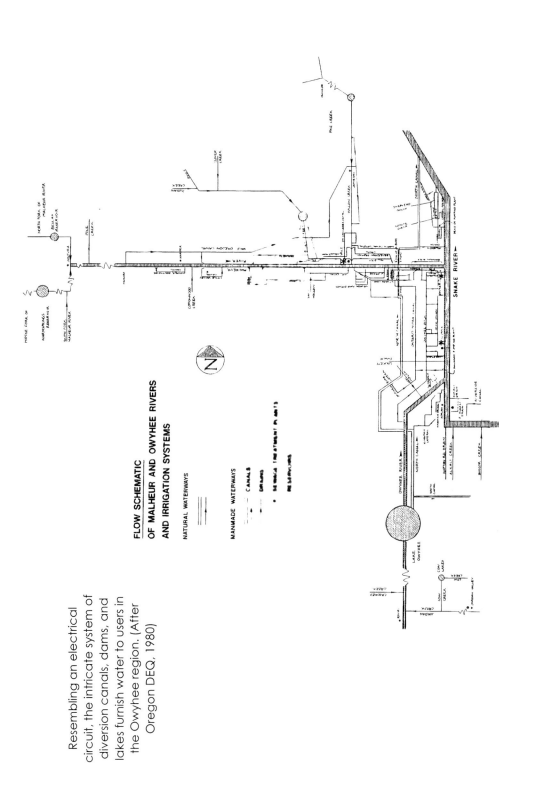

Resembling an electrical circuit, the intricate system of diversion canals, dams, and lakes furnish water to users in the Owyhee region. (After Oregon DEQ. 1980)

FLOW SCHEMATIC
OF MALHEUR AND OWYHEE RIVERS
AND IRRIGATION SYSTEMS

NATURAL WATERWAYS

MANMADE WATERWAYS

CANALS

DRAINS

SEWAGE TREATMENT PLANT

RESERVOIRS

N

in 1978 by the Department of Environmental Quality, identified high sediment loads, high fecal bacteria counts, high nitrates, and high phosphate readings that were degrading streams throughout the basin. With these results in hand, a committee of farmers, soil conservation personnel, and agents from the Department of Agriculture met to map out a Best Management Plan for water improvement. From the outset, the issues were minimized. Kathy Sercu, a water specialist who was hired by Malheur County, attributed high levels of phosphates and sediments to "heavy rains," whereas she felt the problem with high fecal counts was that, "The standards are set for water contact sports … We need to change our beneficial uses to irrigation … then the high fecal coliform levels would not be critical because it does not harm irrigation." [21] Following Sercu's suggestion, the committee "fought for the right to write its own water quality plan because state officials considered the water problem so bad in Malheur County." The "uniqueness" of the county was emphasized along with the need to impress the state and federal governments that, "They cannot set the same standards

Malheur County can be distinguished by its complex of irrigation ditches and canals. (Courtesy Oregon State Archives)

for eastern Oregon as they do for western Oregon." [22] The goals for the management plan were adopted, and in 1991 a groundwater program was approved. The plan provided information on water quality and contamination sources, as well as on recommended solutions; but participation was voluntary, and financial support limited.

Floyd Hawkins, chair of the committee, expressed local feelings. "Our first priority is enough water to grow our crops ... We're conserving the water ... We're using it over and over again." [23] Apparently the Water Resources Department agrees with Hawkins. "On the Owyhee the applicant [for a new permit] shows whether water is available." [24]

Within the 4,000 to 5,000-foot-high Klamath plateau, the Reclamation Service proposed draining swamps and diverting streams through canals to assure that agriculture here succeeded. The Klamath project, which included the Lost River and Gerber reservoirs in Oregon and the Clear Lake in California, was financed, owned, and is still managed by federal reclamation officials. These impoundments were aimed at increasing irrigation water, and in both cases private existing companies agreed to sell their canal systems and water rights and to bind their lands to the federal government. As with similar undertakings, "The people are anxious to obtain irrigation under the provisions of the Reclamation Act." [25]

The Klamath region lies within the Basin and Range province, an area of alternating valleys and eroded elongate hills, underlain by continuous lava flows that erupted some 25 to 30 million years ago. During the Ice Ages, over 12,000 years in the past, the basin was filled by waters of Lake Modoc, which extended over 1,000 square miles. Upper and Lower Klamath lakes, as well as Tule Lake, are remnants of this vast pluvial body of water. Almost all of the drainage is confined within the depression, and only the Klamath River winds in a torturous route out of the basin before exiting to the Pacific Ocean. The Sprague and Williamson rivers run into the Upper Klamath, which, in times past, would overflow into Lower Klamath Lake, while in adjacent California Lost River supplied Tule Lake.

As the nineteenth century began, a combined wetlands and riverine system in this province was rich in fish and bird life and the home to one of the largest osprey breeding colonies in North America. Attracting the attention of plume hunters, who sought feathers and skins for the current fashion in clothing, egrets, terns, gulls, grebes, herons, and pelicans were slaughtered by the hundreds of thousands. It took the intervention of the National Association of Audubon Societies, lobbying the Oregon legislature in 1903, to end the carnage.

Those first farmers in the Klamath area realized the scarcity of well-watered soil and a lack of rainfall would retard the development of agriculture; however, the rivers and lakes scattered throughout the whole area offered "unmatched irrigation possibilities. Indeed, it was clear even to the uninitiated earliest settlers that water could be drawn to flood their fields and increase crop yields." [26] Irrigation began with cattlemen digging small ditches to their own farms near Klamath Falls along the Link River. They utilized ancient abandoned river channels, such as the Olene and Lyttle water gaps, to place their canals and dams.

Informal water organizations emerged after the mid-1800s with the Linkville Water Ditch Company and the Little Klamath Ditch Company. Placing a headgate on the east bank of Link River and extending a canal to Klamath Falls, William Steele provided water for the incipient town with his Linkville ditch. At Steele's death in the 1890s, Henry Ankeny, a rancher-financier, acquired control of the canal, which he incorporated as the Klamath Falls Irrigation Company. The Little Klamath ditch was begun by cattleman J. Frank Adams, who cut an eighteen-foot-deep trench from Little Klamath Lake, through the low hills, to carry water some twenty miles to farms near Klamath Falls. Adams offered stock to finance improvements, but, when he was unable to interest anyone else, he sold to the U.S. Reclamation Service.

In the early 1900s, the Reclamation Service was planning a project that would bring even greater disruption to the wetland ecology of the Klamath basin. In 1904 petitions from residents, businessmen, farmers, and politicians, soliciting federal money, welcomed the arrival of the government. At a town meeting on November 39, 1904, "interest and excitement raised to a fever heat." Californians from adjacent Modoc and Siskiyou counties attended as well, and Secretary of State, C.S. Moore, who made a special trip to assess the situation, reported, "Klamath County is about to enter upon a boom of industrial development, has already entered it, in fact … property is changing hands at greatly increased values, and there are so many people going there." [27]

Local residents formed the Klamath Water Users Association to clear away obstacles, such as previously held water rights, that might stand in the way of a take over by the reclamation agency. Eventually the government purchased all of the regional waterworks and rights: those owned by the Klamath Falls Irrigation Company, by the Jesse Carr Company at Tule Lake, and by the Little Klamath Water Ditch, along with the right-of-way for the Keno cut, belonging to landowner Thomas McCormick. The only hold out was the Klamath Canal Company, demanding and receiving $150,000 for its rights.

As proposed by the Reclamation Service, the ambitious Klamath project was to redeem 300,000 acres of the basin by completely draining Lower Klamath and Tule lakes, thereby making the swampland cultivatable. Among the reclamation activities, this enterprise was unique for its variety of undertakings – irrigation ditches and canals, dredging, river impoundments, bog drainage, and evaporation. Because each swamp was supplied with water from a single source - either from the Klamath or Lost rivers - this plan could be accomplished fairly easily by cutting off the flow at those two points. Evaporation would take care of any remaining water. By constructing a dam across Lost River in northern California and a headworks and tunnel to divert the Klamath River, where it flowed out of Upper Klamath Lake, the two "improvements" would hold spring runoff, which could be used for irrigation as well as to provide a possible source for future power. Once the final plans were fully developed, the Main Canal of the Klamath River would extend from Upper Klamath Lake southeastward through Klamath Falls, branching repeatedly, while another system northward from Clear Lake would divide into east and south branches. Smaller ditches and tunnels moved the water to even more distant users.

Nothing was underway by 1906, but assurances were given that water would soon be coursing through the network. The Clear Lake Dam, begun two years later, was completed in 1912, dewatering Tule Lake, but closing off the water supply to Lower Klamath Lake wasn't accomplished until 1921. A contract, signed by swampland owners belonging to the Klamath Drainage District, agreed to payment of reclamation survey costs of $100,000. Both Tule and Lower Klamath lakes became, in the words of ornithologist William Finley, "a great desert waste of dry peat and alkali. Over large stretches fire has burned the peat to a depth of from one to three feet, leaving a layer of white loose ashes into which one sinks above

The upper portal of a tunnel for a dam on the Klamath project, 1906.
(Photo by D.W. Murphy; Courtesy Oregon State Archives)

his knees. One of the most unique features in North America is gone. It is a crime against our children." [28] Gerber Reservoir across Miller Creek, a tributary to the Lost River, was finished in 1925 as part of the same Klamath project.

For the next fifty to sixty years, a proliferation of inconsistent government policies and a balancing act with private interests led to a tangle of water uses in the Klamath basin. Land and water were alternately set aside for the refuge or taken out and sold to private farmers, depending on which way the current administration was leaning. In spite of lobbying by the Audubon Society to reflood Lower Klamath Lake in 1925, the Klamath Drainage District won out with arguments that the government should honor contracts to supply it with water, even though the district hadn't made payments for huge debts, which it had accrued for reclamation services.

In the end, Lower Klamath Lake was rewatered because of miscalculations by engineers, not for environmental reasons. After most of the original Tule Lake swamplands had been converted to farms, the basin began to refill with excess water from agricultural runoff. To prevent this build-up the Bureau of Reclamation came up with the idea of constructing a tunnel from Tule to Lower Klamath Lake, carrying the water to reflood part of the region formerly occupied by the lake. This latter "correction" in the Klamath project came in 1942, and followed a typical pattern of western reclamation, where swamps were dewatered, rewatered with canals, then the excess carried away. [29]

After drainage of the wetlands, so much new artificially created farm land was being offered so cheaply by the government that the number of farms doubled from 1900 to 1940. Big cattle ranches were replaced by smaller fields of crops, where production of irrigated wheat, barley, oats, potatoes, and especially alfalfa increased dramatically. Overall farming practices throughout the basin consumed the greatest quantities of water. A 1971 Klamath Basin study by the Water Resources Board examined the aftermath of the placement of reclamation dams, noting that the amount of acreage irrigated with federal water increased until the 1970s, when it leveled off at 154,000 acres. However other figures show that at the present

The cultivation of potatoes in Klamath County around 1940 required immense amounts of water. (Courtesy Oregon State Archives)

time the total has risen above 250,000 acres. [30] During dry months, the Lower Klamath Lake and Tule refuges suffered because water they might have acquired was given over to irrigation needs. "As a result, opportunities to manage the refuges to their maximum potential have been limited."[31]

Thus agricultural prosperity, purchased on the ruination of Klamath and Tule lakes, brought grand fair livestock and crop prizes. Farmers received "the award for best oats, barley, and wheat, and award for best irrigated apples."[32] Today the Lower Klamath Lake National Wildlife Refuge of 81,619 acres, set aside in 1908, is touted as a triumph to human efforts at protecting the environment rather than for the eradication it really symbolizes.

Groundwater resources in the Klamath Basin were still considered plentiful into the 1990s. Although localized problem areas were beginning to appear twenty years before this, the Oregon Water Resources Department indicated that overall aquifer levels were not dropping, and "a large volume of ground water" loomed on the horizon for future development plans.[33] Even when the number of wells tripled between 1954 and 1969, the U.S. Geological Survey found that withdrawal of 61,000 acre-feet of groundwater "nearly all for irrigation … had no measurable effect on water levels in the aquifers." [34] These forecasts, however, proved erroneous as needs for wildlife and the necessity of maintaining and augmenting low stream flows began to compete with traditional farm irrigation. The statements were particularly frivolous when the groundwater hydrology of the basin was still poorly understood thirty years later. "No regional-scale quantitative studies have ever been undertaken. There is only limited information with which to evaluate the potential for new ground-water uses … [or] where groundwater development is unlikely to affect streams." [35]

Dependence on underground water grew steadily as surface supplies dwindled in what was a clear misunderstanding of the fundamental relationship between the two. Perhaps the best example of this folly came in 2000 when the Bureau of Reclamation began "mining" groundwater to fulfill surface reservoir quotas. Of the 75,000-acre-feet stored for 2004, it paid for 50,000 acre-feet pumped from deep wells. Predictably, over a three-year period, the water table dropped twenty feet in some regions. Don Rajnus, a spokesman for the Klamath farmers, whose wells were running dry, claimed "their water rights are being usurped … The water belongs to the people, not whoever wants to buy and sell it." The bureau planned to pay $1.6 million for more well water during that coming summer.[36]

Alteration of the entire Klamath ecosystem of lakes, marshlands, rivers, and wildlife began with the advent of settlers. During the first hundred years, little thought was given to preservation, by which time over 280,000 of the original 350,000 acres of wetlands and lakes had been filled or drained. The concerted emphasis on economic betterment throughout that long interval remains unchanged today as decisions concerning the Klamath are still weighed heavily toward business, agricultural, and political interests.

The current tangle of contradictory reports, Band-Aid solutions, backtracking, the lack of adjudication over old water rights, the battles over water ownership, and the dwindling water supply led to the massive fish dieoff in 2001. All point to the inadequacy of historically-followed policies:

April, 2001: The Bureau of Reclamation develops a ten-year management plan to correct the lack of water in the Klamath basin. The plan is to buy water rights, to encourage less water-intensive crops, to restore wetlands, and to keep more flow in the river for protecting salmon.

Spring, 2001: The water supply is already low in the basin. The Endangered Species Act and state law placed water needs of fish before that of farming. Federal water was withheld from irrigation canals.

May, 2001: The Bucket Brigade, passing buckets of stored lake water hand-to-hand into irrigation canals, was formed by farmers as a protest group. Oregon Senator Gordon Smith vowed to reform the Endangered Species Act. "Sucker fish are [not] more valuable than the family farm." [37]

June 29, 2001: An irrigation canal headgate, illegally opened from Upper Klamath Lake, is closed by the Bureau of Reclamation. The gate is opened and closed twice more.

July, 2001: Senator Smith's bill to modify the Endangered Species Act fails to pass.

July 24, 2001: The basin is out of water. The Bureau of Reclamation re-diverted 75,000 acre-feet of water to "relieve farmers" at the initiation of Interior Secretary Gale Norton.

September, 2001: In mid-September in excess of 33,000 fish die in the warm de-oxygenated water of the Klamath River.

February, 2002: A preliminary draft of a Natural Research Council report calls for more biological studies on the fish before a decision on water flow can be made.

March, 2002: More rainfall than in the previous year. The headgates at Klamath Falls are opened by Interior Secretary Gale Norton, providing a full delivery "to help farmers and ranchers recover from losses suffered last year." [38]

Summer, 2002: The drought is said to be less severe.

October, 2002: An U.S. Geological Survey study finds that agriculture generated only $100 million a year as compared to $800 million produced by recreation.

October, 2002: National Marine Fisheries Service biologist Michael Kelly filed a disclosure that the agency's recommended minimum flows for fish had been rejected under "political pressure." [39]

Fall, 2002: President Bush proposes to buy water from those who don't use it, giving it to needy landowners.

Spring, 2003: A wet season with predictions of plenty of water by the Bureau of Reclamation. The bureau promises that the allotment to fish will be increased.

April 10, 2003: Representatives introduce the federal Klamath River Basin Restoration and Emergency Act to establish water conservation, to restore habitats, to increase river flows, and to assist anyone affected by the fish-kill.

June 14, 2003: In response to a lawsuit, a federal judge rules that farming could continue on 22,000 acres of wetlands of the Tule and Klamath refuges, the only two in the nation where farming is permitted.

June 21, 2003: The Bureau of Reclamation ordered farmers to cut water use by one-fourth.

July 17, 2003: The Klamath River Basin Restoration Act is amended to prohibit water and pesticide intensive crops (onions, potatoes, alfalfa) on refuges. The Klamath Water Users Association says the act would not result in much more water and would be an economic hardship on farmers.

July 18, 2003: In a suit brought by conservationists and native tribes, a judge rules that the government is failing to protect salmon but denies any immediate shift in more water to aid fish, a seeming victory for the

Klamath Water Users Association.

July 23, 2003: A federal judge rules that the Oregon State Water Resources Department should determine how much water is needed to maintain the fish and game, which native tribes depend on.

August 3, 2003: More suckers are dying from insufficient water and polluted wetlands. The suckers are close to extinction.

August 6, 2003: Karl Rove, President Bush's political aide, is in the Klamaths; he is accused of wanting to assure that agriculture interests come first.

September 6, 2003: An investigation is begun into Rove's interference.

October 22, 2003: A final Natural Research Council report has a mixed message: it stresses the need to repair the "out of balance landscape" by removing dams, restoring wetlands, and increasing cool water flow to rivers. The council sees a need to take an "ecosystem approach," but thought that the diversion to farms couldn't be blamed for the salmon die-off and that additional polluted warm water would not have helped the fish.

October, 2003: A report by a panel of scientists from Oregon State University, the U.S. Geological Survey, and the Bureau of Land Management disagrees with the NRC report and says the government was right to withhold federal water from farmers. The report also states that more water in the rivers and lakes would have helped the fish.

November 19, 2003: The government admits that giving water to farmers contributed to the fish die-off.

January 21, 2004: Conservationists file a lawsuit to protest increased farming and logging in the Klamath Marsh National Wildlife Refuge.

March 6, 2004: Bush proposes to sent water from the Trinity River to the Klamath area. Trinity water is currently piped to California valley farmers.

March 13, 2004: An inquiry finds President Bush's aide Rove didn't interfere in Klamath water decisions.

Spring, 2004: The weather is dry. There is increased interest in using groundwater to alleviate the water shortage. Groundwater is considered plentiful.

May 20, 2004: Surface water already short, and winter runoff is low, causing the federal government to pay farmers to pump millions of gallons of groundwater onto crops. In places, the groundwater table has fallen more than twenty feet in three years.

Aug, 2004: A study finds more than twice the number of salmon died than previously reported.

August 13, 2004: Groundwater levels are declining rapidly. The Bureau of Reclamation is using water from deep wells to develop a future supply. The State Water Resources Department continues to issue and extend permits for groundwater use.

April, 2005: Water shortages are predicted. The Bureau of Reclamation asks farmers to reduce irrigation voluntarily by fifteen percent to avoid later cutbacks. Wildlife refuges face reductions up to forty percent.

October, 2005: Federal and state officials signed an agreement to restore fish habitat, to improve water quality, and to find more water for irrigation in the Klamath region. The particulars of this catchall program have yet to be worked out.

Most recently, water marketing and water banking have been proposed to alleviate the crisis in the Klamath Basin. Under these measures, irrigation shortfalls would be relieved with the buying and selling of water between rights holders. Any member, who has unused water, can "bank" it, thus allowing the banked portion to be borrowed, then transferred to where needed. Several drawbacks are that historic water rights have yet to be determined in much of Oregon, especially in the Klamath Basin, the transfers might secondarily affect other rights holders, the value of water varies considerably from place to place, and in the opinion of Doug Whitsett, president of the Water for Life, "Separating water rights from land and selling it is somewhat like clear-cutting a forest and not replanting." [40]

A 2005 report by the General Accountability Office noted that the banking program was proving to be extremely costly and could reach in excess of $65 million by 2011. Furthermore, it didn't solve the basin's scant water supply. Democratic congressmen, who read the report said, "The Klamath's upper basin is oversubscribed ... the water bank process has been secretive, and stakeholders have been kept in the dark." [41]

WESTERN OREGON

Large-scale irrigation works came late to the Willamette Valley. Experiments conducted at Oregon State College in Corvallis showed the benefits of sum-

Flooding across a field of alfalfa seedings in Marion County was an early method of irrigating that expended tremendous amounts of water. (Courtesy Oregon State Archives)

mertime watering of crops as early as 1911, but it wasn't until some forty years later that sprinklers were being used extensively after the number of acres and succession of plantings increased. Around 177,000 acres were under irrigation in the western part of the state in 1959. This figure rose to 235,000 by 1978, and close to 300,000 by the 1990s.

Supplemental irrigation allowed the Tualatin Valley to become renowned as one of Oregon's most productive regions. Here the community of Scholls typified the countryside. "Scholls boasts an up-to the minute diversified farming community .. No section of Oregon is better suited for potatoes, berries, nuts, and fruits … Dairying is one of the most important industries of Scholls."[42]

By the middle of the century, however, farmers found themselves being seriously impacted by urban sprawl from Portland and having to vie with a thirsty population for the water supply. It didn't take long for them to realize that they were facing an impending shortage. Reports in 1956 and again in 1963 found that additional water was needed for all three: irrigation, cities, and industry. Initially the idea to impound Scoggins Creek began with local farmers led by Henry Hagg, President of both the Tualatin Valley Water Improvement District and the Dairy Co-Operative Association. Trying to sell the idea of a dam, Hagg pointed out that, "Our whole economy is based on agriculture out here, and we won't have any crops or food processing plants if we don't get some way to control our water." [43]

Experiencing several dry summers, the 1958 flow in the Tualatin was particularly low, forcing the State Engineer to rescind all recently granted water rights along the river. Farmers resorted to nighttime pumping. To complicate the problem, the Oregon Iron and Steel Company in Lake Oswego held historic pre-1909 water rights, and the company was demanding enough water to keep the lake supplied and its electric generator operating. Complaining that, "The amount claimed by the company exceeds actual flow of the Tualatin in roughly three months of each normal year," farmers organized and took their argument to the courts in order to clear the way for their construction.[44] Their attorney expressed the opinion that, "Oswego has been shortsighted … in long opposing a reclamation dam project … now that Oswegans are faced with winding up some summer with a damp swamp instead of a lake … they may be turning toward support of a regulating dam." Residents of Lake Oswego and the Oregon Iron and Steel Company, however, stuck to their demands wanting to keep "Lake Oswego at least knee deep." [45]

Following a court decision favoring the iron company, the Bureau of Reclamation began a study, in which the Secretary of the Interior reported that the, "Present natural stream flow in the Tualatin River is inadequate to meet constantly increasing seasonal water requirements." The secretary also found that expansion of urban, industrial, and agriculture development in the valley "has been virtually stopped in recent years by the seasonal exhaustion of the natural water supply." The conclusion was that a dam across Scoggins Creek would aid in flood control, could provide for added irrigation, recreation, fish and wildlife, and water quality, as well as for municipal and industrial development – all beneficial uses listed by the Oregon Water Resources Department.[46] Many local people felt otherwise. "Behind all discussions loomed the pressure of speculators, bent on turning the Tualatin Valley, a prime agricultural valley, into one vast complex of houses, streets, apartments, and lawns, with a million toilets demanding a dozen dams to flush them." [47]

But construction wasn't to be halted, and Oregon Representative Wendell Wyatt presided over a ceremony that named the future lake after farmer-dairyman Henry Hagg. "In so designating the new lake and the new dam, the history of the valley will be preserved and a tribute to an outstanding civic servant will be proclaimed." [48] Ten years earlier, a "public-spirited" Hagg expressed regret that some fourteen homes would be flooded but opined, "There is never progress without some sacrifice." The Fred Knox family, who had to move to a new home overlooking the scenic lake, agreed. Mrs. Knox commented with feeling, "The Indians were uprooted, too." [49]

The dam on Scoggins Creek, complete with pumping plant and pipelines, was begun in 1972 and completed in 1975. Did this one impoundment accomplish the multitude of tasks set for it by its ambitious planners? Hagg Lake water was primarily intended for agricultural needs, and of the more than 400 water rights on the Tualatin River, eighty percent were designated for irrigation. But with only twenty percent going toward increasing urban demands, water soon was in short supply. Even as the lake was filling in 1976, the Tualatin Valley Irrigation District was laying eighty additional miles of concrete pipe and planning another dam near Gaston. "As fruit and vegetable fields closer to Portland have been wiped out by the outward march of the metro area, the lands in western Washington County would in effect replace the bean fields of Parkrose." These words of Palmer Torvend, manager of the district, fulfilled a prediction made one year earlier.

A 1975 study pointed out the possibility that the dam might actually encourage agricultural production and urban development by "supposedly alleviating a water shortage ... by giving the illusion that plenty of water will be available for increased urbanization." In addition, increased yields would be necessary on the land remaining in production to compensate for that put into municipal growth. After placement of the dam, farmers expanded their crop fields westward, while urban growth in the Tualatin Valley doubled.

The role played by reclamation water, whose original purpose was to supply farmlands, has been modified considerably in recent times. Water rights in the Tualatin Valley, which were initially designated for agriculture, remained tied to land that has since been incorporated into urban bound-

aries. Similarly, farm acreage in the Grants Pass Irrigation District in Josephine
County has been turned into housing. Established in 1916, the district owns
the rights to, and operates with, water from the Savage Rapids Reservoir on
the Rogue River, which was erected by the Bureau of Reclamation. By 1985
the district was serving 400 acres of commercial growers, over 7,000 acres
of urban-suburban lands, and much of municipal Grants Pass itself. Its
officials elected to "encourage the continued supply of irrigation water to
urbanizing land ... within the UGB [urban growth boundary]. The District
feels this benefits the developer," as the cost of supplying water is lower.[52]

The Savage Rapids Dam has deteriorated to the point that the Bureau of
Reclamation recommends tearing it down, but the controversy over removal
has been on-going for over ten years with district supporters claiming government interference. Sixty percent of the members voted for removal in the
face of a 1988 lawsuit by the National Marine Fisheries Service on behalf of
the endangered coho salmon. Two years later a $3 million grant by the Or-
egon Watershed Enhancement Board was approved to help pay for the removal and replacement pumps to supply water in place of the dam system.

Bureau of Reclamation reservoirs carried the promise that large quantities of federal water would always be available even during drought years.
The reality was that when snow and rainfall varied and diminished, there
was little or no water to be utilized. Groundwater pumping became the next
alternative until it, too, dried up.

In greening up the state, irrigated land doubled from 658,652 acres in
1909 to 1,348,284 in 1959, reaching close to 1.6 million acres in the late
1980s, where it remained unchanged for ten years before reaching 2 million
acres in 2000. Today somewhat less water is being used for farming than a
decade ago, a drop that could be accounted for by a shift in irrigation methods, by the cultivation of less water intensive crops, or by the government
paying irrigators to remove land from production.[53] However, even with
updated methods, an abundance of reservoirs, and less irrigation demands,
there is not enough water to go around, and on both sides of the Cascades
new wells are being drilled, older ones deepened, and dams constructed.
Until conservation not consumption becomes the primary goal, maintaining present day agricultural practices and production in the face of increasing needs for fish, municipalities, industry, and recreation is unrealistic.

ENDNOTES: THE GREENING OF OREGON: WATER FOR AGRICULTURE

[1] Charles E. Stricklin, "Oregon's Irrigation," *Oregon Blue Book*, (Salem, 1949-1950), 205.

[2] Michael C. Robinson, *Water for the West; The Bureau of Reclamation, 1902-1977* (Chicago, Public Works Historical Society, 1979), 11.

[3] Robert H. Boyle, John Graves, and T.H. Watkins, *Water Hustlers* (San Francisco, Sierra Club, 1971), 8.

[4] William Hallmark, "Oregon's Water Management Districts" *Oregon Law Review*, 1967-68, v.47, 16.

[5] U.S. Congress, 57th Session I, Chapter 1903, 1902, 388.

[6] Thomas Vaughan, *High & Mighty* (Portland, Oregon Historical Society Press, 1981), 112.

[7] Wallis Nash, *A Lawyer's Life on Two Continents* (R.G. Badger, Boston, 1919), 142.

[8] *Oregonian*, November 3, 1905, 8, col.4.

[9] U.S. Bureau of Reclamation, *Bureau of Reclamation Project Feasibilities and Authorizations* (Washington, D.C., General Printing Office, 1957), 386.

[10] Oregon Water Resources Department. File # G10349; Permit #G9972; Memo from Larry Jebousek to James Sexson, Dec. 27, 1982; Letter from Dave Tolve, Engineering Dept., Avion Water Company, January 6, 1983.

[11] Oregon Water Resources Department, File #G12420; Permit #G-11577, 1992.

[12] 1000 Friends of Oregon, "Gary Harris: Farmer with a Vision." *Newsletter*, Summer, 2004, 6.

[13] Betty Stanard, "Central Oregon Irrigation" In: *A History of the Deschutes Country* (Bend, Deschutes County Historical Society, 1985), 22.

[14] Malheur County Historical Society, *Malheur County History*, 1988, 81.

[15] Ibid., 82.

[16] Eastern Oregon Land Co. v. Willow River Land and Irrigation Company, 201 Fed. Reporter, 1912, 223.

[17] McConnell v. Owyhee Ditch Company, 132 Or 128, 1930, 129.

[18] U.S. Bureau of Reclamation, 1957, 693.

[19] Oregon Water Resources Board, *Malheur-Owyhee Basins* (Salem, 1969), 34.

[20] Ibid., 47-49.

[21] *Daily Argus Observer*, June 24, 1980, 8.

[22] *Daily Argus Observer*, September 10, 1980, 1.

[23] Ibid.

[24] Rick Cooper, Oregon Water Resources Department, Phone interview, October, 2003.

[25] U.S. Bureau Of Reclamation, 1957, 518.

[26] Victor L. Jepsen, *A General History of Klamath Falls from Its Beginning until the Coming of the Railroad in 1909* (Eugene, Masters, University of Oregon, 1939), 66.

[27] Ibid., 72, 73.

[28] *Oregon Sportsman*, September 2, 1925, 1.

[29] Mark Fiege, *Irrigated Eden: The Making of an Agricultural Landscape in the American West* (Seattle, University of Washington Press, 1999), 31.

[30] U.S. Bureau of the Census, Census of Agriculture – County Data. Irrigation, 1992.

[31] Oregon Water Resources Board, *Klamath Basin* (Salem, 1971), 100.

[32] *Klamath Falls Republican*, September 12, 1907.

[33] Oregon Water Resources Board, 1971, 113.

[34] A.R. Leonard and A.B. Harris, *Groundwater in Selected Areas in the Klamath Basin* (U.S. Geological Survey, 1974), 2.

[35] *Klamath Bucket Brigade*, "Upper Klamath Basin Ground-Water Study," Internet, April 25, 2004, 1.

[36] *The Register-Guard*, May 3, 2004, B3.

[37] Ted Williams, "Salmon Stakes, "*Audubon*, March, 2003, 45?

[38] Ibid., 46?.

[39] Ibid.

[40] *Capital Press*, June 18, 2004, 5.

[41] *Oregonian*, March 31, 2005, C8.

[42] Penny Cass and J. Ronald Miner, *The Historical Tualatin River Basin* (Corvallis, Oregon State University, Water Resources Research Institute, 1993), 27.

[43] *Oregonian,* August 31, 1958, 9, col.1-5.

[44] Ibid.

[45] *Oregonian,* June 19, 1960, 31, col.1-3.

[46] U.S. Bureau of Reclamation, 1957, 556.

[47] Robert L. Benson, "The Tualatin River, Mile by Mile." In: *Land of Tuality*, *v.III*, Hillsboro, Washington County Historical Society, 1978, 44.

[48] *Oregonian*, February 1, 1973, 13, col.1.

[49] *Oregonian*, June 19, 1960, 31, col.1-3.

[50] *Oregonian*, June 24, 1976, 13.

[51] Lolita Carter, *The Effect of Human Activity on the Middle Course of the Tualatin River, Oregon* (Portland, PhD, Portland State University, 1975), 123.

[52] Grants Pass, Oregon. Planning Department. *Comprehensive Community Development Plan, Grants Pass and Josephine County* (Grants Pass, 1984), 10.2-10; 10.2-11.

[53] Bruce Pokarney, Oregon Dept of Agriculture, Salem, Phone conversation, October 9, 2003.

CHAPTER 7

WATER TO WASH
AWAY OUR SINS

The sewage must be so largely diluted as to have become almost an inappreciable quantity. To secure this dilution, it is obvious that, if the river be a quiet, slow-flowing stream, it might take ten to twenty miles to produce the required mixing; but if fast-running...a much less distance would have the same effect.[1]

From the earliest days of settlement, Oregon's waterways served as sewers to carry away the raw waste from industry and cities. Clean surface water, which was diverted from springs or rivers, would emerge as sewage or industrial sludge to be sent through yet another conduit into the nearest - and possibly the same - river, beach, wetland, or lake, from which it originated.

It had long been held that flowing water destroyed impurities, an idea modified and adapted to modern practices of diluting toxic and unsanitary wastes with running water in an effort to lower the level of contamination. If the noxious liquids were transported to the ocean, which was boundless, they were thinned even further. This notion didn't originate in the Northwest but was firmly entrenched in the minds of newcomers. The practice, which had been brought to the east coast from Europe, crossed the continent with those wagonloads of pioneers.

The more water that went for human consumption, the more sewage and refuse that came out the other end. The arrival of a public water supply bringing indoor bathtubs, toilets, and washing machines, along with bigger factories processing heavier amounts, greatly amplified the quantity. Generally wastewaters are laden either with chemicals, organic matter, sediment, and bacteria, or they are high in temperature, any or all of which reduce purity. Today these pollutants must be diluted but are rarely eliminated before final discharge. Until the 1930s sewage treatment was largely nonexistent. Settlers focused on waste only after an outbreak of disease, when it was realized that their effluent was discharged into the same waters from which their drinking source was drawn. Since that time laws, enforced by state and federal authorities, were aimed at protecting public health and enhancing water quality.

Concern over water quality arrived late on the Oregon scene, and then regulations emphasized public health rather than pollution. Today the focus has changed, and the goal is to safeguard Oregon's waters. Efforts are directed toward "restoring and preserving the quality and purity of the air and the waters of the state in accordance with rules and standards established by the [Environmental Quality] commission." [2]

In 1889 the only regulations that prohibited contamination were aimed specifically toward domestic or farming activities. Laws protected waterways from "any dead animal carcass or part thereof, excrement, putrid, nauseous … or offensive substance [which] befouls, pollutes or impairs the quality of any spring, river, brook … which is or may be used for domestic purposes or to which cattle, horses, or other kind of domestic stock have access." [3] At that time enforcement came under the auspices of the State Board of Health, which rarely modified or halted any water pollution activity. In one of its few legal actions, the board sought an injunction in 1914 against the city of Silverton in Marion County because its sewers discharged waste onto each bank of Silver Creek. While the court ruled that the board failed to prove the existence of a public nuisance, it did establish the state government's authority over such matters.[4]

Changes began in 1920s, after excessive pollution in the more populous Willamette Basin attracted the concerns of many groups and agencies. Recognizing that its own municipality was the worst offender, the Portland City Club conducted a study that described the river as "ugly and filthy," and the members subsequently encouraged legislation to abate the nuisance.[5] The State Planning Board created the Stream Purification Committee in 1935 to make recommendations on statewide cleanup measures. In highly unusual and forthright findings, the committee reported that pollution control laws were a "Promiscuous adoption of unrelated and uncoordinated nuisance and penal statutes [which] afford only a minimum degree of control and cannot form the basis of a concerted and direct effort to prohibit pollution of streams." [6] Lack of coordination, impracticality, overlapping responsibilities, and uncertain enforcement duties were some of the criticisms leveled at the laws. In 1938, as today, the Legislature failed to take action; so a referendum, the Water Purification and Prevention of Pollution Bill, to set up the State Sanitary Authority, was voted on and passed three to one by the people of Oregon.

Establishment of the Sanitary Authority, a division of the State Board of Health, came in 1939, and its first task was to adopt then enforce water quality regulations. Specific new policies forbade the dumping of any quantity of untreated municipal and industrial waste that would cause the dissolved oxygen content of the stream to be less than five parts per million. This formula marked the beginning of the current pollution abatement program. Initially the Sanitary Authority relied on voluntary cooperation from polluters once they were notified of the requirements for some sort of treatment installation, but it wasn't until the 1950s that legal proceedings were instituted to force compliance.

Oregon's regulations were completely rewritten and strengthened in 1967, redirecting the policy away from pollution abatement to prevention of unregulated effluent disposal and water quality enhancement. Permits for discharging waste from a specific point into public waters were required, and financial assistance was made available for treatment works. Two years later the Department of Environmental Quality was created and given responsibility for examining and establishing water quality standards for each stream, in addition to overseeing a permitting program.

MUNICIPAL SEWAGE: 1800s TO 1930s

At a time when riverbanks were sparsely settled and there were few businesses, the volume and impact of waste was minimal. Conveying sewage from the immediate population center by some system of ditches, gutters, or pipes was the primary concern. For individual households a privy or cesspool stored the refuse, which either percolated slowly into the soil or was transported a sufficient distance in a ditch so as to be out of range of sight and odor. Care had to be taken to keep the sewage separate from the household water source, but, as frequently happened, septic tanks were adjacent to, or upstream from, the domestic supply. Unlined or cracked containers and outfall pipes oozed fecal material directly into the drinking water. As communities expanded, tanks for individual homes were replaced by a network of conduits, that led into a central system, which fed into the nearest surface flow. Creeks or streams were sometimes diverted into a drainage ditch or pipe to aid in dilution.

Most waterways on both sides of the Cascade Range were the recipients of polluted effluent, but no rivers were more overwhelmed than those in the heavily settled Willamette Basin. While the headwaters of a given stream might have escaped from thousands of gallons of liquid wastes, a river like the Willamette, fed by so many tributaries as well as being the focus of development, soon became so contaminated it was already dying by 1900. "The Willamette River is a common sewer for the entire valley between the Cascade and Coast Ranges … all of the filth, the defilement, the infection from this wide territory … ultimately mingles with the Willamette and every person who drinks the river water consumes his portion of these appetizing ingredients." [7] The unsanitary condition of the Willamette was the cause of early outbreaks of disease throughout the valley from Eugene northward to Portland. The onset of epidemics stimulated interest in cleanup efforts and in designing sewage disposal systems.

Lamenting the lack of sewers in 1861, the *Oregonian* newspaper noted that the topography of Portland offered ideal conditions for removal. "The earth can readily be excavated, and the grade from the hill to the river is just about what would be desired for the purpose." [8] Here, as in other communities, it was common practice for the contents of spittoons, chamber pots, and laundry tubs, along with rotting food from vegetable vendors and meat markets to be thrown into city streets awaiting rains to carry it away. It wasn't until three years later that the newspaper was able to report that sewer work was actually going on, "the cleaning up of that abominable sink hole, the receptacle of filth of all the streets between Alder and Morrison. With the proper sewerage Front might be made the prettiest street in the city."[9]

The story of what happened to Portland's Tanner Creek is extraordinary. Once flowing above ground, the creek has not been visible for a hundred years since it was buried beneath the surface and confined in a sewer trough in 1888. Originally the course of Tanner Creek was northward, draining the canyon (now Canyon Road) at the head of Jefferson Street, crossing Multnomah field (PGE Park) before it turned to the southeast through a ravine near upper Alder Street, eventually reaching the Willamette River. Paralleling the creek bed, sections of the old crumbling pipe were replaced with a new one in 1904 designed to encompass and utilize the creek water for moving sewage down from the southwest hills.

Just twenty years after settlement, Portland experienced epidemics of both diphtheria and typhoid. In 1866 California traveller Aubrey Angelo mistakenly attributed diphtheria outbreaks in the city to decomposing vegetation instead of to the raw human sewage being pumped into the harbor. "An annual epidemic, known under the name of Dyptheria, prevails in Portland, more particularly in the immediate neighborhood of the river, caused by a upas malaria [a poisonous tree in Java] from decomposed vegetation lying on the banks." [10] However, by switching its drinking source from the Willamette River to Bull Run Lake in 1895, Portland fared better than most communities.

Salem's sewage system targeted the Willamette as well. In 1893 the Oregon Legislature enacted a law that the "the city of Salem and the county of Marion … shall pay one half of the expense of laying a separate drain from the capitol ground to the Willamette river, on condition that the public grounds … and the grounds adjacent to the county court house may have drainage through such separate drain pipe." [11] West of Salem, McMinnville "never had any sewerage, but one is now being put in … that will drain the business portion of town." The ditch "will be about 2500 feet long … will be from four to eight feet deep" and will stretch to the Yamhill River. [12]

A typhoid outbreak in Salem at the turn of the century recurred in December, 1909, when it spread throughout the city, killing nine people and affecting over one hundred. At first blame was laid on the Salem Water Company, which supplied the city from the Willamette River. One physician pointed out that the intake pipe crossed a big slough, serving as the city sewer "where there is always danger of a slight break and the tainting of the entire water supply." [13] But the state bacteriologist found no bacteria or typhoid germs when he tested municipal water samples and suggested that the contamination might have come from private wells. Adding to Salem's problems that winter was a snowfall, which one physician feared would carry into the river "all kinds of rubbish and infectious material ... The sewers will be clogged and there will be another flood." [14]

While officials warned residents to boil or sterilize their water, the Salem Water Company began an inspection of its pipes and reservoir, eventually concluding that the intake pipe from the Willamette River was cracked. Consequently, the city council decided to purchase the privately held water company and look for a new source. Creating a new position of Sanitary Inspector, the council hired the zealous Amos Long, who plastered the town with warnings "not to spit on the sidewalks, on penalty of the city ordinances." Inspector Long had large quantities of disinfectants dumped into the millraces and creeks, and the municipal landfill was moved to north Mill Creek.[15] Salem's search for better water ended when the city began piping from the North Santiam River in 1936.

Three years earlier Eugene experienced what was called the "worst epidemic in the history of Oregon" when the city's water was found to be the source of typhoid fever.[16] Eugene was supplied by the privately owned Willamette Valley Company that drew water from contaminated wells along the banks of the Willamette River. During the fall, when well water was lowest and pollution highest, six percent of the students at the University of Oregon caught typhoid. The university was not connected to the city sewer. Instead it dumped its effluent into the millrace, "a sluggish stream and unhealthful at the best." [17] Seeking a new reservoir, the water company, the city council, and businessmen sited a well "a few feet from the river bank and a little further up than the present location." However, knowledgeable citizens were suspicious of this area pointing out that an old tannery had operated here for years, disposing of "dirty, greasy hides." [18] Shortly afterward the city government purchased the waterworks and installed filters to prevent further outbreaks of disease.

On the coast, the preferred program was down-to-the-sea-by-sewer. Community collection systems carried their sewage to the ocean whether directly or indirectly by a stream or river, which ended in the bays and estuaries. In Clatsop County, Tongue Point, Warrenton, and Astoria accessed waters of the Columbia River, while Seaside discharged effluent into the Necanicum River. It was the same story on down the coast at Florence, which disposed of its waste in the Siuslaw River, Reedsport utilized the

Umpqua, Newport, Coos Bay, and North Bend their respective estuaries, and Bandon sent effluent into the Coquille River.

Following a winter that saw twelve cases of typhoid, the Coquille City Council decided to consult an engineer from Portland – not because of any deaths, but because their summertime supply from Walker and Rink creeks had diminished. The engineer rejected a proposal to use the contaminated Coquille River, was against filtration, but advocated tapping the river's North Fork, although "there were dead eels and fish found [in the water] every summer … While the thought of that might not be pleasant, it did not constitute a menace to health, nor was it considered pollution." [19]

In Tillamook, Columbia, and Coos counties, where the dairy industry predominated, swamps and swales, with little or no current through them, became heavily polluted after receiving dairy by-products. Among the many ways in which milk could become infected with the typhoid bacillus, the most probable were from diseased cows and unsanitary conditions. A lawsuit involving Clover Hills Farms, a dairy corporation in Columbia County, pointed to the appalling sanitary conditions there, similar to those in other dairies. The farm housed over one hundred cattle in the barn, from which the owners "dump, wash, and empty daily large quantities of washings, manure, slops, garbage, refuse, and offal into [a] … swale and stream," mounding up large piles of manure in and near the swale and pig pens. When it rained, "myriads of maggots and filth and putrid matters" all washed into the stream and were carried down to the home of Albert Adams. Adams brought legal proceedings against the corporation in 1917 contending the company's practices had been ongoing for years. Clover Hills Farms attempted to argue that it had abated the nuisance, but the judge saw otherwise and found in favor of Adams. [20]

Across the Cascades, residents of The Dalles discharged their sewage into the Columbia River, but rather than using the Deschutes River or its tributaries, the towns of Madras, Redmond, Bend, and many private land owners on the Columbia Plateau, came up with the unique solution of sending their raw material from holding tanks into sinkholes, joints, or cracks hundreds of feet into the underlying lava. If the disposal wells became plugged, "shooting" with dynamite to deepen or repair the problem was the standard solution. In 1913 D.E. Hunter, a businessman visiting Bend, thought "he was in a Mexican revolution" one morning when he was wakened by dynamite blasts "going off on the sewer work." [21] The wells, ranging from a few feet to a depth of 400, lay above the groundwater level. "As it will be only a matter of time before the continued and uncontrolled discharge of waste ... will create a ground-water pollution problem, the further construction of disposal wells should be discontinued." [22] This practice continued for more than sixty years, with over 5,000 sumps utilized by municipalities and farms contaminating the very ground beneath the growing communities, before it was halted.

Fortunate to have a nearby water body, Baker City installed a "modern sewer" in 1900, in which the twelve-inch-wide terra cotta pipe "will empty into Powder River about a mile distant from D street." [23]

Eastern Oregon was not exempt from epidemics either. In 1905 and 1906 the town of Nyssa in Malheur County desperately needed a doctor because of an outbreak of disease. Arriving by train. Dr. J. J. Sarazin observed that each year the Snake River overflowed covering "shallow wells and outhouse pits, sometimes it just filled the sloughs and left stagnant water to breed mosquitoes." Dr. Sarazin advised digging ditches to remove standing water, drilling a well to obtain a fresh source, and installing a sewer system.[24]

INDUSTRIAL WASTE: 1800 TO 1930S

By their very nature, industries consume enormous volumes of water and yield tons of unpleasant and toxic liquid. Devouring tremendous amounts of fresh water daily through several stages of cleaning and sludge removal, industrial complexes were, of necessity, almost always placed adjacent to streams and rivers, where the flow could be directed as needed.

The water intake and subsequent effluent from paper mills far outstripped that of other consumers. In the manufacture of paper, millions of gallons of water were needed to convert cloth, straw, or wood pulp through a process called sulphite cooking. This chemical operation began with washing the material in clean water, before boiling it in a solution of caustic soda-ash or sodium hydroxide, producing a fiber slurry. "Next to the fouling of water by the washing of filthy rags, the discharge into rivers of the soda-liquor in which esparto (Spanish [*Stipa tenacissima*] or Algerian [*Lygeum spartum*] grass) has been boiled, is the most formidable source of pollution from paper-mills." [25] Afterward, a dark brown soapy liquid from the "boilings" was diluted with fresh water or "coolings" before being drained away. The pulp was then bleached to produce white paper, generating the third residue that was dumped into the running stream.

At Oregon City the Willamette Falls Pulp and Paper Company began the "first cook of sulphite" in 1880, and the Lebanon Paper Mill on the South Santiam River followed in 1909. By that time the process was well established in over ten pulp and paper companies at Oregon City, Salem, Newberg, Springfield, Astoria, and Coos Bay.[26]

Effluent from the woolen industry was equally calamitous. Wool processing required prodigious quantities of water, and if a river weren't handy, canals were constructed. In the manufacturing process, clean water was converted to toxic liquid during an inordinately lengthy procedure. Sheep wool was washed and scoured with clean running water ten or more times between stages involving boiling it in ammonia, caustic soda, lye or urine, and a variety of other chemicals. Often there were more than forty steps before the fleece was finished. Following the end phase, the dirty, foul-smelling water, laden with oil and grease as well as the detergents, covered the river surface with a sudsy foam.

Toward the mid-1800s, woolen mills were in production throughout the state at Salem, Oregon City, Brownsville, and Dallas in the valley, at Bandon on the coast, at Ashland to the south, and at The Dalles and Pendleton across the Cascades. The plant at Oregon City utilized the latest equipment, handling 600,000 pounds of wool a year. A boiler furnished hot water for cleaning, a furnace blew hot air for drying, and a flume conveyed water to the mill. Most of the woolen production was in the Willamette Valley, but the mills at The Dalles and at Pendleton became famous for their operations. The Dalles Scouring Mill, starting up in 1901, installed new machinery, and employed twenty men to remove dirt and grease from 8,000,000 pounds annually. At Pendleton in Umatilla County the mill dated back to 1894. Over 2 million pounds of sheep wool was run through its washtubs during its first months of operation. One year later, when the wool began to pile up in the warehouse, additional men were hired to keep it moving through the wash cycle night and day. By that fall the mill had scoured 170,000 pounds above the previous quota, the effluent sent into the Umatilla River.

Other businesses such as sawmills, tanneries, and foundries, which were spin-offs from the state's agricultural focus, took in fresh water, to which they added their own high concentrations of chemicals. Thousands of dams and log ponds throughout the state were the most frequent source of contamination. Stored in a pond or estuary near the mill, logs emitted tannic acids that saturated the pooling waters or overflowed into creeks and wetlands. Acidic water and wood debris sank to the bottom, where decomposition removed oxygen, killing aquatic life. Artificial ponds covered many acres and contained thousands of logs. At Cottage Grove in Lane County ten teams and scrapers created a six-acre pond that would hold over one million board feet. The project and accompanying sawmill were backed by "well-to-do businessmen," who were not lacking in funds.[27]

Streams were one way of getting rid of tons of unwanted sawdust, which piled up during lumber operations. On September 8, 1890, C.A. Wright complained to the U.S. Fish Commission that a mill on the Grand Ronde River in Polk County had "for some time past been running the saw-dust from their saw-mill directly into the Grand Ronde River, and that river is now in such a condition that not a fish can live in it any where near the place."[28] Serving as a dump for local mills, the Coos Bay estuary became discolored from "bark and sawdust washes [which are] washed up and accumulate in huge piles along adjacent beach parks."[29]

Tanneries and iron foundries both employed a variety of caustic chemicals, tanneries to dissolve unwanted organic debris and loosen hair and foundries to remove any crust adhering to casting molds. Toxic by-products were carried away with innumerable of gallons of clean water. At Portland, Daniel Lownsdale, a Kentuckian who set up on Tanners Creek in 1845, made leather boots and shoes, sofas, saddles, and whips. When the area of Multnomah Field (PGE Park) was filled in, his tannery vats were left in place and merely covered over. Smaller tanneries sprang up at Milwaukie, Salem, Brownsville, and Eugene in the valley, as well as at Astoria, Marshfield, and Coquille on the coast. The appropriately named Hemlock Tannery in Astoria manufactured leather along with boots and shoes from 3,000 hides annually.

At one time Oregon was thought to possess extensive riches in iron ore, but there was no foundation to this claim. The Oregon Iron Company, which began at Lake Oswego in 1867, became the state's only marginally successful operation, producing 93,404 tons of iron from the mineral limonite. The company closed in 1894 after the cost of processing became too high. Through several washings in fresh cold water, iron products were immersed in acids, heated, then scoured with brushes. Each time the "pickling" water was disposed of in moving streams.

MUNICIPAL EFFLUENT: 1930s TO 1960s

"In 1939 all cities and industries along the banks of the Willamette River were discharging their sewage and waste without treatment into the river." [30] The Willamette was not alone in its decline. What was happening to its waters was commonly taking place throughout Oregon. Surveys of contaminants in the Willamette Basin, begun in 1929, were extended to cover other rivers, showing the poor health of waterways across the state.

The turning point came in 1939. Heightened awareness of the value of water resources and of public health issues, as well as the realization that rivers were becoming unfit for recreation and a menace to fish life, led to the creation of Oregon's pollution regulatory agency, the State Sanitary Authority. The authority was given powers to investigate contamination sources, to hold hearings, to enforce regulations, and to levy penalties. Its program carried through the next thirty years at which time the laws were rewritten to strengthen water quality controls and set minimal treatment standards.

For regulating sewage disposal, the Sanitary Authority classified water bodies into three divisions. Class A and B streams were to be clean enough for swimming and drinking. In addition, all sewage discharged into Class A waters was to be free of solid matter, whereas refuse expelled into Class B water was to be treated so that there were no noticeable floating solids, oil, or grease, and the suspended debris was to be reduced by fifty-five percent. Standards were also set for the oxygen and fecal bacteria content. Class C waters could receive untreated sewage with a permit, provided "such discharge may not be detrimental to any reasonable use." The addition of chlorine could be required at any time. [31]

The authority's first task was to oversee the installation of sewage treatment plants. The program was more or less voluntary, but once it notified

The 1930s brought increased standards for effluent treatment. Three unfinished plants in Oregon were set to begin processing methods that replaced obsolete septic tanks. The one at Ashland installed a round settling tank and a filter that allowed sewage to pass through layers of rock (top). Grants Pass constructed a laboratory, an equipment house, and glass-covered sludge drying beds (middle), while a third plant at Medford was the first in the Northwest to utilize the activated sludge process (heating and drying). (Western City Magazine, 1936)

businesses and munici-palities of their responsi-bilities, the Sanitary Au-thority expected a plan for treatment would be set in motion. By the early 1940s the primary stage of wastewater process-ing, which removed much of the obvious floating solids but little else, was required. Floating scum was trapped by screens, which were cleaned by hand-operated brushes or scrapers. The sludge sank to the bottom of clarifiers, open-air settling tanks, where it was removed, dried, burned, or spread on the land. Oregon's heavy winter rainfall also meant that two conduits were necessary to separate storm-water runoff and septic debris. When both were combined, a downpour practically precluded treatment, often flooding the system and mingling rainwater with unprocessed effluent.

On the mainstem Willamette, Junction City in Lane County and Newberg in Yamhill County were the first to complete satisfactory treatment plants, while on the Tualatin River the facilities at Hillsboro in Washington County were far ahead of those elsewhere in Oregon. As early as 1911 the municipality operated with separate sanitary and storm conduits. But as more people settled and businesses moved in, the newcomers failed to connect to the city system, and their raw septic material was flushed into the Tualatin through open ditches. Facing an additional load of late summer cannery by-products, which utilized the municipal facilities, the city constructed a revolutionary new plant with screens, aeration, lagoons, and drying beds for sludge. In 1940, Hillsboro's plant was the first in the Willamette Valley to treat domestic and industrial material independently.

Other communities ignored the new regulations, forcing the Sanitary Authority to take a more aggressive stance by issuing injunctions. During the 1950s sixteen court cases were initiated against towns such as Mt. Angel and Molalla in Clackamas County, Toledo in Lincoln County, as well as industries along the Columbia Slough. As a result of the authority's efforts, only twenty-one communities lacked treatment by 1960. Among these were Coos Bay, Empire, Eastside, and North Bend, all utilizing the same coastal estuary. Of Coos Bay's twenty outfall pipes, just one had some form of processing, while the others dispensed raw debris. The same was true of Eastside, Empire, and Charleston. Empire was among the "worst offenders." The town had installed a large pipe that reached several hundred feet out from the shore where strong winter tides dissipated the sewage; however, during low summer tides "the odor is strong and the beach is rendered unsightly and foul." [32] Following ten more years of effort by the Sanitary Authority, 200 public sewer systems, which served one million people, roughly one-half of the state's population, were completed.

Industrial Waste: 1930s to 1960s

Under the watchful eye of the Sanitary Authority, industries were struggling to manage their own waste as well. Many relied on distribution through regional municipal sewer systems. Not only do industrial by-products come in heavy loads, they are generally stronger and require a greater degree of treatment than municipal effluent. Throughout the 1930s, as is the case today, the cost of treatment was the deciding factor. The authority reported that "for certain wastes there are no known *economical* [italics added] methods of treatment." It went on to stress the magnitude of the industrial problem. "One [should] stop to consider that the wastes from a single pea cannery may be the equivalent of sewage from 6,000 to 8,000 persons ... and wastes from a sulfite pulp mill equivalent to the sewage from 250,000 to 400,000 persons." [33]

During the 1960s, pulp and paper companies, plywood mills, food processors, dairies, and meat rendering operations failed to treat their discharge at a time when approximately eighty percent of America's pollution load on rivers was due to industrial output. It was well into the 1970s before primary treatment for industries was in place, but in the early stages many companies merely relied on settling ponds.

Growing and harvesting trees and processing lumber have always played a dominant role in Oregon's economy, and lumber, plywood, and paper mills constitute a major source of waterway contamination. Even after cleanup programs were initiated, most mills lagged some twenty years behind municipalities for installing facilities to treat their concentrated liquors. In the Klamath Basin, Weyerhaeuser Company's intensely colored effluent, "essentially free of settleable solids," was visible in the Klamath River for one-half mile downstream. Flow from its hardboard operation was "continuous," but the addition of dilution water "helps to keep the settling basin fresh and hold down foul odors." [34]

Wastes from the paper mills at Lebanon, Salem, Newberg, West Linn, and Oregon City on the Willamette and South Santiam rivers resulted in a zero dissolved oxygen content during summers, killing aquatic life downstream. Following public hearings in 1950, these five mills agreed to develop facilities for their effluent either by creating settling lagoons or by barging and dumping the concentrated sulphite liquor to the Columbia River. Weyerhaeuser Lumber Company in Springfield disposed of "certain of its strong wastes for irrigation on adjacent farm land," relying as well on the McKenzie River and the city's sewer system. Boise Cascade in Salem piped

As late as the 1950s, pulp wastes from the paper mill at Newberg cover the surface of the Willamette River with foam. (Courtesy Oregon State Sanitary Authority)

and stored sulfite waste from it pulp and paper mill to aeration basins on ninety-two acres of Minto-Browns Island before dumping it into the Willamette. Even though the island flooded, the site was favored because of easily accessibility to the river. At Toledo in Lincoln County, Georgia Pacific Paper Company "finally succeeded in abating fairly well the nuisance conditions which had been created along the Newport beach as a result of the discharge … of wastes." The company installed cooling and aerating towers, chlorination equipment, and a second settling pond; however, at its new pulp mill at Gardiner in Douglas County, International Paper Company planned to direct its effluent into the Pacific Ocean, where it would be diluted.[35]

Because of Oregon's agricultural-based economy, the vegetable, fruit, dairy, and meat industries have retained importance over the years. Food processing has become the region's second largest source of wastewater. By-products from canneries and frozen vegetable companies are high in volume of organic material, making them hungry oxygen consumers and giving rise to land disposal as the most practical method. Since the processing times are seasonal, peak loads coincide with low stream flows, and waste discharge frequently overwhelms containment systems.

Many, such as J. R. Simplot's Hermiston potato plant in Umatilla County, Ore-Ida in Malheur County, which handles potatoes, corn, and onions, and Bruce Pac, a meat processor in Marion County, are located in small Oregon towns. In raw potato operations, twenty to fifty percent of the leftovers are discharged as waste. Some can be sold as fertilizer or livestock feed, but much of the effluent finds its way into streams.

In the 1960s few meat companies provided any treatment, although some slaughterhouses practiced surveillance and land disposal. At Klamath Falls, non-edible solids were furnished to the Klamath Tallow Company on the east side of Lake Ewauna. Whatever remained after the Tallow Company processing was sent into the lake. "There was a 3' x 3' sludge deposit of fat and manure scraps at the outfall, but the liquid waste pattern was not evident in the lake more than 30-40 feet away from the outfall." Manure and wastewater from T.P. Packing, also in Klamath Falls, were pumped into an earthen sump. "Overflow from the sump gets lost in several miles of rather undefined drainage ditches which discharge to the Lost River." [36] The nearby Merrill Meat Company abandoned its drain field because it became plugged repeatedly, thereafter discharging from a septic tank directly into the same river. In eastern Oregon the Ontario and Hawley (Vale) slaughterhouses, as well as Valley Sausage (LaGrande), relied on septic tanks, drain fields, and surveillance before sending their waste into the Snake, Malheur, or Grande Ronde rivers.

Threatened with legal action by the Sanitary Authority, most businesses fell into compliance, installing primary processing facilities. Only Pacific Meat Company, discharging slaughterhouse offal into the Willamette at Portland, appealed an injunction to abate the nuisance. The Oregon Supreme Court found that, even though the company had constructed a lagoon and "related engineering devices for the purpose of removing harmful material from water discharged into the Columbia Slough," it did not operate or maintain the system efficiently.[37]

MUNICIPAL AND INDUSTRIAL WASTE: 1960 TO PRESENT

With some satisfaction the Sanitary Authority was able to report that its 1962 accomplishments included contracts awarded to seventy-eight communities for the installation of sewerage projects, close to twenty treatment plants were underway or being improved, and approximately thirty had been completed. New or upgraded facilities for thirteen industries were in similar stages of construction.

While early efforts of the Sanitary Authority made great strides in the establishment of primary treatment, not enough pollutants were being removed, and Oregon's overall water quality was no better. Reports by the authority during the 1960s called attention to the deficiencies in the current processing. Attempting to remedy the situation, the legislature amended its earlier regulations, now requiring secondary treatment for effluent sent into Willamette Basin waters and prohibiting any discharge unless the disposal was permitted by the newly-created Department of Environmental Quality. Secondary treatment depends on bacteria and oxygen to reduce the organic matter further, in conjunction with sedimentation tanks, filters, and chlorine.

It was hoped that these tightened provisions would improve water conditions, and the 1970s found almost seventy percent of Oregon's citizens hooked into sewer systems, while the remainder relied on septic tanks. All of the communities with sewers had secondary treatment facilities except for Cloverdale, Nehalem, Astoria, and Wheeler on the coast, Seneca in Grant County, and, remarkably, Portland, the state's largest metropolis, which accounted for a substantial volume of waste. Raw sewage from the northwest section of Portland received no treatment at all. Fully effective secondary treatment was mandated by 1973, although processing facilities weren't operational until one year later. Cooperating regional programs between smaller cities were initiated as the best means of handling problems.

The department began to operate with a three-point program. It established "beneficial uses" for each river basin throughout the state, it set water quality standards, and it issued permits for effluent release. As with the Water Resources Department, the Department of Environmental Quality was to consider a seemingly impossible and incompatible list of beneficial uses when making a decision: domestic, industrial, municipal, irrigation, livestock, fish, wildlife, recreation, pollution abatement, and hydroelectric power, adding a new category for aesthetic quality. The uses weren't ranked one above another or rated from best to worst, and the "pass or fail test" was generally employed. The proposed use "fails" if it is impaired. That is, for example, if it harmed another or if it were wasteful.[38] Not only are the designations of "good" or "bad" for uses confusing, they are subject to the varying whims of agency personnel, to the political and social setting, or to the period in time.

To protect beneficial uses, standards were set to maintain a level of quality based on parameters such as water temperature, the amount of dissolved oxygen, the bacterial count, or the load of effluent a water body could handle and still remain "unpolluted." Instead of imposing a predetermined level of quality for all streams, the DEQ evaluated each land or water action to determine whether it harmed the standards for that particular waterbody. Total Maximum Daily Loads (TMDLs) are numerical amounts of pollutants that a specific waterway can receive and not be in violation of water quality standards. Depending on the level of degradation already existing, the amounts varied from stream to stream. Favoring a watershed-wide approach, all sources of pollution from agriculture, industry, urbanization, and natural runoff were to be measured. New monitoring technology allowed the Department of Environmental Quality, the U.S. Geological Survey, and other agencies to determine with accuracy the type and volume of outfall effluent river-mile-by-river-mile. As data were gathered, plans were developed assuring that the standards for quality in each water body were not violated.

One function of the DEQ's role in overseeing waterway quality is to issue permits for discharging effluent. The presumption is that the permit will limit or control the discharge of impurities, thereby leading to improved water conditions. Both major and minor industrial and domestic facilities are categorized by effluent type: fish hatcheries, log ponds, food processors, pulp and paper mills, smelters, and urban storm-water outlets. Under this system, an applicant submits a plan, receiving final approval if the operation and the amount of pollutants don't violate quality parameters. The phrase "water quality permit" is something of an oxymoron, because the license doesn't maintain purity but actually allows for some degree of degradation. National Pollutant Discharge Elimination System (NPDES) permits, which are required for facilities that discharge to surface waters, come under both state and federal requirements, while Water Pollution Control Facilities (WPCF) permits are needed when there is no direct effect on the surface flow. General permits are issued for minor discharges that are not considered a threat to water quality. Close to 4,500 NPDES and WPCF permits have been issued – 1,446 for minor industrial and municipal facilities, seventy-eight for major municipal and industrial waste, another 956 for general non-storm-water release, and 2,016 for storm-water runoff. Several hundred new applications are approved annually.

In the case of water quality violations, the department was given the power to enforce compliance to the standards on both private and public property. After an investigation, inspection, and notification, the agency can issue orders to cease and then levy fines. At the outset the department was noted for its "flamboyant positions and threats to local governments" in its enthusiasm to impose sanctions.[39] Attempting to shut down placer operations that were muddying the Rogue River in 1970, the department came up against the Josephine County Sourdoughs, who ignored its injunctions. The miners contended that they didn't need a permit "from a new state agency," having been told by a member of the Rogue River Coordination Board, "So far as I am concerned, the ... Board is still the law on the Rogue River." Threatening to sue, the miners charged that the DEQ allowed local cities and counties to pour "raw sewage into the river," so why shouldn't they be able to pollute with their mining operation?[40] Backed by the authority of the attorney general, the department prevailed.

The Agriculture and Environmental Quality departments both have roles in non-point source contamination. Originating as runoff from urban, agricultural, or timber activities, non-point source pollution is dispersed across the landscape and can't be traced to any one outlet. Runoff carries farm and urban pollutants, along with sediments from erosion, into the surface and groundwater. Whereas logging had long been considered the major contributor to non-point pollution, the real culprit was agriculture. Thirty-five years ago non-point pollution was already of concern as chemicals came to play "an important role in the success story of modern American agriculture."[41] At that time, roughly seventy percent of Northwest streams failed to meet water quality standards with sediment from cropland estimated at forty percent of the total pollutant load. In the Willamette Valley "lots of the 'dirties' are [sic] coming from croplands."[42]

Except for minimal regulations dealing with feed lot operations, Oregon's $3.5 billion agricultural industry has been relatively free of restraints, although its impact on the state's waterways has been significant. But in 1993

Within the Pudding River watershed of the northern Willamette Valley, a spray of unprocessed liquefied manure from a dairy operation blackens a field of corn during the summer of 2004. As of August, 2003, the Oregon Department of Agriculture took over issuing water quality permits for Confined Animal Feeding Operations (CAFO) from the Department of Environmental Quality. Permits are given for hog, mink, chicken, or ostrich feed lots, as well as for dairy holding lagoons. To date, 572 CAFO permits have been issued. Although the permits are designed to protect water quality, operators are able to spray liquefied manure from storage ponds onto fields and floodplains. Agricultural groups can voluntarily modify their practices to assure that water quality isn't harmed, but if these measures fail the department can achieve compliance by levying fines.

the Oregon Legislature passed Senate Bill 1010, which directed state agriculture personnel to work with farmers and ranchers to develop individual management plans for reducing their pollution activities. The plans are aimed at limiting erosion and controlling runoff, but since the plans are voluntary, they probably won't go far in solving problems in the face of a strong agricultural hold on the state's politicians and economy. Judy McClaughry, whose family farmed near Lake Labish in Marion County for four generations, is helping to write regional water quality rules, although she doesn't see the need for streamside buffers. Her property runs along the now-channelized Little Pudding River and includes wetlands that have been drained, diked, and stripped of natural vegetation. "We have always been very careful about erosion … I think most farmers, their attempt is to be a good steward of their soil and their land anyhow [*sic*]. I think that's what farmers have done for years." [43]

On the other hand, property owners such as Peter Kenagy show more accountability. Kenagy, whose 300 acres lie near the Willamette River at Albany, provides a 200-foot-wide streamside buffer of trees, limits his use of fertilizers and chemicals, plants cover crops, and keeps tilling to a minimum. Similar practices have been implemented on the Fisher farm along the Little Pudding River in Marion County, where the family has even installed walkways to keep livestock out of the stream. Several government agencies fund a variety of projects for aiding local landowners or groups to implement better farming practices. Assistance is available for riparian fencing, for removal of noxious weeds, and for the introduction of erosion control measures, as well as for education, evaluation of problems, and monitoring.

"Under the Department's progressive programs, water quality in Oregon reached a peak of reasonably attainable purity by the end of 1972 … Only the Tualatin and Klamath River Basins still largely fail to meet established standards." The DEQ's report went on to add, "Both of these suffer from extraneous conditions quite beyond the effects of controllable waste sources." [44] Water degradation in the Klamath Basin was reported to be caused by an influx of organic matter resulting from the natural aquatic life in the upper Lake "before the infusion of wastes from man's activities," whereas summer withdrawal for irrigation and an overload of sewage were responsible for foul conditions in the Tualatin River

The same year as the Department of Environmental Quality's report, a study by Lolita Carter assessed the impacts of urban and agricultural land modifications on water quality in the Tualatin Basin. She found effluent from fifteen treatment plants serving Beaverton, Aloha, and the West Hills was discharged directly into the river after its flow had already been greatly reduced by upstream demands. During long dry summers, "There are patches of foam … and chunks of cannery wastes in the water which is sometimes

A pickup truck, fitted with long booms and a tank, was adapted for use as a sprayer for pesticides on a field in 1958. (Courtesy Oregon State Archives)

the gray color of sewage." At Rood Road there was zero flow for "extended periods of time." Waters of the Tualatin River and its tributaries were being additionally ravaged by liquefied wastes from local dairies sprayed onto pastures in summertime. Rock Creek "looks like syrup." [45] Thirty years after its construction, Hillsboro's state-of-the-art treatment plant was still in operation, while the city's population had increased from 2,000 to 14,500.

In spite of the anticipation that releases of "clean water" impounded behind the dam on Scoggins Creek, completed in 1975, would dilute and improve quality in the Tualatin, the reservoir didn't hold enough to abate such a load of polluted matter. With a high ammonia and phosphorus content, most of which originated from sewage release, water in the lower reaches "ranged from good to poor." [46]

A federal lawsuit in 1986, filed by the Northwest Environmental Defense Fund, charged the that limits for effluents had not been set or enforced as mandated by the Clean Water Act of 1972. Subsequently the court decreed a that a timetable be set to achieve compliance, making the Tualatin one of the first rivers in the United States for which attempts were made to meet water quality standards. Committees, individuals, urban property owners, and rural residents came together in 1995 to comment on an Agricultural Water Quality Management Plan, drawn up to prevent the runoff of chemicals and erosion from soils. The first hearings in Forest Grove "drew few comments, in part because many farmers believe they already are complying." Local farmers blamed the problem on pollutants "that exist naturally in Tualatin Valley soils," on non-farmers, "who raise small numbers of livestock or exotic animals," on septic tank failures, or on erosion from the construction of roads and houses.[47]

Eventually cleanup efforts by willing individuals and groups brought about a reduction in the daily effluent loads, the control of dairy and nursery releases, and the tertiary treatment of waste, thereby removing ninety-five percent of any remaining organic debris. Among the more progressive innovations, the 710 acres of Jackson Bottom wetlands serve as the final stage in Hillsboro's wastewater processing. Drained at one time for agriculture, the restored marsh and bog land is now home to eagles, herons, otters, beavers, salamanders, and a variety of plants. Working with the scientific community and applying the latest technology, regional groups interested in improving their water quality were rewarded three years later when testing by the Department of Environmental Quality showed, "The Tualatin is almost meeting state standards for oxygen." [48]

Throughout the twentieth century, cities and businesses worked to keep up with changing and tightened standards. Most operated on systems that had been in use for many years and that needed a major overhauling. While remaining within the load of discharge permitted by the DEQ, deficient and crumbling facilities were plagued with overflows and spills. Treatment plants and permits did not end "violation days," and since surface waters received much of the effluent, any mishap or infraction resulted in an excess of contamination. Only after incurring repeated violations did municipalities and businesses take steps toward needed improvements. Except for Astoria on the coast and Portland and Corvallis in the valley, separate storm and sewer lines and more efficient plants were completed by 1995.

Well before the 1930s, the badly degraded rivers and tributaries in the populous Willamette Valley received particular attention when the State Plan-

Jackson Bottom wetlands restoration project was developed as the final stage in Hillsboro's treatment of its wastewater. (Courtesy of Jean Mooney)

ning Board reported to Governor Charles Martin, "This river is essentially a sewer and should be so recognized." [ ] After it assessed all aspects of water use along the Willamette, the board called for "action" to abate the pollution but added realistically, "Public education and legislation have so far been ineffective, largely because the removal of the source of pollution costs much money, from which there is no apparent direct return." [50]

From that point forward, the story of Willamette's troubled waters is one of cleanup initiatives, followed by declarations of success, and then additional testing, discoveries of further contamination, and another call for restoration:

1920s to 1930s: Water quality tests by the State Board of Health found extensive pollution in the Portland harbor. River surveys by Oregon State University showed high dissolved oxygen in the upper Willamette but a drop in oxygen below Salem, Newberg, and at the Sellwood Bridge.

1957: After 1939 the Sanitary Authority reported that reasonably good progress had been made in controlling pollution in the river.

1962: *Pollution in Paradise*, a TV documentary by reporter Tom McCall, showed continuing river pollution.

1964: Governor Tom McCall initiated a Willamette cleanup program.

1967: "Sanitary Authority Urges Closures." The two big pulp mills at Oregon City and West Linn were asked to shut down operations because of the dangerously low oxygen levels in the river there.[51]

1969: "Willamette River now said reasonably safe for Portland area water sport enthusiasts." [52]

1971: "State to move to keep Willamette Valley from falling victim to pernicious pollution." [53]

1972: *The Return of a River; the Willamette River, Oregon*, by George Gleeson concluded that the river had been cleaned and a plan formulated to maintain quality in the future.

1972: A National Geographic magazine article "A River Restored: Oregon's Willamette."

1990: The Department of Environmental Quality began a six-year study of water quality conditions in the entire Willamette watershed. Subsequent results rated the basin as "marginally healthy" with a steady decline northward from Eugene to the Columbia entrance, which received a "poor." [54]

1992: Initiation of the Lower Willamette River Management Plan to address water quality.

1993: The Watershed Health Program was established, with oversight given to the Strategic Water Management Group.

1995: A DEQ study found deformed fish in the river. Lorna Stickel, planner for the Portland Water Bureau, remarked, "What causes problems for fish doesn't necessarily mean harm to humans." [55]

1996: The Willamette River Basin Task Force was formed by Governor John Kitzhaber to assess the current status of the basin water.

1999: The Willamette River Basin Restoration Committee developed a plan for improvement.

2000: The Portland harbor was placed on the EPA's Superfund list because of high toxicity readings in the water and soil.

April, 2004: Governor Kulongoski toured the Willamette River at "the start of his centerpiece environmental initiative." The Willamette cleanup was given priority.[56]

June, 2004: High mercury counts were found in Willamette River fish.
October, 2004: Around $835,000 is requested to cut contamination in the
　　　Willamette River waters.

"We're not only going to clean up the river from its headwaters east of Eugene all the way to the Columbia River – we're going to reconnect the Willamette to … Oregonians who live along the bank. It will once again be part of the spirit of Oregon." [57] With these words Governor Kulongoski set in motion the latest initiative for bringing back the river.

One of the valley's worst offenders, Portland never entirely separated its storm and sewage conduits. Even with a history of more than one hundred spills a year into the Willamette, the municipality still relied on an antiquated system first installed in 1929. On the day it was inaugurated, administrators experienced "great relief" after their "new sewage pumping plant at the foot of Ankeny street … has passed its official tests with flying colors." Engineer O. Laurgaard declared that the plant could "handle all of the sewage and rain water … in the district, even if it should rain as much an inch an hour." [58] This optimism sustained Portland through more than sixty years, while sections of the leaky spill-prone system frequently sent combined sewage and storm water into the Willamette River.

Facing a lawsuit in 1991 from the Northwest Environmental Advocates and pressure from the U.S. Environmental Protection Agency, the city initiated a Big Pipe project along both sides of the river and another on the Columbia Slough. Designed to reduce pollution dramatically by cutting storm water, which floods and overwhelms the sewer system, the fourteen-foot diameter pipe is to be completely functional by 2011. Proponents and opponents lined up to argue over the costs, the effectiveness of the new system, and federal interference. Local officials took a back-off-we're-getting-around-to-it-attitude, although the remedy has been many years in coming. Pete Lavigne, President of the Rivers Foundation of the Americas, responded to unwanted EPA attention with, "Portland is a leader in cleaning up overflows."[59]

Upriver outfall pipes line both sides of the Willamette, but the numbers are concentrated from Milwaukie to Newberg in Clackamas and Yamhill counties. Along this river stretch, twelve major municipal and industrial permit holders discharge directly into the mainstem. On the east side of the river, Clackamas County operates wastewater plants in Milwaukie and Oregon City, while the Oak Lodge Sanitary District manages a third. In 1982 Oregon City officials entered into a sewage-management agreement with the county after its combined storm and sanitary sewer system was given an "inadequate" rating by DEQ officials. Flooding frequently sent unprocessed effluent into the river, causing the department to halt sewer hook-ups and resulting in a virtual "no growth" order from 1977 to 1980.[60] The Oak Lodge Sanitary District experienced similar problems when effluent poured out into the Willamette and adjacent streams at least eight times in recent years. Following a discharge in July and February, 2003, the district was fined $10,800, which it appealed.

In 2004 Clackamas County proposed enlarging the riverfront plant at Oregon City and closing those at Milwaukie and Oak Lodge. Before all parties came to any agreement, Oregon City officials presented a list of demands that included a lower sewer rate for citizens, a payment for "tournament quality baseball and soccer fields next to the plant," a high standard set for the released wastewater, a minimization of the odor, and a requirement that the plant "blend in with the surrounding forested floodplain." [61]

Near Rogers Boat Landing Park in Yamhill County, Newberg's sewage reached the Willamette from a facility that had been built in 1949. Although the treatment plant was updated several times by 1984, odors, foam, floating solids, and other "objectionable conditions have been noted" following the frequent discharge of raw sewage after heavy winter or occasional summer rains, when storm runoff and refuse combined. The water quality was marginally good to fair in the park, where skiing, swimming, and boating are popular activities.[62]

From 1893 when Salem was authorized to send its unprocessed sewage into the Willamette River, the city developed primary, then secondary, treatment facilities. Sewer lines were extended to accommodate the expanding urban boundary and proliferating businesses. Built in 1968 on the low-lying Willow Lake region adjacent to the river, Salem's main wastewater treatment plant frequently suffered from heavy floods; however, the damage "must be traded off against pumping cost savings realized when the plant is kept low." Ultimately a protective wall was erected to hold the river at bay.[63]

In answer to Salem's need for additional facilities some ten years later, consultants for CH2M-Hill unveiled an extraordinary disposal and expansion plan to inject sludge into the soil of the 770 acres around the Willow Lake plant. City Council members, as well as local residents, expressed uncertainty and questioned the procedure. Sidney Laswell, of the consulting company, termed their queries about effects on wells and irrigation as "unanswerable." He countered that "the land will be closely monitored … and that danger levels can be detected well before the situation gets out of hand … the sludge injection method would be the least expensive and most resourceful." The idea was rejected.[64]

By 1984 Salem's Willow Lake facility was judged as "critically near system capacity for peak flow," and at present six or seven discharges of about 120 to 160 million gallons of raw sewage each are typical during the winter months.[65] Such was the case in January, 2004, when city workers opened diversion gates, expelling unprocessed wastewater after heavy rainfall overwhelmed the facility. Currently a new plan to be implemented addresses flow releases during high rainfall, rehabilitation of the system, and other changes.

Oceanside communities and businesses continued to discharge their effluent onto the beaches or into estuaries and the ocean until treatment systems were finally installed at the instigation of the State Sanitary Authority. By 1968 only Astoria, Cannon Beach, and Seaside in Clatsop County had installed municipal works, and it was well into the 1970s before other towns complied. Once Astoria was notified to stop sending its raw effluent into the tidal waters of the Columbia River and Youngs Bay, city officials made plans to fill thirty acres of the Columbia estuary as settling lagoons. The proposal was endorsed in 1971 by the Environmental Quality Commission, and even Oregon Fish Commission biologist Irv Jones didn't oppose the plan but added matter-of-factly, "The [Fish] commission can only guess about the net effects of the project." [66] Since then, Astoria operates secondary municipal facilities with a DEQ permit for discharge to surface waters. Taking a biologic approach, Cannon Beach created a wooded marsh habitat as the final stage of its processing.

On the south coast, the estuary at Coos Bay received debris from "open toilets … from waterfront buildings and industries; refuse dumped into the bay as if it were a garbage disposal site … soap and detergents which run directly … from a laundromat, and small fills that seem to be made without permission from anyone." [67] That was in 1970, but two years later the city passed sewage treatment bonds for constructing new facilities in order to meet secondary treatment guidelines mandated by state water quality regulations. Since then the system has been upgraded and extended several times to reach Charleston and other outlying districts. From 1994 to 1998 Florence in Lane County struggled with 184 violations when partially treated effluent clouded the Siuslaw River during heavy rains. Recognizing the need for improvement, the city designed a new plant completed in 2000.

Astoria, Cannon Beach, Florence, and Coos Bay are not alone. The coastal region is especially susceptible to pollution from sewage release by municipalities and businesses because the narrow coastal topography favors strip development and ready discharge to the ocean. Cities here, which tend to be modest in size, but distributed lengthwise along the shoreline, must accommodate large numbers of summer visitors. The same is true of RV parks, motels, casinos, campgrounds, or private homes. This type of growth particularly relies on individual septic tanks that are not hooked into a larger regional system. Tanks are pumped regularly by vacuum truck or are connected to extensive leach fields. Although a permit is now necessary for installation, many small septic tanks are unregistered. The overall number of unregistered tanks in Oregon is difficult to determine, but it is close to fifty percent.

In 2000 Congress passed the Beaches Environmental Assessment and Coastal Health Act, requiring beach cleanup standards to be adopted to protect swimmers from unsafe contamination. Warnings and closures were to be posted when guidelines weren't met. Just two states, Oregon and Louisiana, were named as "Beach Bums" by the National Resources Defense Council because they had no regular monitoring program to test, identify, and take steps to eliminate sources of pollution. The council reported that beach waters "are generally cleaner now than they were 25 years ago," but leaky septic tanks, crumbling sewage treatment plants, and urban runoff are worsening.[68]

Since that time, the Oregon Department of Environmental Quality has begun checking for fecal bacteria at fifty-two beach locations to ensure the level remains below the 158 count. Anything higher can lead to skin rashes, ear, eye, and nose infections, diarrhea, or stomach problems. Testing during the fall of 2003 disclosed high fecal bacteria from Lincoln County south to

Coos County, when people were asked to stay out of the water and tide pools. Enterococci bacteria at D River and Beverly Beach State Park in Lincoln County indicated the presence of human or animal feces.

Particularly troublesome spots, such as Seaside, Cannon Beach, and Oswald State Park, will be checked weekly during summer months, and a closer examination was scheduled for Sunset Bay State Park, which was posted with warnings for 103 days between November 21 and May 14, 2003. Officials were uncertain whether Big Creek, flowing along the south side of the park, or the two sewage lagoons were causing the contamination. This broad cove with a narrow opening, which restricts tidal flushing, contains ideal conditions for contamination. "It [creek water] affected the whole cove because the [contaminated] freshwater just kind of built up," remarked DEQ coordinator Larry Caton.[69] Tests here showed 1,860 colony-forming units of bacteria per 100 milliliters of water. Routine monitoring serves to warn beach users but doesn't halt the contamination sources.

The Deschutes Basin is no longer a sparsely-settled dry land of isolated farms and ranches. Undergoing tremendous growth, the landscape, once

An urban solution to runoff at the Chinook Winds Casino in Lincoln City: excess water from the large parking lot is piped onto the beach. A plastic basket "filter" lies along the cliff base.

considered unfriendly, is filling with retirees, second homes, entire vacation villages, and commuters in addition to the original residents. Throughout the Deschutes watershed small towns are expanding faster than in any other region of Oregon. Since the 1960s, when "the practice of disposing of sewage into lava sink holes" resulted in "little evidence of ground water pollution," individual wells and septic tanks have been replaced by municipal and regional treatment systems.[70]

In Sisters, most homes and businesses were still using separate septic systems in 1999, but the influx of residents and summer inundation of tourists, whom the city accommodates with sixty or more portable toilets, forced officials to seek federal funding for a treatment plant. In operation by 2001, the plant was designed to last for twenty years, but by 2005 the system was near capacity. A similar boom in growth and tourism forced Bend to construct a treatment facility, which manages sewage under permits from the Department of Environmental Quality. The town's effluent is stringently processed, then sprayed on golf courses or piped to evaporation ponds.

The great number of septic tanks located in Deschutes County between Sunriver and La Pine signal trouble. Doubtless, one of the most extensive health hazards in Oregon occurs here where the porous soil and a shallow subsurface of volcanic debris allow septic sludge to mingle with the drinking water. During the 1960s, before the state initiated land use planning, what Governor Tom McCall called "sagebrush subdivisions" permitted 13,000 lots to be carved up in this region. Such practices, combined with the desire of many people "to settle on a small acreage in the pine forest … and own a piece of land in the country," created a sprawling unincorporated community at La Pine.[71] There were no services for the roughly 8,200 residents, each living on one to two acres. "This is a ticking time bomb" were the words of Richard Benner, Director of the Land Conservation and Development Commission in 1998. Even though Benner anticipated imminent water quality problems, "if not a single additional septic tank is placed there," the issuance of new housing permits continued.[72]

Plans to solve the contamination problem included incorporating a large area under a unified disposal system or upgrading existing tanks. An on-site sewage plan, implemented in 1999, applies advanced filtering technology to individual waste systems, with funds available for those who wish to participate. Solutions are slow in coming, however, and in 2004 La Pine school officials were forced to shut off faucets after remarkably high counts of bacteria were found in the drinking water.

The bulk of industrially generated solids still originates with the pulp and paper industry. Historically lagoons, aeration, and landfills were the favored disposal methods for paper mill sludge, but much of the company's solid waste is now applied to soil as an amendment. The non-compliance of major industrial waste sources is not infrequent, and in 1993 alone Evanite Hardboard (Corvallis), James River (Halsey and Wauna), Smurfit (Newberg and Oregon City), and Weyerhaeuser (Springfield) all exceeded effluent limits or lacked adequate permits. Three paper processors - James River and Boise Cascade at St. Helens on the Columbia River and Pope and Talbot on the Willamette - released chlorine, dioxins, and furans, but all were scheduled to comply with new regulations by 1995.

Sewage treatment ponds for Boise Cascade Paper Company in Salem lie adjacent to the Willamette River in 1972. The Marion Street bridge is in the back center. Today the pond area is still clearly visible. (Courtesy Salem Public Library)

On the mainstem Willamette River, permits from the Department of Environmental Quality to James River Paper, Pope & Talbot, Weyerhaeuser, Blue Heron, West Linn, and Simpson Paper companies rely on surface waters for a final dilution to bring them into compliance. Near Oregon City, the Blue Heron Company has three permitted outfall pipes, and West Linn has two, all discharging near the same spot. In 2003 the department reported that "data from the point sources was found to be limited. Many water quality constituents, such as nutrients, were not monitored in the point sources. Data was collected on a monthly basis or less frequent." [73]

Since 1987, Smurfit Newsprint Corporation, which became Blue Heron, has garnered a number of penalties for breaking pollution laws. As recently as 1998, the company was fined $65,000 after dumping "pink liquid and red foam … into Cotton Creek," a tributary of the South Santiam River. In spite of the fact that the wastewater contained phenol and formaldehyde, Smurfit President Jay Lamb assured the public that, "there was no lasting environmental damage" and said that company officials were misled by several of their employees. [74]

It was a different story with Rosboro Lumber Company in Springfield, Lane County. Threatened with a lawsuit in 2004 by the Northwest Environmental Defense Center for washing grease and oil into the Springfield Millrace, the company and the environmental group were able to reach an amicable agreement. In this case, where the Department of Environmental Quality failed to act on 129 violations between 1997 and 2003, the company repaired its faulty equipment and paid $15,000 toward restoring the millrace for wildlife.

Food processing is still a major generator of wastewater in Oregon. Potatoes in the eastern part of the state and fruit and vegetables in the western region generate immense quantities of by-products. NORPAC, a member-owned company, processes over 300 million pounds of fruit and vegetables annually in its five northern Willamette Valley plants. Rich in nutrients, the waste is screened, then applied as fertilizer to land without discharge to surface waters. However, there are exceptions. In 1994, following several occasions where its effluent exceeded limits, Ore-Ida was fined $250,000. In addition the potato processor in Ontario had to complete $12 million worth of improvements after it was discovered that, "17,000 gallons

The outfall pipe from a small fish processing company runs along a jetty and into the bay at Charleston in Coos County.

of sludge had collected along the banks of the Snake River just down from [the plant's] discharge pipe." Currently the sludge is applied to the land.[75]

The use of sludge from industries and cities as a soil amendment on fields, public parks, and golf courses was not well regulated in 1991, when a lawsuit by Citizens Interested in Bull Run, asked the U.S. Environmental Protection Agency to limit the dioxin content. After 1989 findings that dioxin levels in Portland's sewage sludge were the highest in the nation, the Oregon Health Division recommended that the concentrations be reduced. During disposal, Portland first sends its toxic waste to Triangle Lake, a lagoon near the mouth of the Columbia River, where it is mixed with less contaminated material, before being transported to the community of Echo in Umatilla County. There it is spread on cropland owned by Madison Farms. Even though dioxins, ingested through meat, milk, and fats, disrupt many human physiological processes, protection from field applications is currently lacking, and the EPA ultimately concluded in 2003 that the high levels in Portland's sludge did not pose a health threat.

Present-Day

The Department of Environmental Quality is not keeping up with water degradation in the face of a greater municipal and industrial sewage load, of more complex chemicals, and of a diminishing water flow. It is beset with notoriously porous laws compounded by a lack of compliance to existing regulations. Too few employees and politically motivated decisions favoring development and businesses all work to the detriment of the state's water resources.

Effluent loads (TMDLs) have not yet been set for many rivers and streams, but for those in which the water quality falls below the standards - where the beneficial uses are not protected - the Department of Environmental Quality declares that the particular stream is water quality limited. The list of impaired waters includes over 13,300 stream miles where at least one water quality standard is violated. Between 1998 and 2003 about 6,000 miles were removed from the list, however, since then approximately the same number of new miles have been added, so there has been no overall gain in cleanup. In addition, data are lacking for many streams and waters with suspected problems. In 2000 the U.S. Environmental Protection Agency established a ten-year plan for those 13,300 miles of waterways, setting milestones for the DEQ in accordance with the Clean Water Act. Nina Bell, an attorney with Northwest Environmental Advocates, remarked, "(DEQ) has such a poor record of getting things done on time that I'm sure meeting a 10 year target is going to be difficult anyway."

The agency also struggles with having to upgrade its standards. Following a lawsuit brought by Northwest Environmental Advocates in 2003, a district court found that the state's water quality standards themselves were inadequate. The agency was ordered to rewrite them, lowering temperature parameters and increasing the levels of dissolved oxygen necessary to protect salmon and bull trout.

Over the years the DEQ has learned to work with the local communities and citizens, encouraging voluntary cooperation. However, the permitting process still continues to generate dissension, with objections to its fines, complaints about the backlog of applications, and worry over legal loopholes. During 2003, the DEQ levied roughly 200 separate fines amounting to $1.9 million. Its largest penalty in 2004 was $205,658 against Florida-based MasTec North America in connection with construction of a sixty-mile-long natural gas pipeline near Coos Bay. Fines or serious offenses average $10,000 per day, but only one violator in seven pays the entire fine. Under a new proposal, more polluters could draw the maximum amount, prompting Jeff Dresser, representative of the Associated Oregon Industries, to remark,

"The state risks coming across as unfriendly to business if the rules seem too hard-line ... and it sends the message that you can't make any mistakes at all." [76]

In 2003 the DEQ's backlog of wastewater permits was called the worst in the nation. DEQ Director Stephanie Hallock promised to reassign staff, "stepping up the pace of renewing permits that regulate how much sullied water may be released to Oregon rivers, mainly the Willamette." Hallock pointed to "chronic underfunding," adding that she had been denied new positions by the Legislature. Renewal of the oldest expired permit for the Wah Chang foundry in Albany had been pending for ten years.[77]

By the 1990s, the DEQ was dealing with a variety of complex industrial chemicals. Dioxin in effluent from the state's three chlorine-bleaching pulp mills, gold mining using cyanide heap leaching, runoff from acres of urban concrete, and concentrated agricultural chemicals represent ongoing challenges. The appearance of pharmaceuticals and personal-care products in surface waters is the most recent cause for concern. In 2002 the U.S. Geological Survey found thirty-one antibiotics and antibacterial compounds, eleven different birth control and hormonal supplements, along with steroids and nonprescription drugs in waters throughout the United States. In Oregon, such chemicals have been detected in the lower Willamette River and along the Snake River near Ontario in Malheur County. These chemicals are discharged into streams from treated wastewater, from land applications of sludge, from concentrations of septic systems, or from animal feed lots and lagoons. Little is known about the extent or the long term effects of their environmental occurrence and the fate of the chemicals.[78] Hampered by a shortage of staff and resources, the DEQ samples most of their 151 stations just six times a year, while some Willamette Basin locales are tested twelve times.

Since the period of unlimited and unregulated sewage discharge of the 1930s, agencies, laws, and enforcement have aimed at improving water quality. More than sixty years later, however, the water purity from the early days has not been regained. The Department of Environmental Quality attributed this "to the sheer loss of stream flow to consumptive water uses. Many major streams and tributaries are reduced to sluggish warm flows and others are dried completely." [79] The underlying assumption is that if the stream current were sufficient and not overallocated by the Water Resources Department, it would carry away all pollutants. Virtually any amount or quality of discharge would be permissible. Oregon has come a long, but not necessarily a progressive, way in its thinking since 1965 when Assistant Attorney General Cecil Quesseth noted that the Sanitary Authority hadn't set specific flow amounts to provide for pollution abatement. "Apparently the board has recognized that our waters are too valuable to wash away other's sins." [80]

ENDNOTES: WATER TO WASH AWAY OUR SINS

[1] James P. Kirkwood, *A Special Report on the Pollution of River Waters* (New York, Arno, 1970), 28.

[2] *Oregon Revised Statutes* 468.035 (1)(a)) 2001.

[3] *General Laws of Oregon,* Chapt. 264, Sect. 115, 1919.

[4] Smith v. Silverton, 17 Or 379, 1914.

[5] George W. Gleeson, *The Return of a River* (Corvallis, Water Resources Research Institute, Oregon State University, 1972), 13.

[6] Ibid, 20.

[7] *Oregonian,* February 28, 1905, 9.

[8] *Oregonian,* November 11, 1861, 3.

[9] *Oregonian,* February 6, 1864, 3.

[10] C. Aubrey Angelo, *Sketches of Travel in Oregon and Idaho* (Fairfield, Washington, Ye Galleon Press, 1988), 21.

[11] *General and Special Laws of Oregon*, 1893, 23.

[12] *Oregonian,* July 7, 1900, 4.

[13] *Oregonian,* December 7, 1909, 6.

[14] Ibid.

[15] *Oregonian,* December 23, 1909, 6.

[16] *Register Guard,* February 10, 1906, 5.

[17] *Register Guard,* February 12, 1906, 3.

[18] Ibid., 4.

[19] *The Coquille Valley Sentinel,* March 4, 1921, 1.

[20] Adams v. Clover Hill Farms, 86 Or 140, 1917, 142.

[21] *Bend Bulletin,* February 19, 1913,1.

[22] Jack Sceva, *Liquid Waste Disposal in the Lava Terrane of Central Oregon* (Corvallis, Federal Water Quality Administration, Pacific Northwest Water Laboratory, 1968), 7.

[23] *Oregonian*, September 17, 1900, 6, col.1.

[24] Malheur County Historical Society, *Malheur County History* (n.p., 1988), 99.

[25] Kirkwood, 1970, 53.

[26] W. Claude Adams, "History of Papermaking in The Pacific Northwest: I" *Oregon Historical Quarterly*, 1951, v.52, 33.

[27] *Oregonian*, November 19, 1905, 19.

[28] Joseph E. Taylor; *Making Salmon; an Environmental History of the Northwest Fisheries Crisis* (Seattle, University of Washington Press, 1999), 57.

[29] *Oregon Journal*, June 3, 1970, J5.

[30] Cecil Quesseth, "Water Pollution Control Laws of Oregon – Problems of Enforcement" *Willamette Law Journal*, 1965, v.3, 287.

[31] Oregon State Sanitary Authority, *Biennial Report to the Governor of Oregon ...for the Period July 1, 1940, to June 30, 1942* (Salem, 1942), 6.

[32] D.A. Long, D. McKey-Fender, and J.A. Macnab, *A Preliminary Survey of the Sources and Kinds of Pollution in Coos Bay* (Portland, Portland State College, 1964), 8.

[33] Oregon State Sanitary Authority, 1942, 11.

[34] Oregon State Sanitary Authority, *Final Report on the Quality of Klamath Basin Waters in Oregon, July, 1959, to December, 1963* (Salem, 1964), 8.

[35] Oregon State Sanitary Authority, *Twelfth Biennial Report on Water Pollution Control for the Period July 1, 1960 to June 30, 1962* (Salem, 1962), 31.

[36] Oregon State Sanitary Authority, 1964, 8.

[37] Sanitary Authority v. Pacific Meat Co., 226 Or. 494, 1961, 495.

[38] Email, Audrey Eldridge, Oregon Department of Environmental Quality, November 17, 2003; opinion of Mark Charles, DEQ.

[39] W. Bruce Shepard and D. Hay Doubleday, *Political Efficiency and Political Effectiveness in Water-Related Policy Areas* (Corvallis, Water Resources Research Institute, 1977), 17.

[40] *Oregonian*, March 23, 1970, 19.

[41] Logan Norris, "Forests and Rangelands as Sources of Chemical Pollutants" Oregon State University Water Resources Research Institute, *Nonpoint Sources of Water Pollution* (Corvallis, 1976), 17.

[42] Ibid, 48.

[43] *Statesman Journal*, November 7, 1999, col.1, A6.

[44] Oregon Department of Environmental Quality, *Water Quality Control in Oregon; a Status Report* (Portland, 1975), 36.

[45] Lolita Carter, *The Effect of Human Activity on the Middle Course of the Tualatin River, Oregon* (Portland, PhD, Portland State University, 1975), 16-17.

[46] Ibid., 120.

[47] *Oregonian*, September 27, 1995, D2.

[48] *Oregonian*, December 25, 1998, B2.

[49] Oregon State Planning Board. *The Willamette Valley Project; Report … to Governor Charles H. Martin on the Development of the Willamette River Watershed, May 8, 1935*. (Salem, 1935), 96.

[50] Ibid., 24.

[51] *Oregonian*, September 7, 1967, 26.

[52] *Oregonian*, July 7, 1969, 27.

[53] *Oregonian*, January 8, 1971, 27.

[54] Department of Environmental Quality, *Willamette River Basin, Briefing Packet* (Portland? March, 1999), [5].

[55] *Oregonian*, August 21, 1995, A1.

[56] *Oregonian*, April 13, 2004, B4.

[57] *Capital Press*, May 14, 2004, 17.

[58] *Oregonian*, May 3, 1929, 26.

[59] *Oregonian*, October 18, 2002, C1.

[60] Oregon City, Oregon. Planning Department, *Comprehensive Plan* (Oregon City, 1982), I-3.

[61] *Oregonian*, June 9, 2004, C2.

[62] Newberg, Oregon. Planning Department, *Sewerage Master Plan Update* (Portland? Kraemer, Chin & Mayo, Inc., 1984), 4.2.

[63] U.S. Army Corps of Engineers, Portland District, *Final Environmental Impact Statement, Operations and Maintenance of the Willamette Reservoir System* (Portland, 1980), 2.8.

[64] *Capital Journal*, May 30, 1973, Sect.2, 17.

[65] Task Force on Wastewater Management, *Report [to the Mayor and Salem City Council]* (Salem, 1984), 5.

[66] *Capital Journal*, September 18, 1971, Sect.2, 18.

[67] *Oregon Journal*, June 3, 1970, J5.

[68] *Oregonian*, August 9, 2001, B4.

[69] *Oregonian*, May 30, 2004, B18.

[70] Oregon State Water Resources Board, *Deschutes River Basin* (Salem, 1961), 95.

[71] *Oregonian*, March 10, 2002, A17.

[72] *Oregonian*, April 21, 1998, A1.

[73] Oregon Department of Environmental Quality, "Point Sources" Internet, April 22, 2003, 2.

[74] *Oregonian*, November 10, 1998, C4.

[75] *Oregonian*, June 29, 1994, B20.

[76] *Statesman-Journal*, January 29, 2004, C3.

[77] *Oregonian*, April 25, 2003, C1.

[78] U.S. Geological Survey, *Pharmaceuticals, Hormones, and Other Organic Wastewater Contaminants in U.S. Streams* (USGS Fact Sheet FS-027-02, 2002), 1-4.

[79] Oregon Department of Environmental Quality, *Water Quality Control in Oregon: A Status Report* (Portland?, 1975), 37.

[80] Quesseth, 1965, 314.

CHAPTER 8

WHERE HAS ALL THE WATER GONE? — WATER SUPPLY

The average home uses water in the following manner: 41 percent for toilet flushing; 37 percent for bathing; 6 percent for kitchen use; 5 percent for drinking water; 4 percent for washing clothes; 3 percent for general household cleaning; 3 percent for lawn and garden watering; and 1 percent for car washing.[1]

During long dry western summers, residential water use rises considerably to 200 gallons just for maintaining a green lawn, while keeping the family automobile clean takes fifty gallons. Aside from care for lawn and car, the average overall daily consumption is between 100 and 200 gallons for each person, while it takes 7 billion gallons a day to supply all Oregonians. Where does all of that water come from and where does it go? About ninety percent originates as surface flow and ten percent as groundwater, primarily replenished by precipitation. Water is used for municipal systems, for hydroelectric power, for industry, and for agriculture, but nothing consumes more than farming. Agricultural practices account for seventy-seven percent of the total, or close to 5.3 billion gallons each day.

The simple withdrawal from shallow wells, springs, and streams, adequate during pioneer days, has been replaced by the utilization of thousands of miles of pipes, lateral lines, pumping stations, valves, deep wells, reservoirs, canals, and treatment plants. The larger the operation, the more complex the system. Generally water is pumped from a storage facility to a plant where it is filtered to remove impurities, treated with chlorine to destroy bacteria, and then passed through carbon to enhance the taste, before being delivered to customers.

Settlers didn't require a great quantity for their homes, but copious amounts were needed for the territory's growth and development. Individual households could store water in tanks or barrels, but, once people clustered together, a village required a regular means of garnering and maintaining a plentiful supply. Of the two arrangements to obtain water - wells or aqueducts - all large towns relied on aqueducts supplemented by wells. Early communal systems were built piecemeal by private individuals, who often incorporated formally as a water company. Pipes, stretching from the company's source, supplied customers until reservoirs or cisterns were constructed. Businesses, on the other hand, required an even greater quantity of water to keep operating, and resorted to building long flumes, canals, and dams to maintain a steady flow during slack water periods.

Today, what it comes down to, is how much water is available to go around, where is it going, and who controls the supply? The Oregon Water Resources Department has responsibility for those tasks – delegating the amount, the time, the place, and the purpose of water use.

In 1909, businessmen and government leaders prevailed upon the Legislature to enact the Oregon Water Code. Embracing four principles, the code decreed that the state's waters belonged to the public; anyone wanting the right to appropriate water had to receive a certificate granted by a state agency. Those with the oldest permits had priority over newer users, and permits could be issued only for beneficial uses with no waste. Instead of limiting water appropriation to riparian property owners, the code encouraged procedures to move water away from the streambed through ditches and canals to where it was needed. Landowners some distance from the surface flow could thus secure the right to a waterway. In 1955 groundwater was declared as belonging to the public and came under similar regulations.

Responsibilities under the code were originally assigned to the State Engineer and two superintendents, forming the Board of Control. These officials had the monumental task of overseeing all aspects of water allocation, adjudication, surveying, stream gauging, and formation of control districts. In 1920 the Legislature created the State Water Board, which underwent several transformations, merging with the office of the State Engineer in 1975 as the Water Resources Department. Although all water belongs to the public, in order to use it legally application has to be made and permission granted by the department, which is to consider the parameters set forth in the Water Code before making its decision. There is one exception. Up to 15,000 gallons a day can be used for domestic purposes without application.

A steam shovel is used to excavate an area for the Tumalo Dam in Deschutes County, an irrigation project overseen by the Water Resources Department around 1914. (Courtesy Oregon State Archives)

From the outset, the bureaucracy was charged with sorting out the tangle of claimed water rights in what proved to be such a lengthy and tedious process of adjudication that most of the controversies are still unresolved. A water right is permission to use a specific amount, at a specific location, for a specific purpose, and, for the most part, a water right remains tied to the land. Because the claims of many users were overlapping or the beginning dates were unclear, all petitions had to be examined, determinations made, and orders issued by the State Engineer. These decisions then went to the court, where a hearing took place, objections were heard, and a final water right certificate granted. Many of the conclusions were challenged, and settlements took years to process through the courts. One of the most protracted cases revolved around the State Engineer's findings on the

Deschutes River, which were entered in February, 1928, but not finalized until December, 1959. By the mid-1980s water rights in sixty-seven percent of the state, almost all in eastern Oregon, had been determined. Approximately thirty percent of the rights in the Willamette Basin had been completed, while surveys in the Klamath region had just begun. Today these figures remain little changed. Even though facing situations where many rights are unresolved, the Water Resources Department continues to issue hundreds of new permits annually.

1800s TO 1900s

The franchise to provide for Portland's needs was obtained by the Pioneer Water Works, established in 1857 by Jacob Cline, Robert Pentland, and Stephen Coffin. The company drilled Douglas Fir logs to serve as a pipe, carrying water to the downtown from Caruthers Creek. This source was supplemented by enlarging and enclosing year-round springs. Instead of connecting to the communal water organization, many residents continued to rely on their own shallow wells. Six years later Pioneer Water Works was sold to H.C. Leonard and John Green, who incorporated 5,000 feet of

Portland's reservoir No. 3 was one of three on Mt. Tabor in 1902.
(Courtesy The Irwin-Hodson Company, Portland)

California redwood logs into a new system complete with a pumping station that tapped Balach Creek on Willamette Heights. Additional water from the Willamette River was piped throughout the city. This complex was updated in 1883 with the installation of iron mains and purchased thereafter by the publicly owned Portland Water Works. Ultimately, four reservoirs scattered throughout the town stored approximately sixty million gallons, and twenty-five cisterns, primarily for fire protection, had a collective capacity of 407,000 gallons. The city's Chief Engineer, Joseph Buchtel, monitored the works, reporting whenever repairs or replacements were needed.

As local streams and wells became polluted from overflowing septic tanks, Portland's water source was switched to the west bank of the Willamette River. However, fearing contamination from the river itself and responding to increased public demands, the city constructed a waterworks at Bull Run Lake on the northwest flank of Mt. Hood. Sylvester Pennoyer, the Mayor of Portland from 1896 to 1898, opposed efforts to tap Bull Run, regarding the Willamette River as extremely drinkable. Sampling that from Bull Run, he grumpily declared, "Lacks body." [2] The first flow of water through the conduit from the reservoir in January of 1895 caused pleased Portland officials to predict that no shortage of water would occur for many years. The headworks were raised in 1920, a second impoundment was completed in 1929, and yet a third one was under consideration by the late 1990s.

Municipal water systems on the coast came together in the same manner. Initially a private corporation, owning a flume or canal from a creek or springs, levied a fee to supply the community until the works was purchased by a public agency. Water for citizens of Coos Bay and North Bend originally came from the Marshfield Water Company. Established in 1897, the business underwent many changes to become the Coos Bay Water Corporation, supplying approximately 1,000 customers from a small dam on Pony Creek. The system was purchased from the corporation in 1947 by the publicly operated Coos Bay-North Bend Water Board.

Water in eastern Oregon was not readily available, but most municipalities here managed by "hustling" a supply from some distance away. At the small town of Sisters in Deschutes County, citizens, who formed the Sisters

Domestic Water System, "took some boards and nailed them together to form a pipe" and ran water to town from a farm pond, which was fed by Squaw Creek. In the words of watermaster Aubrey Perry, "it wasn't very successful, but it kind of worked." Throughout the early 1900s, the system evolved from a ditch connected directly to the creek, to one that harnessed five springs, which "wasted away in the [Pole Creek] swamp." A trench from the springs sent water along the bed of Pole Creek for one mile, then into a small reservoir, and from there through a steel pipe into Sisters. Town officials took the formal step of applying for water rights from the State Engineer before commencing the construction.[3]

In the nearby town of Bend, the first 226 inhabitants could have fresh Deschutes River water delivered to their doorsteps daily for 25 cents a barrel; however, Alexander Drake's Pilot Butte Development Company established a more reliable service by transporting water through a three-mile-long canal from the Deschutes. The year 1905, when Bend was incorporated, marked the beginning of the city's more efficient system that ended the process of "hauling water from the river." Street mains and hydrants, private connections, a 30,000 gallon storage tank, and a ram pump, owned by the Bend Water Light and Power Company, a private organization, were "connected up" bringing "pure water" to residents. The city government purchased the waterworks in 1924, three years after a vote defeated Mayor E.D. Gilson's attempt to sell it his own system. The mayor had been granted the municipal water franchise by the council, but his move was stymied when it was pointed out that the Water Resources Department had refused his application for rights to Spring River.[4]

The first water pipes at The Dalles were laid by private businessmen in 1862 at the same time that wooden sidewalks were constructed downtown. Passing through several hands, the system was purchased by the city some forty years later when the municipality was said to have enough water for 20,000 persons, as well as the "best and purest water in the U.S." – a declaration that would no longer be true a hundred years later. Water reached the town from Mill Creek through The Dalles Lumber Company flume, a "masterpiece of bridge engineering and tressel [sic] work 16 miles in length."[5] Spanning deep ravines sometimes fifty feet above the canyon floor, the flume had catwalks on both sides, which were used for patrolling. On hot summer days the wooden trough served as entertainment for the children, who rode

down on the logs or sent along ripe watermelons to the mill workers below. When the city took over in 1904, it replaced the wooden trough with iron pipes and a reservoir on 16th Street.[6]

In the southern part of the state, Grants Pass in Josephine County worked with a patched together system, which was improved at the suggestion of the Oregon Insurance Rating Company. Upgrading its fire pumping engine in 1927, city officials purchased a new 1,000 gallon capacity truck, but the old water hydrant failed to handle the modernized equipment, because the "screen was

Wooden flumes, which were sometimes miles in length, often did double duty by carrying logs to mills as well as furnishing water to expanding cities. (Courtesy The Irwin-Hodson Company, Portland. 1902)

clogged with sand, crawfish, and periwinkles." Following some discussion, the council contracted for an entirely new system of mains, an intake from the Rogue River, and a filtration plant for $350,000.[7]

Well into the twentieth century Oregon was said to be fortunate in its water, which could be found in abundance "in almost every section of the state." [8] A 1937 study of 144 incorporated cities revealed that ninety used surface water as their source of supply, while groundwater wells served the remaining fifty-four. Of these systems, 127 were publicly owned, whereas the remaining seventeen were private. Portland had twenty-two storage reservoirs, supplied from Bull Run Lake, Klamath Falls had six, filled from eight deep wells, and Coos Bay had five, replenished from Pony Creek. Other cities functioned with just one or two tanks, and some, such as Reedsport, managed by simply pumping directly from a stream.

Instead of constructing their own systems, industries frequently depended on the regional municipal facilities. Sawmills, canneries, paper mills, and woolen mills not only tapped into the waterworks of the larger cities such as Portland, Salem, Albany, Corvallis, Eugene, and Medford, they also utilized water from the smaller towns such as Silverton, Creswell, Toledo, Warrenton, Nyssa, Ontario, and Redmond.

WESTERN OREGON: 1950 TO 1970s

In western Oregon, growth after the 1950s was steady, but water resource planning for the future remained minimal and information was lacking. In 1953 a profusion of government boards and committees such as the Water Resources Committee, the Irrigation and Securities Commission, the State Irrigation Board, the Klamath River Commission, the State Hydroelectric Commission, the Willamette River Basin Commission, the Upper Columbia River Basin Commission, and the State Reclamation Commission shared duties to evaluate water issues. A Legislative Interim Committee on State Water Resources concluded that there was little coordination among water bureaucracies, resulting in a tendency to "create conflicts among water agencies having broad powers and to encourage single-purpose development." [9] In addition, the committee found that water policy had evolved as a series of discrete, uncoordinated laws, each with separate goals. It favored a multiple-use approach for the state's waters, which were to be administered by a single bureau. In response to comments, the legislature created a Water Policy Review Board, which later became the Water Resources Commission, directing its members to formulate a program for use and control of the resource. Operating under broad guidelines, the board was to study Oregon's water picture and determine the means and methods of conserving and augmenting the supply for existing as well as for contemplated future needs.

The Water Policy Review Board reacted to the legislative directive by dividing the state into eighteen basins and preparing reports for each. The reports listed water allocation, set minimum perennial stream flows (how much water can be removed from a stream before someone's rights were violated or fish habitat endangered), determined as much as possible water availability and existing water rights, and predicted potential development. Waters were classified according to their highest and best uses. Although the beneficial uses were generally similar for each basin, they were not ranked in any order. These encompassed every imaginable purpose: domestic, municipal, irrigation, power development, industrial, mining, recreation, wildlife, fish life, pollution control, flood abatement, reclamation, drainage, and reservoirs. Because no hierarchy was set up (Was industry preferred over fish? Was recreation more necessary than irrigation?), the board had what would appear to be the unenviable task of juggling a wide diversity of contrasting and contradictory demands for uses on each stream and in all watersheds.

A closer look at the reports reveals that they were geared more toward the development of the resource rather than toward its protection, and frequently the two were mutually exclusive. In the case of the 1969 plan for the Malheur and Owyhee basins, the department concluded that "Some aquifers *may* easily be overpumped." However, "An additional 380,000 acre-feet per year *could be* developed," or "There *would appear* to be at least a limited *possibility* for development" (ital. added).[10]

Except for the relatively recent one on the Willamette Basin, most reports are hopelessly out-of-date and out-of-step with current trends in urban growth, with development of fish habitat, and with recreational needs. They also predate or are in conflict with mandated land-use regulations. Comprehensive reports for the Klamath and Malheur basins were never written. Ultimately the reports formed the basis for administrative rules that became the operating program for the department after the 1980s. Unlike the basin plans, which contained some concrete data, the rules are written in language that allows a considerable amount of latitude for interpretation and response to political pressure. Little down-to-earth direction is provided by such phrases as "the maximum economic development of this state" or "the attainment of an integrated and coordinated program for the benefit of the state as a whole." [11]

But in the early 1950s, no hovering specter of a shortfall was visible. Deficiencies experienced in certain regions during long dry summers were ignored. Thirty-three cities experienced shortages in flow, but in general supplies were said to be "more than adequate." [12] In fact, the State Water Resources Board and the U.S. Geological Survey foresaw no problems for the Willamette basin. "The U. S. Geological Survey states that there is a great quantity of available water for future development." [13] In the hills west of Portland, only Forest Grove and Hillsboro, entirely dependent on surface flows, were facing possible shortages. On the other hand, the urban areas of Beaverton, Sherwood, Tigard, Cooper Mountain, and Bull Mountain, which drew from wells drilled into the Columbia River basalts, appeared to have unlimited quantities. This was the same source utilized for irrigation. Lake Oswego and surrounding communities counted on wells supplemented with water purchased from Portland's Bull Run system. Protected by Oregon law, Portland's rights to Bull Run Lake and the Little Sandy River appropriated the largest amount of water for any one public supply.

As people and businesses migrated toward the metropolitan areas of Portland, Salem, and Eugene, ongoing expansion and improvement were inevitable. During the mid-1930s, the Salem City Council had decided to obtain water from the North Santiam River instead of relying on its three existing wells. The new complex necessitated $750,000 for a transmission line and $185,000 for a filtration works. Following general approval at a council meeting in May, 1936, the Portland engineering firm of Stevens and Koons laid pipe and drilled three shallow wells in Stayton (now Geren) Island on the Santiam River. Two years later, algae and sandy turbidity caused officials to agree "with the people of Salem … that the fantastic and ridiculous water system for which they have spent so much money is a flop. There is not enough water and its quality is nauseous." [14]

Again encountering water shortages by the late 1950s, Salem constructed the 100-million-gallon Franzen Reservoir on a hill above Turner. Even though

For its expanded drinking water system during the 1930s, Salem placed a submerged, thirty-six-inch steel pipe across lower Mill Creek. (Courtesy Western City Magazine, 1937)

designed to feed water into other storage basins around the community, it couldn't fulfill peak demands during dry summer days. However, curtailment of use was "not acceptable to the elected City Council or the residents of Salem. It was the community tradition to use large amounts of very cheap water for irrigating lawns and ornamental plants … if we are running out of water we just need to find a way to increase the supply." [15] Arguments for and against drinking from the Willamette River were resolved with a $3,750,000 bond to pay for new transmission lines and filters to improve the taste from Stayton Island.

Faced with periodic shortfalls over the next twenty years, Salem purchased old water rights from Boise Cascade and gained further access to the North Santiam River. That wasn't the end of its water dilemma, and a new Master Plan, adopted in 1994, recommended additional lines from the river as well as rehabilitation of the Franzen Reservoir. At the same time the council decided to initiate a back-up aquifer storage and recovery program. The plan was to inject 440 million gallons of treated North Santiam River water into wells drilled in the basalt at Salem Heights. Worried about the impact of the injection, the Department of Environmental Quality monitored the project closely. Ultimately five injection wells were productive, but the entire operation was not as successful as hoped. Management of the complex system was difficult and time consuming, and the water quality was poor. Even though the water met all the technical regulations for purity, a musty taste and smell caused city residents to complain. Eventually the city decided to halt any expansion of the project. Today Salem operates from eighteen reservoirs and is renovating the Franzen storage facility. At the same time it has begun a program of conservation, urging residents to use water-saving devices and not to green-up their lawns.

Eugene's system underwent modernization in 1941. Prompted by increased usage, the Eugene Water and Electric Board augmented its booster pumps to their McKenzie River line. Examining its options, the board completed a 15 million-gallon reservoir, the second on College Hill, as well as a 100,000-gallon tank. Several new storage facilities and a filtering plant, combined with additional water from the McKenzie River, were added during the next twenty-five years, and today, EWEB is examining the possibility of raising the height of Leesburg Dam to increase its capacity.

Eugene and Salem were fortunate in that the Environmental Quality Commission enacted the Three Basins Rule in 1977 to protect the pristine condition of the North Santiam, the McKenzie, and the Clackamas rivers, prohibiting any direct discharge of pollutants into the surface waters of these basins.

South of Eugene in Douglas County the picture was somewhat different. In the late 1950s virtually all municipalities tapped surface flows. Residents in many areas found that supplies "in the last few years have just barely been adequate and those communities dependent upon groundwater supply have been in difficulty." [16] Typically, individual homeowners in the South Umpqua basin, whose wells dried up from July through November, hauled in water from elsewhere. Forty years later municipal water supplies in this region were still unreliable during the summer irrigating season.

Douglas County officials saw the placement of dams as the solution to their water woes. The advantages, they felt, were steadiness of supply and improved quality as well as the ability to provide for recreation. The major disadvantage was cost, not environmental degradation. Between 1967 and 1985, the government was able to develop six major dams to serve regional municipalities and industries, but more recently it lamented the fact that lands under consideration for potential future dam sites already had "conflicting uses" such as housing, schools, or churches, rendering costs prohibitive.[17]

EASTERN OREGON: 1950S TO 1970S

People living in eastern Oregon counted on supplying water from deep wells more commonly than from springs or rivers. Among the communities there, Bend was the exception, utilizing upstream reservoirs supplied from the Deschutes River until 1924, when an algae growth rendered the water so unpleasant that mechanical filters were installed. The offensive taste remained, forcing the city to abandon utilization of the river and purchase rights to Bridge Creek from the Tumalo Irrigation District. By 1971 a burgeoning population finally compelled the city to drill its first well near the Deschutes, and since then it has consistently tapped groundwater to sustain growth.

In Wasco County, the community of The Dalles employed a gravity-fed, filtered water system from a reservoir on Mill Creek, combined with two wells from "an underground source described as inexhaustible." It served 13,000 residential, commercial, and industrial customers in addition to some irrigators. A daily pumping capacity of five million gallons provided for "whatever expansion might come in the future … water for the municipal swimming pool, city parks and cemeteries are free." [18]

1970S: GROUNDWATER

Headlines in 1977 - "Here Comes California" and "The Southwest Wants Our Water" - resurrected earlier strategies to pipe water from the Columbia River to southern California, Nevada, and Arizona. Los Angeles County Supervisor Kenneth Hahn said the Columbia's "wasted" water could "turn our deserts into Gardens of Eden." Senator Mark Hatfield warned that Oregon and Washington must be prepared to justify their claims to all of the Columbia water or risk losing it. Fortunately the pipeline never came to pass because Oregonians were beginning to experience their own water deficiencies by that time:

1915: "Water Supply Abundant"
1924: "Shortage in Portland Unlikely"
1953: "Oregon Blessed with Much Precious Water"
1965: "100-year Study to Find if State has Water Surplus"
1966: "Solon Asks Sustained Yield Plan for State Water Users"
1966: " 'Cheap Water' Depleting Supply, Consultant Says"
1973: "Water Shortage Leads to Restriction in Counties" [20]

Groundwater was to be the remedy as Oregon headed toward the new century. Typically when the surface flows diminish, underground water becomes the next stopgap. Once that point is reached, serious competition for a supply arises between all users. Oregon's most cherished myth is that limitless volumes of pure water run beneath the ground in streams, which are replenished each year with precipitation. Neither of these notions is close to the truth. For the most part, the workings of aquifers are poorly understood and have yet to be mapped, but it has become evident that the surface flow drops as groundwater is removed. Surface and groundwater don't act independently but work together hydraulically as one inter-connected system. Freshwater aquifers, natural underground storage reservoirs, vary in

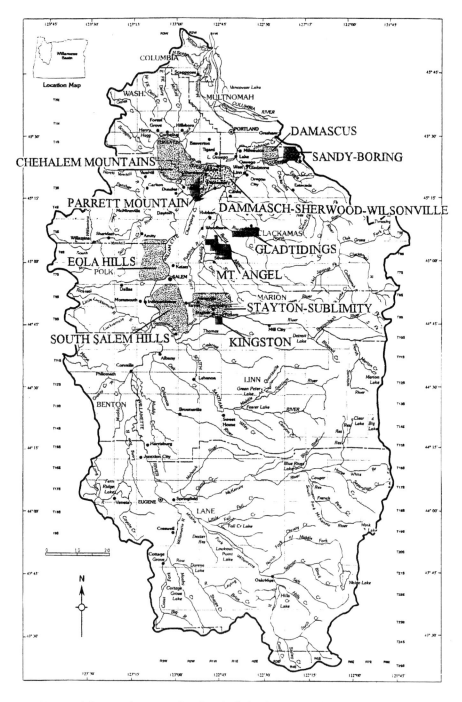

Maps of Oregon's groundwater deficient areas. (After Oregon Water Resources Department, 1984; 1992)

thickness from less than twenty to more than 600 feet. Here the water moves extremely slowly through cracks and openings in rock, or in the tiny openings and spaces in sand and gravel layers. In general terms, the Oregon Coast Range and High Lava Plains have only modest amounts of groundwater, the Willamette Valley possesses large quantities, while the Great Basin and Columbia Plateau are moderately abundant.

Oregon's first groundwater laws requiring an application and permit from the Water Resources Department were adopted on May 28, 1927, but the regulations applied only east of the Cascade Mountains. It wasn't until 1955 that the entire state came under the same regulations, when the department began to realize that groundwater was being used faster than it was being replenished. At present virtually none of the early groundwater rights or dilemmas have been examined and resolved, even though numbers of new permits for use and extension are being issued monthly.

Almost 700 million gallons of water pumped from the ground each day serve seventy-seven percent of Oregonians in one way or another, but farm operations take the most, a trend that has increased steadily. "Development of the groundwater resource for irrigation was almost nonexistent in the

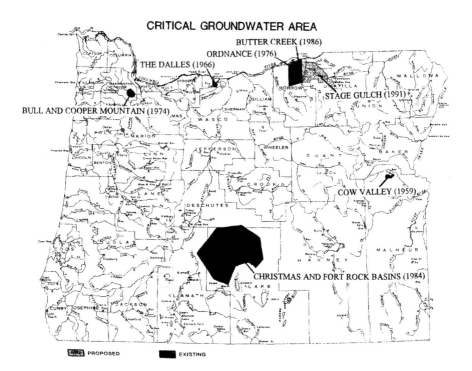

CRITICAL GROUNDWATER AREA

1950s."[21] More efficient drilling methods enabling wells to reach deep basalt aquifers, new irrigation techniques, inexpensive electricity, and high crop prices favored agriculture. The tragedy is that today municipalities are looking to drink from polluted rivers, while clean groundwater goes for irrigation, where quality standards are lower than for household consumption.

If the amount drawn from the aquifer exceeds the estimated natural long-term recharge, the Water Resources Commission declares the region to be a groundwater critical or groundwater limited area. The groundwater limited designation allows the commission to limit future use. Within a groundwater critical region more severe restrictions can give certain users preference over others, can reduce the amount of a water right, can cap polluted wells, or can limit the number of wells for a single right holder. At present in Oregon there are six critical groundwater areas, all except one east of the Cascades. By contrast, eleven groundwater limited areas, established in 1992, are all in western Oregon.

Because it is hidden beneath the surface, groundwater has always been viewed as pristine, and only recently has examination of this resources begun. Following enactment of the Groundwater Protection Act and Groundwater Quality Protection Rules in 1989, the Department of Environmental Quality began to monitor domestic wells, to set procedures for well construction and decommissioning, to establish pollution levels, and to identify geographic areas of concern. One of these areas encompassed the shallow aquifer in the southern Willamette Valley impacted by a rapidly growing population. Conducting an assessment of the groundwater between the years 2000 and 2002, the department found dangerous nitrate levels in domestic wells from Corvallis south to Eugene. Non-point sources for the nitrates include fertilizers, septic systems, and animal wastes. Regions around Junction City and Coburg in Lane County had the highest readings. These levels exceeded safe drinking water standards, although private well owners don't have to meet any health requirements, and currently there are no legal restrictions for drilling new domestic wells into areas of polluted groundwater. Following this discovery, the DEQ held public hearings in 2002 before placing the region into a Groundwater Management Area. Most comments were favorable with the exception of those by Joanne Hathaway representing the Benton County Farm Bureau and the Oregon Farm Bureau. Hathaway questioned whether the entire area should be included. "She also pointed out her understanding that houses and septic systems are the sources of the groundwater problems, not farmers." [22] Hathaway went on to remark, "Don't ever say Best Management Practices to a bunch of farmers. That is like a red flag. You are going to tell them how their soils should be handled, when they've spent twenty years figuring out how to do it." [23] Implementation of the groundwater plan would allow additional research, monitoring, education, and working with participants to improve the quality in the southern Willamette aquifer.

EASTERN OREGON

In the eastern part of the state, crop irrigation, not population, has been responsible for the serious reduction of the groundwater table. Cow Valley in 1959 and The Dalles in 1966 were the first regions in the state to be declared as groundwater critical. Located between Brogan and Ironside in northern Malheur County, aquifers in Cow Valley were being drained faster than they were being recharged, and even under a management program water levels remain unchanged at fifteen feet below normal almost fifty years later. In Wasco County, residents and farmers in and around The Dalles were experiencing serious deficiency problems in 1966 when groundwater levels were declining at the rate of five to six feet a year. At that time Water Resources placed a moratorium on new wells drilled into the regional aquifer. A legal challenge to the department's decision dragged on in court for over six years, delaying any immediate action and resulting in even greater depletion of the water level. When water from the Columbia River became available to The Dalles Irrigation District through a Bureau of Reclamation project, farmers turned to that source. The decline in the aquifer has slowed, while the number of irrigated acres has steadily increased.

No part of the state has seen the groundwater more heavily impacted than the Boardman-Ordnance-Hermiston area in Morrow and Umatilla counties. Although this section of the Columbia Plateau receives only eight or nine inches of rainfall annually, the government still encouraged agricultural and industrial production. Development was rapid after 1963, when Governor Mark Hatfield brokered an option for the Boeing Company on nearly 100,000 acres near the Boardman bombing range. A seventy-seven year lease, costing Boeing $2 an acre, included nine water rights for irrigating more than 63,000 acres. Boeing's original intent was to test missiles, but in 1971 the company elected instead to farm part of the land, contracting out the remainder. Needing prodigious amounts of water, Simtag, the largest potato-growing enterprise in the world, acquired use of 25,000 of the acres. Roughly ten years later, basalt and gravel reservoirs near Ordnance experienced excessively low groundwater levels after large irrigation wells multiplied, some reaching 1,500 feet deep. As levels dropped more than 100 and as much as 300 feet, the Water Resources Department placed the area on the critical groundwater list.

This restriction did not halt the 1995 application of Hermiston businessman Bob Hale and his partners in the Inland Land Company. The company intended to draw off 144,000 acre-feet of Columbia River water - more than Portlanders use in a year – to irrigate 23,000 acres of land leased from Boeing. Whereas the Water Resources Department declared a moratorium on new withdrawals from the Columbia in order to protect salmon, it routinely issued numerous extensions of time for water rights permits, some well into the future. In the case of the Inland Company, the department approved an extension. WaterWatch of Oregon and several other groups filed a petition to have the extensions reviewed. Jim Myron, of Oregon Trout, said, "I mean, this is the public's water and land we're talking about." [24] Failing to alter the department's determination, the groups were forced to file a lawsuit against Water Resources and Boeing in 1996, alleging that the numerous extensions violated state law, that extensive habitat destruction would result, that public input was necessary, and that the moratorium on new withdrawals would be violated. As the result of negotiations, the quantity of land to be farmed and the amount of water to be taken from the river were reduced, while tracts were set aside for habitat protection.

To the southeast near Butter Creek, the basalt aquifer became similarly critical, following severe declines in the groundwater that began in late 1960. Within twenty years, levels had fallen more than 300 feet in some wells, with an average of 100 to 200 feet total during that interval. As the state Water Resources Department continued to issue permits, Curt and Neal Perkins were authorized to appropriate 15.89 cubic feet per second of water for irrigation of just over 2,000 acres. Most permits allowed for less than one cfs.[25] By the time the department set new limits in the mid-1980s, cutting available water by one-third, many of the older drilling and production records had been lost, and "most of the water level data collected since 1975 has been in the winter months when large-capacity wells are not pumping." [26] These restrictions met severe opposition from local wheat and potato farmers, and at a Hermiston meeting farmers protested the taking away of their prior held water rights. Larry Hansen, of Echo, suggested the state should compensate farmers "whose rights were interfered with." [27] Appealed to the Oregon Supreme Court, the restrictions were upheld in a 1989 decision. Over two decades later the aquifer in the Butter Creek area has yet to recover.

In the Basin and Range Province of southcentral Oregon, where shallow playa lakes shrink and expand periodically, reliance on aquifers has always been the case. Because streams and rivers there were so sparse and far between, settlers looking to farm the barren landscape drilled wells to reach what they imagined was "a largely untouched natural resource – a bountiful supply of groundwater – [that] flowed beneath the parched, dusty land, remarkably close to the surface." [28]

Receiving less than twelve inches of rainfall each year, Fort Rock Basin consists of Christmas Lake, Silver Lake, and Summer Lake. Fort Rock and Christmas valleys are ancient, dry lake beds, whereas Silver and Summer lakes are shallow flat expanses where the water level has varied considerably throughout the historic past. Homesteaders converged on the Fort Rock Valley from 1905 onward only to find water was elusive, and it wasn't until fifteen years later that the Oregon Legislature funded four test wells. Supervised by geologist Henry Parks of the State Bureau of Mines and Geology, the drilling was a success, the wells producing 700 to 1,000 gallons a minute. A banquet, band, and dance marked the occasion, and the *Silver Lake Leader* predicted, "Now that the question of water has been solved " farming will thrive.[29] In anticipation of profits from lush irrigated fields, the Fort Rock Development Company was organized and financial backing secured from San Francisco and New York. But when the rickety wooden flumes leaked, when seepage drained ditches, and when water hustling proved too costly, irrigation of the farmland fell by the wayside. It never completely ceased, however, and gradually the number of watered acres began to increase.

In 1953 the U.S. Geological Survey and Oregon Water Resources Department were still predicting plentiful groundwater in the basin, whereas

Oregon State College scientists reported that irrigation should be limited to 32,000 acres. When the area was divided into ranchettes for California retirees and some would-be hobby farmers, the land was speedily sold. Between the 1970s and 1980s the Water Resources Department issued 60,000 new water rights permits as settlement was spurred on by low-interest federal and state-sponsored government farm loans. Before then, pumping averaged less than 20,000 acre-feet annually with no discernible drop in the water reservoir, but a steady expansion in withdrawal to 80,000 acre-feet began to depress the groundwater table.

Almost all of the groundwater removed goes for irrigated agriculture. "Today this land of prehistoric lakebeds is spiraled with circles of green … the center-pivot-irrigation machine, sending out a tremendous stream, comes by at approximately three-day intervals." [30] Currently land under irrigation remains at 40,000 acres, although valid groundwater rights exist for 65,000 acres. From 1984 to 1986 the Water Resources Department halted the issuance of permits, but it started up again in October, 1986, by accepting applications for 6,000 additional acres to be watered. Donn Miller in the department realized that, "Limitations on new appropriations would help prevent overdraft of the main ground water reservoir." One year later all new well applications were again being denied, when the basin was declared a critical groundwater area.[31]

Miller also reflected that, "The slow depletion of ground water storage allows understanding of reservoir conditions before conflicts arise among users." Miller's cautionary note was expressed but not heeded in 1986. Twenty more years of pumping, in conjunction with periods of drought, brought conflict to Summer Lake residents over prior water rights and water designated for wildlife, irrigation, and recreation. Located in the southwest portion of the Fort Rock Basin, the lake is fed by rainfall, intermittent runoff, and many springs rising from basalt aquifers. Currently the lake is rapidly shrinking. During 1950 and 1961 it was reduced from 45,000 acres to a ten-acre wet area surrounded by vast mudflats. Today a similar episode of water loss is being challenged by homeowners, who want the level to be maintained by diverting the springs, which feed into a wetland and bird sanctuary. Much of the water is being drained off for older rights held since the 1930s by the Summer Lake Irrigation District. Practicing flood irrigation, some thirty ranchers get their water off the top, whereas the remainder goes to the refuge, which locals feel is being maintained by fish and wildlife personnel for the enjoyment of duck and geese hunters.

An enclosed irrigation flume for the Goose Lake Valley Irrigation Company in Lake County is seemingly endless. A car travels on a dirt road paralleling the flume (1915). (Courtesy Oregon State Archives)

When the Fish and Wildlife Department failed to acquire permits for rebuilding a Summer Lake dike in 1997, it had to backtrack and make application to the Division of State Lands for wetlands improvements as well as to update its management plan. This gave residents a foothold to intervene in a move to readjust some of the prior held water rights, causing the ranchers, in turn, to worry about their irrigation. Meanwhile, the Division of State Lands approved the dike, although the federal permit for work by the U.S. Army Corps of Engineers is pending. Also pending is a hearing on updating the area's management plan.

Darrell Seven, owner of Summer Lake Inn, wants the lake filled but doesn't "want the irrigators to suffer ... Farmers and ranchers have it tough enough." The ranchers feel, "Homeowners want the lake full for aesthetics." Susan Haig of the U.S. Geological Survey speaks for the wildlife. "What they [lakeside residents] don't get is that they're in a desert and the lake dries up historically. That's the way the desert works." [32] The Water Resources Commission, on the other hand, is an advocate for the farmers. Rejecting previous requests from the Oregon Department of Fish and Wildlife to provide water for native trout and other fish in Thomas Creek, lying within in the Goose and Summer lakes watershed, the commission "concluded that irrigation use is a more important use of water." [33]

While subsequent decisions by the commission closed Thomas Creek to new appropriations for irrigation, a permit was still granted for two wells to water over 1,300 acres. The application went through a number of ups and downs after being filed in 1990. Initially rejected on a finding that the wells were too close to the creek and that groundwater withdrawal would interfere with surface flows, the denial was appealed, then approved in 1997. Approval came after the department received "new" information that this particular section had been channelized so the creek "now flows in excess of 1000 feet from the proposed wells." [34] During the summer of 2000 the Water Resources Department realized that both wells were too shallow, essentially drawing surface water, a violation of the initial agreement. Irregardless, a time extension to complete and repair the system was given in 2004, because the "new owners didn't know about the problem." [35]

WESTERN OREGON

Twenty years after water restrictions were established in areas east of the Cascade Range, rainy western Oregon began to experience its own shortages. Urban pressures and industrial growth were demanding a greater percentage of the available supply both on the coast and in the Willamette Valley. Along the coast, the normal surface flow was thought to be more than adequate, while the groundwater was very limited in quantity and quality. Generally, numerous small systems provided service, and throughout Clatsop County residents were served by twenty-eight separate companies. Coos Bay and North Bend were the exceptions, both of which supported lumber and pulp mills that were harvesting and processing sizeable stands of virgin timber. As far back as 1948 these communities had already determined that even with sixty-two inches of rainfall a year, "paradoxically, lack of water has blocked further industrial expansion." [36] Figuring in its own needs, as well as the costs of accommodating Weyerhaeuser Lumber

Company's new mill, the Coos Bay Water Board planned to lay bigger lines to a small dam on Pony Creek around 1950.

Ten years later, freshwater was "discovered" beneath the sand. Encouraged by drilling tests, Pacific Power and Light believed that one million gallons of clean water a day could be drawn from the dunes around Coos Bay, leading engineers to anticipate that this would "become the second major sand dune water supply source in the world" behind waterworks in Holland.[37] This immense flow of water never materialized, and officials gradually expanded their Pony Creek system by adding added a dam on Joe Ney Slough. By 2000, Coos County was in the final stages of tripling its existing storage as well completing twenty wells to pump from the aquifer beneath the Oregon Dunes National Recreation Area. The reality is that the population of Coos County has only increased by a few thousand over the past thirty years, and much of the pristine aquifer water goes to support industries. The long-term effects of lowering the groundwater in the dune field are uncertain, but permits from the Water Resources Department haven't ceased. Today, the community sees itself in an environmental light. "Wetlands, wildlife, and fish were protected through a comprehensive mitigation plan," while the long-term capacity of the well field is being studied.[38]

Meanwhile, costal development continues unchecked with little or no thought given to water resource planning or conservation. At Bandon newly developed golf courses on the dunes, along with an astonishing 5,300 new units along the coast, exhibit little concern by planners and government for increased water consumption.

In California, along the Gulf, and on the East Coast, dunal water resources have proven to be extremely susceptible to over-pumping. Excessive withdrawal can pull deeper marine saltwater up into an aquifer, ruining it for the foreseeable future. Such was the case in the late 1960s at Gearhart and Warrenton in Clatsop County, where two deep wells into dunes were abandoned after producing brackish, low saline water.

Population expansion on the coast found other communities struggling with the same shortfall by the mid-1990s. After the town of Florence, in Lane County, became involved in ongoing disagreements with its supplier, Heceta Water District, residents and businesses were forced to depend on their own seven dunal wells. Officials relied on earlier reports, which found

"This dunal aquifer is a vast natural reservoir … The capacity of this aquifer, while not unlimited, is vast." [39] "Vast" was the operative word, but after the city actually began to pump from the wells, it found the supply was insufficient during summer drought months, when it accommodated the annual influx of tourists. After three years of shortages, Florence officials signed an agreement in 2003 to secure water from Heceta Water District at increased rates. However, the district was facing its own roadblock with limitations on the quantity of water it could divert from Clear Lake. Hoping to protect fish habitat, landowner Aaron Jones, along with the Lane County Commissioners, restricted drawdown of the lake. The Heceta Board accused the officials and Jones of wanting the lake for themselves. They "think we're going to drain the lake like a bathtub … They feel like it belongs to them." Others suggest that Florence's water problems, which have been growing for years, were ignored by bureaucrats. [40]

With its population density, its concentration of industries, its plant nurseries and irrigated fields, and its contaminated and disappearing surface and groundwater supply, the Willamette Basin was destined to experience a combination of water problems unique to Oregon. Even while recent focus has been on the Klamath River and regions east of the Cascades, where water has all but disappeared, the Willamette Valley has been exhibiting increasing signs of distress. Water districts merged, arguments and competition arose between agencies and companies and cities and farms, alternate days were assigned to the watering of lawns, conservation was mandated for fish needs, water costs increased, and the buying and selling of water became part of the equation in the search for additional sources.

The notion of a water shortage in the Willamette Valley is hard to believe, but in no place is this more true than in the northern part of the basin. Here city dwellers are forced to drink contaminated surface water, while farmers, holding the oldest rights, have access to a clean source. Reports in the 1990s that Wilsonville residents in Clackamas County would drink from the polluted Willamette River were greeted with good-humored denial, followed by abhorrence, then by consternation. Attempts by Wilsonville officials to tap into the nearby Troutdale aquifer were stymied by Charbonneau water rights holders as well as by Clackamas County officials. Having depleted its own water source, the city had hoped to obtain "the five or six years' worth of water needed to provide relief for the failing aquifer" from yet another groundwater source. Over the past ten years Wilsonville has boomed with new construction for housing and industry, heedless of falling water levels, but, eventually facing this dilemma, officials imposed a moratorium on all new construction in 1998. "If we go to turn on a faucet on a hot late August day and there's no water because they've destroyed the water table, it's too late," Joe Casale, a farmer just east of Charbonneau, concluded about Wilsonville's expansion.[41]

Requiring new sources, Wilsonville chose the Willamette River, and in 2002 its new water treatment plant opened for business. Capable of processing 15 million gallons a day from the river, the facility treats the water to meet drinking water standards, although officials feel that the plant is "over-designed" in that several extra steps are taken to assure high quality. In both the raw water and river sediments, "ALL [sic] of the 140(+) organic chemicals were below the laboratory detection limit in the UNTREATED [sic] river water. The exception was DDT "which is no longer in use…" Found only in a trace amount, "the dioxin of concern for drinking water was not detected … A far less harmful species of dioxin was detected in the sediments, but at such a low level it was nearly" equivalent to pure water.[42]

The newly-constructed and beautifully-landscaped Willamette River Water Treatment Plant opened in 2002 near Wilsonville.

Other reports don't speak quite as glowingly about the water and sediment quality in the Willamette River, which has been the focus of cleanup efforts for decades. Before wastewater regulations were implemented during the 1940s, sewage and industrial discharge caused severe degradation within the basin. Despite the fact that the river is significantly cleaner, "recent surveys indicate that concentrations of several pollutants (e.g., metals, pesticides, PCBs, dioxin, and bacteria) in water, sediments, or fish tissue exceed regulatory or guidance criteria for the protection of aquatic and human health … indicating that further improvements in water quality are needed." Overall the river health received a marginal rating, with some sections falling below that standard.[43]

In 2005 the Willamette River Water Coalition, an intergovernmental group, is launching a campaign to inform citizens about the Willamette River treatment plant at Wilsonville. Anticipating that many small northern valley communities would need to purchase future drinking water, coalition members hope that "Informed voters are more likely to choose the Willamette River," although their goal was not to "persuade people" but to inform them.[44]

Much persuasion may not be necessary as the search for water is so pressing that other urbanized regions are already looking at the Willamette. Forced to locate additional sources by 2007, following disagreements with Portland over the rising rates on Bull Run water, the Tualatin Valley Water District is considering an option on the river through the Wilsonville facility. But when Portland officials had taken a look at the Willamette River ten years earlier, they were opposed by residents. "You have to put the health of the city first," the city council was told. "Drinking out of the Willamette is an appalling thought." Others blamed the ongoing absorption of land into the urban boundary for development. "There are so many houses, it's insanity. Developers want every piece of land to build a house. Where is it going to end?"[45]

It won't end in Canby, just east of Wilsonville, which is encouraging development "as subdivisions continue to crop up and demand for water increases." Ignoring their lack of a sufficient municipal supply, officials hope to utilize agricultural wells to augment their only source, the Molalla River. One of the most productive wells is owned by farmer Harvey Tofte, who has been steadily selling his property to builders. Dirk Borges, Canby Utility Manager, wishes "to find a 1.5 million-gallon underground supply that could be used in emergencies … Canby's a thirsty town … known for its commercial nurseries and greenhouses. And residents pour a lot of water on their yards and gardens."[46] Tapping the Willamette River for industrial and drinking water needs may be the city's main option.

Throughout the northern Willamette Valley water levels in basalt aquifers are not being recharged fast enough to offset withdrawal. The eleven areas declared by the Water Resources Department to be groundwater limited or groundwater critical can be grouped into six broad regions from Salem northward to Damascus on the east side of the valley and from Salem almost to Forest Grove on the west side.

The Clackamas River Basin is groundwater limited from Sandy westward past Damascus. In August, 2002, Clackamas River Water [District], servicing the southeast Portland metro area, experienced such low water levels in conjunction with hot weather, with excessive effluent discharge, and with a lack of rainfall that a "foul odor" and growth of algae affected the water supply of several local cities utilizing the river. Water experts blithely assured, "Despite the musty odor and strange taste of tap water, residents shouldn't worry about any health risks from drinking the water or using it for cooking." Gordon McGhee, water quality specialist for Clackamas River Water, suggested using hydrogen peroxide then allowing the water to sit a while, although there was no guarantee that this process would cure the problem. John Collins, acting manager of the South Fork Water Board, which furnishes water to the district, noted, "We used to get these [algae problems] every five to seven years, but now they're coming with more frequency – like every 18 to 24 months." [47] Clackamas River Water along with Gresham and others are considering merging with the Rockwood Water People's Utility District. As a cost-saving measure, in 2005 the Rockwood District began blending Bull Run water with that from its own newly-drilled wells.

The Sunrise Water Authority, supplying Damascus, is doubling the capacity of its Clackamas River plant, which it shares with the Oak Lodge Water District. For the future, however, the authority is looking at a merger in addition to producing income from selling nonpotable water from its nine wells. The water, which is high in flouride, can go for irrigation without processing. Having to buy water from the South Fork Water Board, which relies on the Clackamas River, the West Linn City Council approved a ninety-eight percent rate increase in 1995. This move was contested by residents, who say they are paying for services to new housing areas instead of the builders being charged for expanding the system. The council pointed out, on the other hand, that the South Fork Board itself had raised its rates by 146 percent.

Not only is much of the Tualatin Valley groundwater limited, but both Bull Mountain and Cooper Mountain have been placed on the critical groundwater list. Tigard, which obtains its water from the Tualatin Valley Water District, asked residents to conserve after high demand during the hot summer of 2003 put a strain on the system. A sanguine Jeff Bauman, Public Works Director, pointed out, "There are no water restrictions in place. No worries … It's hard for me to believe I am saying this. We are telling people not to waste it. But as long as people wish to use it, there is no limitation."[48] On the other hand, Tigard planned to hang a large banner on one of its reservoirs to promote conservation. Serving 180,000 customers in Washington County, the Tualatin Valley Water District is supplied through the Bull Run and Barney impoundments.

Both Tigard and Beaverton have begun aquifer storage and recovery programs to supplement their low summertime supply. Beaverton pumps water from its treatment plant into underground basalt layers for an additional 400 million gallons. The city installed two new recharge wells in 2004, bringing its total to four. Tigard located its first aquifer recharge well in 2001, and a second one in 2003, but a third site experienced difficulties and proved unusable.

Small communities operating from regional systems sometimes experience the most problems, and mergers are commonly the answer. In Marion County, cities within the Mt. Angel groundwater limited area have raised their rates, and in Silverton seventy-seven "water-starved" residents to the south of town, whose water table had been dropping for some six years, were annexed into the city system. The adjacent Oregon Garden found its water pressure dropping too low to irrigate its seventy-acre botanical area. Promised an unlimited supply of wastewater through an agreement with the city "to pump all the water needed to irrigate the grounds," the garden now finds there is not even enough from that source.[49] Throughout the garden, wetlands serve as the final stage for Silverton's wastewater treatment processing.

Dayton in Yamhill County declared a water crisis in July, 2003, because city reservoir levels were at less than thirty-percent capacity. All outside watering except for gardens and animals was prohibited until after the completion of two new wells, set to become operative the following year.

Extravagant urban water use during hot summer days keeps sidewalks and roadways wet.

PRESENT-DAY

Viewed as an unlimited resource by Oregonians, water was consumed lavishly to supply needs and encourage growth, and recent unmistakable signs of depletion in both surface and groundwater have failed to limit the approval of new water rights permits by the Water Resources Department. Today the actual number of legitimate water rights permits frequently leads to over allocation or over appropriation – a condition where the quantity of surface or groundwater is not available to meet needs during a certain period. It is not unusual for a streambed to become dry during late summer, the flow having been entirely pumped out by permit holders. Even in the face of diminishing quantities of water, the department continues to approve new water rights permits, denying few. "The Water Resources Department shall approve all applications made in proper form which contemplate the application of water to a beneficial use." [50]

Administrative rules, water availability, and public interest are the main criteria for which a water rights application is scrutinized. A detailed department publication, *Water Availability for Oregon's Rivers and Streams*, contains statistical data on water flow, rights, and basin characteristics for thousands of streams throughout the state. It can be easily consulted to provide a basis for making a decision as to what unallocated water remains at a given spot for both instream and out-of-stream uses. Public interest is an imprecise concept never really defined in the statutes, although Dwight French, head of the Water Rights Section of the Water Resources Department, considers that public interest has been served if the above criteria, along with any other restrictions, such as those for endangered species, are met.[51] Public interest has also been interpreted to mean whether complaints have been made about the application. "The practice of not regulating a diversion until an appropriator *complains* [ital. added] is adequate to solve problems between individual users, but is wholly inadequate to attain maximum beneficial use of water resources or effective enforcement of state water resources board policy." [52] Operating today at the "complaint" level, Water Resources is failing to fulfill its duties of protecting the public's waters.

Between the years 1950 to 1999, the agency granted an average of 2,000 certificates annually, and French acknowledges that today ninety percent are passed on, sometimes with conditions or limitations attached.[53] Approximately 60,000 individual out-of-channel diversions are recorded in the department.

A 2001 mission statement adopted by the Oregon Water Resources Commission emphasizes "resource stewardship and addressing long-term water supply needs." [54] Its five core water policies are water resource stewardship, water supply solutions, information management, citizen services, and funding for local and state management. Stated more specifically, the Water Resources Department is to improve instream flows and overall supply through the encouragement of conservation and efficiency practices, by enforcement, by the manipulation of water rights, by the creation of additional storage, and by reservations of water for the future. To achieve these goals, the department relies on Oregon law, which allows transactions or modifications to water rights certificates. The character or nature of the use can be changed (for example, from irrigation to urban), and the point where water is diverted or appropriated can be moved. Water can be transferred between persons, a surface right can be substituted for a groundwater right, and the date for completion of a project can be extended for what the department considers a reasonable length of time, often in excess of five years. Additionally, by reserving quantities of unappropriated water for future economic development, the department is not only furnishing water to current users, but it has been given the responsibility of doling out water for years hence.

In carrying out its duties, the department streamlined (a euphemism for "speeded-up") its water right permitting process and expedited applications for construction of small dams. Although its strategic plan concludes, "These small projects [dams] ... make less impact on other natural resources," that is actually not the case. Little hard data is available on the cumulative effect of single small dams, but they may flood more land or lose more water to evaporation than the larger ones. In addition, there is virtually no comprehensive long range planning, no inspection, and no

During wintertime, virtually no water flows over Zollner Creek Dam in Marion County. There is no inspection or oversight by the Water Resources Department for small dams of less than 2,000 acre-feet, such as this one, although they number in the thousands. Most are in the hands of rural landowners.

oversight for impoundments of less than 2,000-acre-feet, even though they number in the thousands. Permits for new ones average three a month, but there are intervals when applications are much more frequent. In the first half of March, 2005 alone, eleven applications were filed. Whether these methods will actually augment stream flow and "find" water remains to be seen. Historically, storage behind dams has not proven to be the panacea once thought, and the effectiveness water transfer policies has yet to be proven.

ENDNOTES: WHERE HAS ALL THE WATER GONE – WATER SUPPLY

[1] Ellis Armstrong, ed., *History of Public Works in the United States, 1776-1976.* 1976 (Chicago, American Public Works Association, 1976), 243.

[2] *Oregonian,* January 1, 1895.

[3] Tillie Wilson and Alice Scott, *That Was Yesterday* (Sisters? Authors publishers, 1974), 7-8.

[4] *Bend Bulletin,* July 28, 1905, 1-2.

[5] William H. McNeal, *History of Wasco County, Oregon* (The Dalles? Author?, 195?), 209.

[6] Ibid., 13.

[7] *Grants Pass Daily Courier,* April 3, 1935, 16.

[8] Herman Kehrli, "Rates and Related Facts Regarding Water Systems in Oregon Cities" *Western City (Magazine),* January, 1937, v.13,11.

[9] W. Bruce Shepard and D, Hay Doubleday, *Political Efficiency and Political Effectiveness in Water-Related Policy Areas* (Corvallis, Water Resources Research Institute, 1977), 10.

[10] Oregon Water Resources Board, *Malheur-Owyhee Basins* (Salem, 1969), 50-51.

[11] Oregon Water Resources Department, *Oregon Administrative Rules,* Division 400, Sect. 690-501-0005, 2003.

[12] Oregon Water Resources Board, *Mid-Coast Basin* (Salem, 1965), x.

[13] Oregon Water Resources Board, *Lower Willamette River Basin* (Salem, 1965), 48.

[14] *Capital Press,* September 16, 1938, 1.

[15] Frank Mauldin, *Sweet Mountain Water* (Salem, Oak Savanna , 2004), 88.

[16] Oregon Water Resources Board, *Umpqua River Basin* (Salem,1958), 33.

[17] Douglas County, Oregon. Planning Department, *Douglas County Comprehensive Plan* (Roseburg, 1995), 4-3.

[18] *The Dalles Chronicle* (*Progress Edition*), April 25?, 1952, 7.

[19] *Capital Journal*, December 27, 1977, col.1-3, A4.

[20] *Oregonian*, September 14, 1915; May 3l, 1924, 4; February 8, 1953, 17; *Capital Journal*, November 22, 1965, 4; *Oregon Statesman*, January 15, 1966, sect.1, 2; *Capital Journal*, January 19, 1966, 5; *Capital Journal*, July 24, 1973, sect.2, 13.

[21] Michael Zwart, *Groundwater Conditions in the Stage Gulch Area, Umatilla County* (Salem, Oregon Water Resources Department, 1990), 9.

[22] Oregon Department of Environmental Quality, memo, from Audrey Eldridge to Keith Andersen, Jan. 14, 2004, [2].

[23] Oregon Department of Environmental Quality, Memo, From Jack Arendt to Keith Andersen, Jan. 1, 2004, Attachment A [2].

[24] *Oregonian*, December 27, 1996, B6.

[25] Oregon Water Resources Department, Permit G-4354; Certificate 41330, 1968.

[26] Marc Norton and William Bartholomew, *Update Ground Water Conditions and Declining Water Levels in the Butter Creek Area, Morrow and Umatilla counties, Oregon.* (Salem, Oregon Water Resources Department, 1984), 31.

[27] *Oregonian*, December 6, 1984, col.3, D8.

[28] Merritt Parks, "The Fort Rock Basin: Valley in Transition" *Oregon Historical Quarterly*, Spring, 1997.

[29] *Silver Lake Leader*, October 6, 1921.

[30] Parks, 1997, 57.

[31] Donn Miller, *Ground Water Conditions in the Fort Rock Basin, Northern Lake County, Oregon* (Salem, Oregon Water Resources Department, 1986), 48.

[32] *Oregonian*, June 21, 2004, A1.

[33] Oregon Water Resources Department, *Goose and Summer Lakes Basin Report* (Salem, 1989), 29.

[34] Oregon Water Resources Department, Permit G12148; Agreement and Stipulated Final Order, 1997, [2].

[35] Lisa Juul, Water Resources Department, phone conversation, November 3, 2004.

[36] *Oregonian*, April 4, 1948, col.2-3, 24.

[37] *Oregonian*, March 31, 1957, 32.

[38] Coos Bay-North Bend Water Board, *Coos Bay-North Bend Water Supply*, pamphlet, nd., @2000.

[39] Florence, Oregon. Planning commission, *City of Florence Public Facilities System Plan* (Florence, 1988), 7.

[40] *Eugene Register-Guard*, July 12, 2003, B1.

[41] *Oregonian*, November 12, 1998, C2.

[42] Wilsonville: Tualatin Valley Water District, "Water Quality Study," Internet, July 4, 2004.

[43] Oregon Department of Environmental Quality, *Willamette River Basin Water Quality Study; Summary Report* (TetraTech, Bellevue, Washington, 1992),1; *Summary of Recent Scientific Reports on the Willamette River* (TetraTech, Richmond, Washington, 1995), 12.

[44] *Canby Herald*, April 7, 2005, 3.

[45] *Oregonian*, October 19, 1995, C2.

[46] *Oregonian*, July 29, 2003, B1.

[47] *Oregonian*, August 18, 2003, D2.

[48] *Oregonian*, July 31, 2003, C3.

[49] *Silverton-Appeal Tribune*, August 13, 2003, 1.

[50] *Oregon Revised Statutes* 537.160 (1) 2003.

[51] Oregon Water Resources Department, Dwight French, phone interview, December 6, 2003.

[52] Oregon State Engineer, *Thirty-fifth Biennial Report, July 1, 1972 [to] June 30, 1974* (Salem, 1974), 36.

[53] Oregon Water Resources Department, French, 2003.

[54] Oregon Water Resources Department, *Strategic Plan for Managing Oregon's Water Resources, 2001-2003* (Salem, 2001), 2.

[55] Ibid, 31.

CHAPTER 9

OREGON'S WASTE-OUR-WATER WAYS

Who cares? Did I miss the announcement that we were in a water shortage?[1]

For over 150 years Oregon's waters have been engineered to benefit irrigation, impounded to produce power and electricity, dammed to prevent flooding and to provide a supply, drained to create land, contaminated by effluent disposal, and dredged for navigation. Channels have been straightened, overlain and confined by concrete, stripped of vegetation, relocated, disconnected, and divided. Manipulation and control have prevailed since settlers first began to take charge of their environment. Rules and regulations, in ever increasing numbers, reinforced the process. "We and our contractors … enjoy pushing rivers around" were sentiments expressed by the Bureau of Reclamation when assessing a project to pipe Klamath River water to southern California in 1951."[2] Historic policies have pursued the principle of humans dominating rather than adapting to nature.

During the era of settlement, Oregonians moved optimistically toward a future of growth and prosperity through utilization and exploitation of their resources, which were perceived as unlimited. Pioneers, who came to farm, altered the landscape and locked up rights to the state's waters. Industries required water for powering mill wheels, for processing commodities, for disposing of by-products, and for moving goods to distant ports. River channels and estuaries were subjected to dredging and jetty building to assure that commerce wasn't impeded. Cities, placed at streamside, flourished and expanded their boundaries year after year. When communities were inundated, dams were built to control water and to keep it away from the developments. Needs for a water supply and electrical power brought more dams. Water was taken up for municipal use, then flushed back into the river as waste alongside that from industries. Across the state, water privileges were freely given away by officials, and the specific uses acquired such importance that they were eventually cemented into state laws by the legislature.

From the 1800s forward, state and federal bureaucracies were charged with stewardship of the lands and waterways. The Oregon Water Resources Department, the Division of State Lands, the Oregon Department of Environmental Quality, the Oregon Department of Agriculture, and a variety of commissions, along with the U.S. Army Corps of Engineers and the Bureau of Reclamation were placed in the role of protectors and managers. Subscribing to the notion that the state held boundless resources, these agencies pursued lavish water-utilization programs to encourage and boost economic goals. By measuring and collecting data, by setting standards, by publishing reports, and by overseeing a permitting system, they perpetrated the impression that Oregon's water quality and quantity were being safeguarded, even as the resource was being depleted and polluted.

But a new way of thinking crept in during the 1960s. Environmental awareness brought a change in attitude as people began to realize that the state's resources were finite and that the intrinsic qualities of their surroundings might be of value. The importance of economic development gained at a cost to the landscape was questioned, as were the actions of bureaucracies mandated to protect the environment. This awareness accelerated as the cumulative effects of unbridled pollution and overuse became obvious. The illusion that the state's natural riches had been preserved was dispelled with the revelation that the Willamette River continued to be badly degraded year after year. By the 1990s, deformed fish inhabited the waters near Newberg, and Portland's harbor was placed on the U.S. Environmental Protection Agency's Superfund list. The Willamette Basin was not alone in its woes. Eighteen regions across the state experienced catastrophic drops in their groundwater levels. Malheur County and other parts of eastern Oregon suffered from both a lack of water and from polluted sources, whereas contaminated and diminished waters in the Klamath Basin killed thousands fish in 2001 and over 100,000 in 2005. It was apparent that the purity, flow, and beauty of Oregon's waterways had been impaired.

The realization that policies followed historically, favoring consumption and contamination, have not worked was expressed by well-known author, Michael Crichton: "Even our most enlightened past efforts have had undesirable outcomes – either because we did not understand enough, or because the ever-changing world responded to our actions in unexpected ways. From this standpoint, the history of environmental protection is as discouraging as the history of environmental pollution … policies have been carried out with utter conviction … [providing] ample evidence of the obstinate egotism that is a hallmark of human interaction with the environment." [3]

Ambitious environmental goals have been modified, set aside, or ignored. What happened to the movement? The environmentalist way of thinking began over forty years ago at a time when "transforming the natural environment to make it serve man's needs" was the accepted plan of action.[4] To achieve that goal, the landscape was to be fit into rigid parameters. As the Army Corps stated, "The Coos Bay estuary provides an example of a human society adapting to favorable natural conditions by modifying the ecosystem according to a narrowly circumscribed set of values in order to improve its usefulness for particular functions." [5]

This outlook changed with enactment of regulations directed toward preserving the natural resources and saving or reestablishing the intrinsic physical character of natural surroundings. The purpose of the National Environmental Protection Policy Act of 1969 was to promote "enjoyable harmony between man and his environment; to promote efforts which will prevent or eliminate damage to the environment." [6] This legislation was followed by the Clean Air Act in 1970, the Clean Water Act of 1972, the Ocean Dumping Act in 1972, and the Safe Drinking Water Act of 1974, as well as other laws, all reinforcing similar aims.

As a consequence, agencies were forced to pay attention to impact of an action on the surrounding habitat. The new regulations were approached with seeming amiability. The Oregon office of the Army engineers surmised, "The Portland District engaged in both traditional and innovative tasks … The usual dredging, jetty maintenance, multi-purpose dam construction and operation, and water resource planning … in a new social context that required altered thinking and work methods." [7] Simultaneously trying to cater to industry and satisfying requirements of protecting the public's waters, bureaucracies found themselves placed in adversarial roles against environmental advocates. Their past activities and actions were assailed as destructive, as economically unsound ("wasteful pork"), and as adversely affecting natural habitats.

Gradually modifying their projects, agencies now feel that they are moving forward with water management while still preserving environmental quality. One of the means by which they support this belief is through an environmental impact statement (EIS). An EIS details the repercussions that an action might have on the natural, social, and economic setting, as well as lists possible alternatives to the proposed activity. Notices have to be posted, comments solicited, public meetings held, and all data incorporated into a final written assessment.

Impact statements have grown increasingly lengthy over the years, but the act of description and compilation itself, not modification, has come to satisfy any legal or environmental requirements. The notion seems to be that if a problem is *mentioned* somewhere in the EIS, then the issue has been addressed or resolved. Close scrutiny reveals their inconsistent and speculative nature. For a 1976 dredging operation, Army Corps engineers held: "Since our present understanding of most of these processes (biological and physio-chemical) is exceedingly limited, our predictive capabilities for determining the effects of man-induced perturbations on the natural system are correspondingly crude." The agency goes on to surmise that food web "relationships *may*…be jeopardized," that the tidal circulation patterns "*may be* altered," and that, with "our limited understanding of the processes," an analysis of the impact is imprecise (ital. added).[8] Since eagles "did not appear to be adversely effected [*sic*] by the [1976-1979] dredging project," the Corps concluded that its 1994 activity would have "no effect" either, although it did note a high rate of breeding failure among the eagles following completion of the prior undertaking.[9] Meaningful adjustments are rarely made, and the "No Project – Cease Dredging" never seems to be the selected option.

Whereas projects affecting the environment met with favorable comments early on, since then challenges, strong objections, and legal motions question the validity of this course of action. But meaningful changes are extremely difficult in the face of economic pressures, and legal challenges to loopholes in regulations are often the only way to bring about compliance. Northwest Environmental Advocates won a victory when nearly a dozen industrial wastewater permits were revoked. Under a "mixing zone" rule, where a stretch of a river serves to dilute toxic chemicals enough to avoid any violation of standards, agricultural districts are allowed to spray herbicides into canals, and companies such as Allvac, an Albany titanium plant, can dilute its waste in Oak Creek and the Calapooia River. Arguing that its 900,000-gallons-a-day discharge augmented low summer stream flows, Allvac was given the go-ahead by the Oregon Department of Environmental Quality before its activity was halted by the lawsuit. Awaiting a replacement permit for effluent release, the company is planning to store part of the waste temporarily, then discharge it during wintertime when stream flow is high so the pollution levels would be acceptable. Similarly, Georgia Pacific's permit for its paper mill at Clatskanie in Columbia County allowed the company to set up an 110,000-square-foot "toxic mixing zone" around its effluent pipes in the Columbia River, an extensive area in which the waste could be watered down to meet standards. A 2003 lawsuit filed by Columbia RiverKeepers and the Northwest Environmental Defense Center disputed the DEQ's renewal of the permit.

Today environmentalists and other interest groups have reached an impasse, which has diminished the effectiveness of both sides. Farmers blame urbanites or the government, environmentalists are accused of caring more about a few animals and plants than about farm families, and businesses try to maximize their profits over all else. Collaboration among individuals is one solution in which local conflicts can be set aside. Designed as a grass-roots movement in 1995, watershed councils are composed of local citizens, representatives of businesses, and elected officials, who come together to examine and resolve watershed issues. These groups seemingly meet the collaboration criteria but face several disadvantages. To date, the ninety-two councils, which have been formed, occupy a somewhat nebulous position in the state's political hierarchy, as they have no regulatory or defined legal authority. Their members have the monumental task of overseeing an assessment of watershed health and initiating projects for improvements of water quality and habitat. Since technical support generally comes from outside of the membership, councils are funded by Oregon lottery money through the Watershed Enhancement Board. Facing recent cutbacks, councils are forced to choose among projects, solutions, and even their own extinction.

Past measures, taken to protect the state's waters, are woefully weak, subject to political pressures, and in need of rethinking: An *Oregonian* newspaper story in the summer of 2003, praising the million-dollar houses constructed in the Estates at Parrett Mountain in Washington County, fails to relate the real impact of that development on the regional groundwater. Extolling the nature of the surroundings, which provide "elbow room" for the residents, the newspaper notes that the luxury homes offer high-speed internet service, natural gas, nearby recreational and metropolitan centers, as well as "private water system[s]." What it fails to mention are the eight years of planning, legal wrangling, and political maneuvering that made the houses possible. Acreage at Parrett Mountain was purchased in 1993 by Manke developers, whose plans were denied during the initial hearings process. An appeal to the county commissioners brought approval, but, when the declining water table came to the attention of the Oregon Water Resources Commission, it initiated a study of the basalt aquifers. Local residents rely on groundwater wells, which were experiencing drops and a mingling of water between levels. As a result of its findings, the commission proposed restrictions on further appropriations from the aquifer. However, after a court appeal by Manke, the homes, which rely on wells ("private water system[s]"), were constructed.[10]

These past social, legal, and political activities leave Oregonians facing two crucial water issues today. One is water scarcity and the other is water degradation, trends which signal the transformation of Oregon into an urban community although it is still perceived as an agricultural one. But modifications to alter the entrenched methods used in the past, in order to accommodate changing regional patterns, are still not part of the equation. State agencies are attempting to support the notion of all-out consumption, while devising new schemes to shore up the existing system.

Historically agricultural irrigation has dominated water use, but when the demands by growing cities and industries, for fish and wildlife, and for recreation are figured in, farmers find themselves competing with urbanites and businesses for water that is no longer there. The Water Resources Department admits to the predicament. "Put very simply, there is not enough water where it is needed, when it is needed, to satisfy both existing and future water uses. This situation jeopardizes the high level of livability that Oregonians enjoy. It seriously limits the ability of Oregon's economy to grow, and threatens existing users' water supplies and the sustainability of the natural systems on which our economy relies." [11]

The lack of sufficient water also seriously compromises policies followed by the Department of Environmental Quality. The department operates with the understanding that there would always be a sufficient quantity to dilute the volumes of sewage dumped into river channels. Even though stream flows have diminished considerably over the years, and effluent loads have increased dramatically, the DEQ continues to pursue the solution-to-pollution-is-dilution course of action.

Having enough water is pivotal. If there were enough water, any amount could be expended for irrigation, for municipalities, and for industry. Any amount of sewage could be diluted by flowing streams. Today's water woes have not shaken the confidence of Oregonians in their perceived water surplus. It just awaits the winter rains or discoveries by scientists, engineers, planners, and the government employing marvelous new techniques. Once located, the water can then be manipulated and redirected for easy utility. Where is Oregon's "found" water to come from? Oregon's water laws, which allow for the transfer of a water right ownership and for a change in the use or in the place of diversion, have generated several imaginative and creative methods to replace diminished sources – in something akin to a shell game. One of the first, groundwater recharge, was followed by its later modification, aquifer storage and recovery. More recently setting aside amounts of water for future use, water banking, and reassigning federal water are being examined for possibilities.

Artificial groundwater recharge allows winter water to be stored in an aquifer then used during high demand summer months. This strategy was tested in the 1950s when field water was introduced into wells at Pine Flat east of Klamath Falls. Spring and creek water went into municipal wells for St. Helens in 1952, water from the Willamette River poured into Springfield city wells in 1960, and water sprayed onto stacks of concrete pipe at the American Pipe and Construction Company in northeast Portland from 1958 to 1962 was cycled back into the same source where it originated. More formal methods were utilized at The Dalles between the fall of 1960 and spring of 1961, by the Salem Heights Water District, and by the Buell-Red Prairie Domestic Water Association in Polk County in the 1970s. Problems arose when there was no measurable build-up of the groundwater table, when the water-bearing zones quickly became clogged, or when a large amount of sediment was carried into the well.

Oversight by the Department of Environmental Quality imposed rigorous demands on the quality of the injected water. "The City of Salem … indicated that the DEQ 'threw in the kitchen sink' when the water quality testing program [for recharge] was developed." [12] Subsequent lobbying by the Tualatin Valley Water District brought about approval of a new "statutory scheme" termed aquifer storage and recovery. Passed by the legislature in 1995, the program also allowed for diversion, underground storage, and recovery but relegated the Department of Environmental Quality to "a commenting role." This reworking of the law eased regulations, encouraged development, and, as with many vague legislative rulings, is rife with issues that, no doubt, will have to be decided in court. Rules for aquifer storage and recovery fail to answer questions such as where do permits fit into the scheme of prior water right ownership? Does the law comply with the federal Clean Water Act? Does it address the serious lack of knowledge about the workings of groundwater or about the chemical reaction between injected water and the aquifer material? [13]

Other plans to produce water involve both reserving and banking water to insure availability where needed, but the approaches differ. One calls for the setting aside, locking up, or reserving of specific amounts of unallocated water that *could* be needed for economic development, whereas the other involves the banking of water through a selling, buying, or leasing program. What it comes down to is that water quantities, which might not actually exist in already overallocated rivers, in overdrawn aquifers, or behind dams, are being juggled on paper.

The setting aside or taking of enormous quantities of water based on anticipated future goals, growth, or development is rife with pitfalls, even for limited periods of time. Under this legislation, 25,000 acre-feet in the Powder River and 80,000 acre-feet in the Hood River basins were reserved by the Water Resources Department in 1996, following requests by the Department of Agriculture. Petitions to secure 364,000 acre-feet of water for irrigation in the Willamette Valley twenty years into the future have been put on hold while a study conducted by both the U.S. Army Corps of Engineers and Oregon Water Resources determines the actual amount of irrigated acreage. Once the number of acres has been calculated, the figures can then be utilized to decide how much unused water remains behind federal dams. The idea is that federal water, impounded early in the twentieth century, was allocated for irrigation, but that designation doesn't address present day needs for fish, cities, and recreation. Because much of the water may not be needed for agriculture, the League of Oregon Cities and government agencies hope to reallocate the unused quantity more realistically to current purposes. But since this means asking Congress to reconsider and reassign the historically designated usage, reallocation will doubtless be an uphill battle politically.

In 1990 the Coos Bay Water Board applied for 25 million gallons a day from Tenmile Creek to be reserved or held for five years into the future in order to meet needs for predicted development. When the board failed to act on its certificate within the designated time, WaterWatch of Oregon and a number of conservationists went to court to halt renewal of the permit by the Water Resources Department. Environmentalists were "worried about policies that allow governments to tie up unused water, some times for decades." WaterWatch attorney Brian Posewitz noted, "Take this case from [*sic*] example. The use of the water occurs, 20 or 50 years down the road, with no opportunity to ask, 'Is this in the public interest now?'." [14] In 2004 the Court of Appeals found for WaterWatch.

Under the water banking program, monitored by the Water Resources

Department, unused water rights can be put into a bank in exchange for credits. That water right can, in turn, be sold, but more often leased, to a new user. Most rights are leased for a limited period of time so the arrangements are temporary, and the trades are managed through a supervising agency that acts as a clearinghouse for the exchanges. In the Deschutes Basin the department coordinates with the Deschutes Resources Conservancy that manages the lease agreements.

What is the overall status of Oregon's water health today? Oregonians have long thought of themselves as being in the forefront environmentally, but reports by both state and federal agencies fail to substantiate this notion. Two state publications, both issued by the Oregon Progress Board - *Achieving the Oregon Shines Vision: the 1999 Benchmark Performance Report*, and *Oregon, State of the Environment Report 2000* - evaluate water resources. Unfortunately, the conclusions in one disagree with those in the other. The *Oregon Shines Vision*, which ranks state-achieved benchmarks, gives the preservation of forest land and wetlands an "A" grade. "Oregon has … no [loss of] net acreage of either [forest or wetlands] during the 1990s … fifty-two percent of monitored streams had significantly increasing water quality trends, compared to zero percent with significantly decreasing trends. Similarly, streams with adequate water supply 12 months per year jumped from 44% in 1990 to 70% in 1997."[15] These conclusions are contradicted by those reached in *Oregon, State of the Environment*. Hailed as "the first scientifically credible, comprehensive assessment of Oregon's environment … [providing] … much needed scientifically sound information," the report is, for the most part, forthright. The science panel, which compiled the document, found inadequate water supplies, poor water quality, loss of wetlands, and degraded riparian areas as among problems to be resolved by Oregon residents.[16]

Findings by the federal government, as well, have revealed that the quality of water in Oregon rivers is not being protected. In 2005 the U.S. Environmental Protection Agency notified the Oregon Department of Environmental Quality of "widespread deficiencies" in the handling of wastewater and sewage from industries and municipalities. Threatening a federal takeover in order to enforce water quality standards, the EPA urged Oregon to commit more money to bring about compliance to existing laws. It cited several problems with the issuance, oversight, and enforcement of permits.

No one solution has worked in the past and that will be the case in the future. All will cost money and will not satisfy everyone. But something of a balance must be resurrected from the depleted landscape. With the changes they have undergone, ecosystems will never be completely restored, but a balance can be re-established between the needs of humans, animals, plants, and the economy. Adherence to an economic dogma alone is no longer acceptable. Oregonians are still in the historic "exploitation" way of acting and thinking, begun by the pioneers, but now they need to move on toward preserving what remains of the state's natural resources. In the view of former state geologist John Beaulieu, "Our history is littered with evidence of oversight mistakes, unbalanced priorities, bad analyses, etc. The future needs more analyses, better scientific understanding, and better choices; also more creativity in terms of design. Such an approach started earlier would have modified or avoided some of our historic mistakes … In terms of the future we need to keep the door open to finding elegant solutions."[17]

In 1949 the State Engineer Charles Stricklin expressed the hope that, "Oregon may well treasure its greatest natural resource, water." [18] Oregonians haven't done so in the past, and the longer they wait to change their ways of thinking and acting about their water, the harder it will be in the future. If there is a bright side, it's that rivers and waterways are wonderfully forgiving. They will recover purity if given the chance.

ENDNOTES: OREGON'S WASTE-OUR-WATER WAYS

[1] *Willamette Week. Hydro Hogs IV*, September 8, 2004, 26; Words of Dr. William Coit, President of Diagnostic Imaging Northwest, when asked about the 947,716 gallons of water used annually at his Dunthorpe home in the Palatine Hill Water District.

[2] Time Magazine, July 30, 1951, 51.

[3] Michael Crichton, *Prey*, New York, HarperCollins, x.

[4] William Willingham, *Army Engineers and the Development of Oregon* (Washington, D.C., General Printing Office, 1983), Preface.

[5] U.S. Army Corps of Engineers, *Draft Supplement, Coos Bay, Oregon, Deep Draft Navigation Project, Environmental Impact Statement* (Portland, 1975), 7-1.

[6] National Environmental Policy Act of 1969 [NEPA]; 42 USCA, 4321 to 4370b.

[7] Willingham, 1983, 208.

[8] U.S. Army Corps of Engineers, Portland District, *Draft Environmental Impact Statement, Operation and Maintenance Dredging, Coos Bay and Coos and Millicoma River Navigation Project, Oregon* (Portland, 1976), x-xi.

[9] U.S. Army Corps of Engineers, Portland District, *Feasibility Report on Navigation Improvements with Environmental Impact Statement; Final, Coos Bay, Oregon* (Portland, 1994), v.1, Syllabus: Exhibit 7 (Endangered Species Coordination Letters and Biological Assessments), 3.

[10] *Oregonian*, September 18, 2003 (Feature Story, New Home Monthly Magazine)

[11] Oregon Water Resources Department, *Strategic Plan for Managing Oregon's Water Resources, 2001-2003* (Salem, 2001), 6.

[12] Report of a meeting between the Department of Environmental Quality, the Oregon Water Resources Department, and Salem officials, March 12, 2003. Minutes of the East Valley Water District, July 14, 2003, 2.

[13] "Aquifer Storage – a Good or Bad Idea?" *Oregon Scientist*, Winter 1999/2002, E2.

[14] *The World* (Coos Bay), May 22, 2004, A5.

[15] Oregon Progress Board, *Achieving the Oregon Shines Vision: the 1999 Benchmark Performance Report, 1999* (Salem, 1999) 9. Such statements of the board, based on *monitored* streams only, are misleading. Overall the miles of polluted stream segments have remained unchanged.

[16] Oregon Progress Board, *Oregon, State of the Environment, Report 2000; Statewide Summary* (Salem, SOER Science Panel, 2000), 1-2.

[17] John Beaulieu, Former Director of the Oregon Department of Geology and Mineral Industries, personal communication, 2005.

[18] Charles Stricklin, *Oregon Blue Book*, 1949-1950 (Salem, 1950), 205.

SOURCES

The following references, which can be found in the endnotes, are not listed in the bibliography:

Newspaper articles from the *Capital Press*, the *Coos Bay Harbor*, the *Coos Bay Times*, the *Corvallis Gazette*, the *Bend Bulletin*, the *Daily Argus Observer*, *The Dalles Chronicle*, the *Eugene Register Guard*, the *Grants Pass Courier*, the *Marshfield Sun*, the *Mt. Angel News*, the *Oregonian*, the *Oregon Journal*, the *Oregon Statesman*, the *Silver Lake Leader*, the *Silverton-Appeal and Mt. Angel News*, *Time Magazine*, the *Walla Walla Statesman*, *Western City Magazine*, the *Willamette Week*, and *The World* (Coos Bay).

Personal and phone interviews

Minutes from meetings

Court cases

Legal statutes

Well logs from the Department of Water Resources

Water quality permits from the Department of Environmental Quality

Water use permits from the Department of Water Resources

Most journal articles

The Oregon Blue Book

Emails, memos, and letters

BIBLIOGRAPHY

Aikens, C. Melvin, 1984. Archaeology of Oregon. Eugene, U.S. Bureau of Land Management, 134p.

Angelo, C. Aubrey, 1988. Sketches of Travel in Oregon and Idaho. Fairfield, Washington, Ye Galleon Press, 185p.

Armstrong, Ellis., ed., 1976. History of Public Works in the United States, 1776-1976. Chicago, American Public Works Association, 736p.

Bancroft, Hubert H., 1888. The Works of ... History of Oregon. San Francisco, The History Company, 2 vols.

Bartlett, Richard., 1984. Rolling Rivers, an Encyclopedia of America's Rivers. New York, McGraw-Hill, 30?p.

Bartram, Colonel W.B., 1930. Flax Fibre in Oregon. The Oregon Magazine, v.26, no.1, pp.10-31.

Bastasch, Rick, 1998. Waters of Oregon. Corvallis, Oregon State University Press, 278p.

Bateson, Cornelius, 1966. The Water Gap – and a New Approach to Its Solution. Oregon Law Review, v.45, pp.278-287.

Battaile, Connie H., 1998. The Oregon Book; Information A to Z. Newport, Saddle Mountain Press, 677p.

Beaulieu, John., 1974. Geologic Hazards of the Bull Run Watershed; Multnomah and Clackamas Counties, Oregon. Portland, Oregon Department of Geology and Mineral Industries, Bulletin, 82, 77p.

—and Hughes, Paul W., 1975. Environmental Geology of Western Coos and Douglas Counties, Oregon. Portland, Oregon Department of Geology and Mineral Industries, Bull.87, 148p.

Beckham, Stephen D., 1977. The Indians of Western Oregon. Coos Bay, Arago Books, 236p.

Bend. Planning, Development & Resource Management, 2003. About Bend's Water Supply, Internet, July 26, 3p.

Bibby, Max, 2000. The Pioneers of Lake Labish. Brooks, The Sons of Labish, 99p.

Boyle, Robert, Graves, John, and Watkins, T.H., 1971. Water Hustlers. San Francisco, Sierra Club, 253p.

Brimlow, George, 1980. Harney County, Oregon, and its Range Land. Bend, Maverick Publ., 316p.

Brogan, Phil., 1964. East of the Cascades. Portland, Binfords & Mort, 304p.

Caldwell, Rodney R., 1998. Chemical Study of Regional Ground-Water Flow and Ground-water Surface-Water Interaction in the Upper Deschutes Basin, Oregon. U.S. Geological Survey, Water Resources Investigations, Report 97-4233, 49p.

Canniff, KiKi, 1981. Sauvie Island: A Step Back in Time. Portland, Ki2 Enterprises, 142p.

Carey, Charles H., 1935. A General History of Oregon Prior to 1861. Portland, Metropolitan Press, 2 vols.

Carter, Lolita M., 1975. The Effect of Human Activity on the Middle Course of the Tualatin River, Oregon. PhD, Portland State University, 166p.

Cass, Penny L., and Miner, J. Ronald, 1993. The Historical Tualatin River Basin. Corvallis, Oregon Water Resources Research Institute, 59p.

Citizens for Florence, 2004. Treatment Plant Law Suit; Memorandum from Florence Public Works. Internet, May 21, 2004, 4p.

Claeyssens, Paul, 1987. A Cultural Resource Evaluation Report of the Klovdahl Tunnel and Headgate Structure, Waldo Lake … Eugene, Willamette National Forest, 22p.

Clatsop County, Oregon. Commissioners, 1968. Engineering & Planning Report, Water Supplies & Sewerage. Carl E. Green & Associates, Consulting Engineers and Planners, Portland, 194p.

—Department of Planning and Development. Clatsop County Comprehensive Plan; Goals and Policies, 1994. Astoria?, 180p.

Collier, Michael, Webb, Robert, and Schmidt, John, 1996. Dams and Rivers; A Primer on the Downstream Effects of Dams. U.S. Geological Survey, Circular 1126, 94p.

Coos Bay-North Bend Water Board, 1996. Water Supply Project, Coos Bay, 4p.

—2000. Coos Bay-North Bend Water Supply. Coos Bay, Pamphlet.

—2002. Source Water Assessment, Summary Brochure. Coos Bay, 3p.

Coos County, Oregon. Planning Commission, 1967. A Preliminary Development Plan for the South Coast Area of Coos County. Eugene, Bureau of Municipal Research and Service, University of Oregon, 26p.

Corbett, Tara H., 2003. Breaking Environmental Gridlock? Stakeholder Involvement in Water Quality Management. Eugene, Masters, University of Oregon, 202p.

Corning, Howard, 2004. Willamette Landings. Portland, Oregon Historical Society, 3rd ed., 261p.

Crichton, Michael, 2002. Prey. New York, HarperCollins, 367p.

Daughton, Christian., 2001. PPCPs as Environmental Pollutants; Pharmaceuticals and Personal Care Products in the Environment. Internet, American Chemical Society, 28p.

David Newsom: the Western Observer, 1805-1882. Portland, Oregon Historical Society, 1972, 299p.

Dawson, Robert, and Brechin, Gray, 1999. Farewell, Promised Land. Berkeley, University of California Press, 233p.

Deschutes County Historical Society, 1985. A History of the Deschutes Country in Oregon. Bend?, 530p.

—1986. Deschutes Country; Yesteryear. Bend?, 32p.

Deschutes Resources Conservancy, 2004. Deschutes Water Exchange; Permanent Mitigation Credit Auction. Internet, August 23, 2p.

Dicken, Samuel, and Dicken, Emily, 1985. The Legacy of Ancient Lake Modoc: a Historical Geography of the Klamath Lakes Basin, Oregon and California. Eugene, University of Oregon Bookstore Distributor, various pagings.

Dietrich, William, 1995. Northwest Passage; the Great Columbia River. New York, Simon & Schuster, 448p.

Douglas, David., 1972. The Oregon Journals of David Douglas… Ed. by David Lavender. Ashland, The Oregon Book Society, 87p.

Douglas County, Oregon. Planning Department, 2001. Douglas County Comprehensive Plan. Revised. Roseburg, various pagings.

Douglas County Water Resources Survey, 1987. Galesville Dam Project, Douglas County, Oregon. Final Report. Roseburg, Morrison-Knudsen Engineers, Inc., various pagings.

Douthit, Nathan, 1982. The Coos Bay Region, 1890-1944; Life of a Coastal Frontier. Coos Bay, River West Books, 163p.

—1986. A Guide to Oregon South Coast History. Coos Bay, River West Books, 157p.

Drewes, Jorg, *et al.*, 2003. Fate of Pharmaceuticals during Ground Water Recharge. Ground Water Monitoring & Remediation, Summer, 2003, pp.64-72.

E&S Environmental Chemistry, Inc., 2002. Results of Storm-Based Monitoring of Water Quality in the Tillamook, Kilchis, Trask, and Wilson Rivers … from 1996 to 2002. Corvallis, 48p.

Eicher, George, 1959. The Effects of Round Butte Dam on the Deschutes River Downstream. Portland? Portland General Electric, 6p.

Eugene Water & Electric Board, 2003. From Source to Tap; All About Your Drinking Water. Eugene, Pamphlet.

Ewart, Shirley, Anderson, Jane, and Anderson John, 1991. A Long and Wearisome Journey: The Eakin Family Diaries – 1866. Bend, Maverick Publ., 263p.

Fiege, Mark, 1999. Irrigated Eden: the Making of an Agricultural Landscape in the American West. Seattle, University of Washington Press, 323p.

Florence, Oregon. Planning Commission, 1988. City of Florence Public Facilities System Plan, Florence, 68p.

Foxworthy, B.L., 1970. Hydrologic Conditions and Artificial Recharge Through a Well in the Salem Heights Area of Salem, Oregon. U.S. Geological Survey, Water Supply Paper 1594-F, 56p.

—and Bryant, C.T., 1967. Artificial Recharge through a Well Tapping; Basalt Aquifers at The Dalles, Oregon. U.S. Geological Survey, Water Supply Paper 1594-E, 55p.

French, Giles, 1964. Cattle Country of Peter French. Portland, Binfords & Mort, 167p.

Friends of South Slough, 1995. South Slough Adventures; Life on a Southern Oregon Estuary. Coos Bay? Authors?, 276p.

Fuller, George W., 1938. A History of the Pacific Northwest. New York, Knopf, 383p.

Gannett, Marshall W., 1990. Hydrogeology of the Ontario Area, Malheur County, Oregon. Salem, Water Resources Department, 39p.

—and Caldwell, Rodney R., 1998. Geologic Framework of the Willamette Lowland Aquifer System, Oregon and Washington. U.S. Geological Survey, Prof. Paper 1424-A, 32p. and maps.

—et al., 2001. Ground-Water Hydrology of the Upper Deschutes Basin, Oregon. U.S. Geological Survey, Water Resources Investigations Report 00-4162, 77p.

Gatke, Robert M., 1943. Chronicles of Willamette; the Pioneer University of the West. Portland, Binfords & Mort, 702p.

Gibbs, James A., 1955. Sentinels of the North Pacific. Portland, Binfords & Mort, 232p.

—1962. Shipwrecks of the Pacific Coast. Portland, Binfords & Mort, 316p.

Glanzman, Charles, 1976. Land Use Planning and Non-Point Source Pollution. Corvallis, Oregon State University, Water Resources Research Institute, Seminar, Spring, 1976, pp.59-67.

Gleeson, George W., 1972. The Return of a River; the Willamette River, Oregon. Corvallis, Oregon State University, Water Resources Research Institute, 102p.

Goble, Dale., and Hirt, Paul, 1999. Northwest Lands, Northwest People; Readings in Environmental History. Seattle, University of Washington Press, 552p.

Grants Pass, Oregon. Planning Department, 1984. Comprehensive Community Development Plan - Grants Pass and Josephine County. Grants Pass, various pagings.

Graves, Jonathan, and Rushmore, Carol., 1993. The Columbia River Estuary Atlas of Natural Resources. U.S. Environmental Protection Agency, 34p.

Gray, Edward, 1993. William "Bill" W. Brown, 1855-1941: Legend of Oregon's High Desert. Salem, Your Town Press, 222p.

Green, Carl E., 1936. Four Oregon Cities Aid in Clean-up of Rogue River by Constructing New Sewage Treatment Plants. Western City (Magazine), v.12, pp.14-15.

Greenhow, Robert, 1844. The History of Oregon and California and the Other Territories of the North-West Coast ... Boston, Little and Brown, 482p.

Hall, Roberta A. ed., 1995. People of the Coquille Estuary. Corvallis, Words & Pictures, 224p.

Halper, Ruby, 1977. Water Policy in Oregon. Eugene, Oregon Student Public Interest and Research Group (OSPIRG), 65p.

Hatton, Raymond R., 1978. Bend, in Central Oregon. Portland, Binford & Mort, 144p.

Hauth, Vincent, 1998. Tales of Mt. Angel. Mt. Angel, Mt. Angel [Abbey] Press, 79p.

Heceta Water District, 2004. Source Water Assessment; Summary Brochure. Internet, 3p.

Henshaw, F.F., Lewis, John H., and McCaustland, E.J., 1914. Deschutes River, Oregon, and its Utilization. U.S. Geological Survey, Water-Supply Paper 344, 200p.

Hiatt, Isaac, 1997. Thirty-one Years in Baker County; a History of the County from 1861 to 1893. Baker City, Baker County Historical Society,108p.

Highsmith, Richard M., 1958. Atlas of Oregon Agriculture. Oregon State College, Corvallis, 42p.

Hodes, Sister Ursula, 1932. Mt. Angel, Oregon, 1848-1912. Eugene, Masters, University of Oregon, 136p.

Hunter, Bob, 2004. Another Year, Another Round in the Klamath Basin. Instream [Newsletter], Portland, Water Watch of Oregon, Summer, 12p.

An Illustrated History of Baker, Grant, Malheur and Harney Counties, 1902. Spokane, Western Historical Publication Company, 787p.

An Illustrated History of Central Oregon, 1905. Spokane, Western Historical Publication Company, 2 vols.

The Irwin-Hodson Company, Portland, Oregon, 1902. Travelers' Protective Association of America; Oregon and Washington Division, National Convention, Portland, Oregon, June 3d to 7th, 111p.

Jaeger, W.K, 2004. Potential Benefits of Water Banks and Water Transfers. Corvallis, Oregon State University, Extension Service, 4p.

—2004. The Value of Irrigation Water Varies Enormously Across the Upper Klamath Basin. Corvallis, Oregon State University, Extension Service, 4p.

Jennings, Todd., Mighetto, Lisa, and Schnaiberg, Jill, 2003. Currents of Change; a History of the Portland District, U.S. Army Corps of Engineers, 1980-2000. Portland, 247p.

Jepsen, Victor L., 1939. A General History of Klamath Falls from its Beginning until the Coming of the Railroad in 1909. Eugene, Masters, University of Oregon, 127p.

Johannsen, Dorothy, and Gates, Charles., 1957. Empire of the Columbia; a History of the Pacific Northwest. New York, Harper, 685p.

Johnson, Robert, 1958. John McLoughlin, Father of Oregon. Portland, Binfords & Mort, 153p.

Jones, Edward G., The Oregonians Handbook of the Pacific Northwest. Portland, Oregonian Newspaper, 631p.

Kirkwood, James, 1970. A Special Report on the Pollution of River Waters. New York, Arno, 408.

Klamath Bucket Brigade, 2004. Upper Klamath Basin Ground-Water Study. Internet, April 25, 3p.

Komar, Paul D., 1997. The Pacific Northwest Coast. Durham, Duke University Press, 195p.

—et al., 1991. Bandon, Oregon: Coastal Development and the Potential for Extreme Ocean Hazards. Shore and Beach, v.59, pp.14-22.

Kuennecke, Bernd H., 1974. Distribution of Irrigation in Eastern Oregon. Eugene, Masters, University of Oregon, 87p.

Kuhn, V.E., 1937. Salem Completes a New Water Supply source and Improves Distribution. Western City (Magazine), v.13, pp.35-37.

Laird, J. Clint, 1971. Economic Development in Charleston, Oregon. Coos Bay, Coos County Economic Development and Coordinating Committee, 66p.

Lancaster, Samuel C., 1915. The Columbia; America's Great Highway through the Cascade Mountains to the Sea. Portland, Author Publ., 140p.

Lang, H.E., ed., 1885. History of the Willamette Valley. Portland, Geo. Hines Publ., 902p.

Leonard, A.R., and Harris, A.B., 1974. Ground Water in Selected Areas in the Klamath Basin, Oregon. Salem, Oregon State Engineer, Ground Water Report No.21, 104p.

Lev, Esther, 2001. Heroic Tales of Wetland Restoration. Tualatin, The Wetlands Conservancy, 75p.

Lincoln County. Board of Commissioners, 1970. Lincoln County; Regional Water and Sewerage Plans. Clark & Groff, Engineers, Inc., Salem, various pagings.

Lockley, Fred, 1928. History of the Columbia River Valley, from The Dalles to the Sea. Chicago, S.J. Clarke Publ., 3 vols.

Lomax, Alfred, 1941. Pioneer Woolen Mills in Oregon. Portland, Binfords & Mort, 312p.

—1973. Later Woolen Mills in Oregon. Portland, Binfords & Mort, 301p.

Long, D.A., McKey-Fender, D., and Mcnab, J.A., 1964. A Preliminary Survey of the Sources and Kinds of Pollution in Coos Bay, Oregon. Portland, Portland State College, Public Health Laboratory, 27p.

Lyman, William D., 1963. The Columbia River; its History, its Myths, its Scenery, its Commerce. Portland, Binfords & Mort, 367p.

Lynch, Vera M., 1973. Free Land for Free Men; a Story of Clackamas County. n.p., Artline Publ., 680p.

Maddux, Percy, 1952. City of the Willamette; the Story of Portland, Oregon. Portland, Binfords & Mort, 229p.

Malheur County Historical Society, 1988. Malheur County History, 2 vols.

Many Hands, 1998. Jefferson County Reminiscences. Portland, Binford & Mort, 396p.

Marion County. Planning Department, 2002. Lake Labish Wetlands Restoration Project. Salem [3]p.

Mauldin, Frank, 2004. Sweet Mountain Water; the Story of Salem. Salem, Oak Savanna, 285p.

McGee, George, 1937. Hillsboro, Ore. Uses Revenue Bonds for New Sewerage Works. Western City Magazine, April, v.13, pp.44-47.

McNeal, William H., 195? History of Wasco County. The Dalles? Author?, 471p.

Merriam, Paul G., 1976. Riding the Wind: Cape Horn Passage to Oregon, 1840s-1850s. Oregon Historical Quarterly, v.44, pp.37-60.

Miller, Donn W., et al., 1994. Groundwater Conditions of Basalt Aquifers, Parrett Mountain, Northern Willamette Valley, Oregon. Salem, Water Resources Department, 144p.

Miller, Emma G., 1958. Clatsop County, Oregon; a History. Portland, Binfords & Mort, 291p.

Murphy, Martha A., ed., 1988. A History of Josephine County, Oregon. Grants Pass, Josephine County Historical Society, 304p.

Nash, Wallis, 1904. The Farm, Ranch, and Range in Oregon. Salem, The Lewis and Clark Centennial Exposition Commission for the State of Oregon, 32p.

—1919. A Lawyer's Life on Two Continents. Boston, R.G. Badger Publ., 212p.

Newberg, Oregon. Planning Department, 1984. Sewerage Master Plan Update. Kraemer, Chin & Mayo, Inc., various pagings.

Norris, Logan., 1976. Forests and Rangelands as Sources of Chemical Pollutants. Corvallis, Oregon State University, Water Resources Research Institute, Seminar, Spring, pp.17-51.

North Bend, Oregon, 2004. City of North Bend, Oregon. Internet, May 21, 3p.

North Fork Siuslaw Watershed Analysis Team, 1994. Siuslaw National Forest. Corvallis, various pagings.

Norton, Marc A., and Bartholomew, William S., 1984. Update of Ground Water Conditions and Declining Water Levels in the Butter Creek Area, Morrow and Umatilla … Salem, Water Resources Department, 203p.

Oliphant, J. Orin, 1933. Voyage of the *Sequin*, 1849. Oregon Historical Quarterly, v.34, pp.254-258.

Oregon City, Oregon. Planning Department, 1982. Comprehensive Plan. Oregon City, various pagings

Oregon Department of Agriculture, 1930? Oregon. Salem?, 36p.

—1998. ODA's Story of the Week – Oct. 7, 1998; CAFO: an Important Link to AG Water Quality. Internet, 3p.

—1999. The Oregon Department of Agriculture SB 1010 Planning Program; Enforcement and Compliance Process and Procedures. Salem?, 15p.

—2004. New CAFO Rules: How Do You Stack Up? Internet, June 26, 2p.

—Natural Resources Division. 2002? Water Quality and Agriculture in Oregon; Implementation of Senate Bill 1010. Leaflet.

Oregon Department of Environmental Quality, 1975. Water Quality Control in Oregon, Portland? 68p.

—1980. Oregon's Hazardous Waste Management; Status Report. Portland?

—1981. Malheur County. Nonpoint Source Water Quality Management Planning Program; Two-year Sampling Program. Salem? 153p.

—1992. The Nomination of Tillamook Bay, Oregon, to the National Estuary Program, Salem, Office of the Governor. Portland, various pagings.

1992-1995. Willamette River Basin; Water Quality Study. Portland, Tetra Tech, 6 vols.

—1994. Oregon's 1994 Water Quality Status Assessment Report. 305(b) Report. Portland, various pagings.

—1995. Sixth Annual Environmental Cleanup Report, Submitted to Governor John Kitzhaber… Portland? 27p.

—1998. Listing Criteria for Oregon's 1998 303(d) List of Water Quality Limited Water Bodies. Portland?

—1998. Oregon's 1998 Water Quality Status Assessment Report. Section 305(b) Report. Portland, 84p.

—1998. Permits Handbook; A Guide to Oregon Department of Environmental Quality permits and Requirements. Portland? 104p.

—1999. Briefing Packet, Willamette River Basin. Portland, various pagings.

—1999. Portland Harbor Sediment Management Plan. Portland, v.1, various pagings.

—2002. TMDLs: Tools to Improve Water Quality in the Willamette Basin. Internet, February, 1 p.

—2003. Fact Sheet: The 2002 303(d) List of Impaired Waters in Oregon. Internet, February, 1 p.

—2003. Hazardous Waste Program. Internet, November 8, 2p.

—2003. Water Quality. Facility Summary Data … for Permits. Internet, various pagings.

—2004. Declaration of a Groundwater Management Area … Southern Willamette Valley. Portland, 4p.

—2004. Oregon On-Site Sewage Program [La Pine]. Internet, 4p.

—2004. Oregon Water Quality Index Summary Report, Water Years 1994-2003. Portland, 8p.

—2004. Southern Willamette Valley Groundwater Management Area Declared; Fact Sheet, leaflet.

Oregon Department of Land Conservation and Development, 2001. Experimental Program Enables Collaborative Local Strategy Building [at La Pine]. Internet, 5p.

Oregon Division of State Lands, 1972. Biennial Report, 1970-1972. Salem, 27p.

—1978. Biennial Report, 1976-1978. Salem, 25p.

—1979. Navigability Studies. Salem, various pagings.

—1983. Report and Recommendation on the Navigable Waters of Oregon. Salem, 168p.

—1990. Report to the State Land Board and the People of Oregon on Division ... Activities from July 1987 to June 1989. Salem, 43p.

—1991. Wetlands Update. Salem, v.2, no.2, 6p.

—1992. Lower Willamette River Management Plan; Final. Salem, various pagings.

—1995. Proposed Asset Management Plan; a Plan to Guide the Care and Management of Land, Waterways, and Minerals ... Salem, various pagings.

—2002. Oregon's Removal-Fill Program for Waters of the State 1999-2002. Salem, 18p.

—2002. State Ownership of Navigable Waterways. Salem, Memo, March 15, 2002, from Ann Hanus, Director. [17]p.

—2003. Biennial Report, 2001-03. Salem. [10] p.

—2004. Navigability Study Requests. Internet, November 13, 2p.

Oregon Progress Board, 1999. Achieving the Oregon Shines Vision: The 1999 Benchmark Performance Report. Salem, 24p.

—2000. Oregon, State of the Environment Report 2000; Statewide Summary. Prepared by SOER Science Panel. Salem, 74p.

Oregon State Engineer, 1958. Twenty-seventh Biennial Report to the Governor of Oregon, July 1, 1956 [to] June 30, 1958. Salem, 79p.

—1966. Thirty-first Biennial Report to the Governor of Oregon, July 1, 1964 [to] June 30, 1966. Salem, 105p.

—1974. Thirty-fifth Biennial Report to the Governor of Oregon, July 1, 1972 [to] June 30, 1974. Salem, 132p.

Oregon State Land Board, Advisory Committee, 1972. An Inventory of Filled Lands in Tillamook Bay Estuary. Salem?, 5p.

Oregon State Planning Board, 1935. Willamette Valley Project; Report to Gov. Charles H. Martin on the Development of the Willamette River Watershed, Salem?, 128p.

Oregon State Sanitary Authority, 1942. Biennial Report to the Governor of Oregon and the Forty-second Legislative Assembly for the Period July 1, 1940 to June 30, 1942. Portland?, 13p.

—1957. Interim Report on Status of Water Pollution Control in the Willamette River Basin. Portland, 17p.

—1962. Twelfth Biennial Report on Water Pollution Control for the Period July 1, 1960 to June 30, 1962. Portland, 60p.

—1964. Final Report on the Quality of Klamath Basin Waters in Oregon, July, 1959, to December, 1963. Portland?, 14p.

—1967. Implementation and Enforcement Plan for the Public Waters of the State of Oregon. Portland, 28p.

—1969. Water Quality in Coos Bay. Portland?, 10p.

Oregon Water Policy Review Board, 1979. Final Report to the Pacific Northwest Regional Commission on Oregon's Drought and Conservation Activities. Salem, Oregon Water Resources Department, 74p.

Oregon Water Resources Board, 1958. Umpqua River Basin. Salem, 200p.

—1961. Deschutes River Basin. Salem, 188p.

—1965. Lower Willamette River Basin. Salem, 148p.

—1965. Mid-Coast Basin. Salem, 122p.

—1969. Malheur-Owyhee Basins. Salem, 84p.

—1971. Klamath Basin. Salem, 288p.

Oregon Water Resources Commission, 1995. 1993-1995, Biennial Water Management Program for Oregon. Salem, 72p.

Oregon Water Resources Committee, 1954. A Report on Water Supply Sources and Water Use in 187 Oregon Cities. Eugene, Compiled by the Bureau of Municipal Research and Service, 31p.

Oregon Water Resources Department, 1984. Report for the Period January, 1983, to December, 1984. Salem, 57p.

—1985. Rogue River Basin. Salem, 293p.

—1986. John Day River Basin. Salem, 264p.

—1988? Surface Water Records for Oregon. Salem, 76p.

—1988. Umatilla Basin Report. Salem, 246p.

—1989. Goose and Summer Lakes Basin Report. Salem, 112p.

—1992. Biennial Report for the Period January, 1991 to December, 1992. Salem, 79p.

—1992. Willamette Basin Report. Salem, 350p.

—2001. Strategic Plan for Managing Oregon's Water Resources, 2001-2003. Salem, 55p.

—2001. Water Rights in Oregon. Salem, 50p.

—2004. Aquifer Storage and Recovery. Internet, May 7, 2p.

—2004. Artificial Ground Water Recharge. Internet, May 7, 1p.

—2004. Oregon's Water Law and Water Rights System. Internet, July 26, 3p.

Oregon Watershed Enhancement Board, 2002. Investments in Oregon's Future. Salem, 43p.

—2003. The Oregon Plan for Salmon and Watersheds; Biennial Report. Salem, 56p.

Oregon Wetlands Joint Venture, 2004. Coast Range; Basin and Range; Columbia Basin; East Cascades; Blue Mountains. Internet, November 13, various pagings.

Orr, Elizabeth, and Orr, William, 1999. Geology of Oregon. Dubuque, Kendall-Hunt, 254p.

Outwater, Alice, 1996. Water; a Natural History. New York, Basic Books, 212p.

Pacific Northwest River Basins Commission, 1978. The Oregon Coast; an Informational Report on the Water and Related Land Resources. Corvallis, Oregon State Study Team, 103p.

Parsons, William, 1902. An Illustrated History of Umatilla County and of Morrow County by W.S. Shiach. W.H. Lever, Publ., 581p.

Pollock, Cheryl, McGehee, David, and Neilhaus, Ronald W., 1995. Effectiveness of Spur Jetties at Siuslaw River, Oregon; Report 1: Prototype Monitoring Study. Washington, D.C., U.S. Army Corps of Engineers, 101p.

Port of Portland, 2003. Harbor Clean-up; Lower Willamette Superfund Site. Portland, 4p.

Portland General Electric, 1989. Bull Run Hydroelectric Project; Marmot Dam Rehabilitation; Design Report. San Francisco? EBASCO Services Inc., 15p.

—2004. Bull Run Hydroelectric Project Decommissioning Agreement Facts. Internet, July 4, 3p.

Price, Don, Hart, D.H., and Foxworthy, B.L., 1962. Artificial Recharge in Oregon and Washington. U.S. Geological Survey, Water Supply Paper 1594-C, 65p.

Raven, Christopher, and Elston, Robert G., eds., 1992. Land and Life at Malheur Lake; Preliminary Geomorphological and Archaeological Investigations. Silver City, Nevada, Intermountain Research for U.S. Fish and Wildlife Service, 151p.

Rees, Helen., 1982. Shaniko; from Wool Capital to Ghost Town. Portland, Binfords & Mort, 166p.

Robbins, William G., 1988. Hard Times in Paradise; Coos Bay, Oregon, 1850-1986. Seattle, University of Washington Press, 194p.

Robinson, Brittain B.,1936. Fiber Flax in Oregon. Corvallis, Oregon State Agricultural College, Agricultural Experiment Station.

Robinson, Michael., 1979. Water for the West; the Bureau of Reclamation, 1902-1977. Chicago, Public Works Historical Society, 117p.

Robison, E. George, 1991. Water Availability for Oregon's Rivers and Streams. Salem? Water Resources Department, 68p., plus appendix.

Salem, Oregon. Public Works Department, 2003. Annual Report on Salem's Drinking Water. Salem, Pamphlet.

Salem, Oregon. Task Force on Wastewater Management. Report [to the] Mayor, 1984. Salem?, 54p.

Sauvie Island Soil Conservation District, 1947. Report. Sauvie Island? No publ., [22]p.

Sceva, Jack, 1968. Liquid Waste Disposal in the Lava Terrane of Central Oregon. Corvallis, Federal Water Quality Administration, Pacific Northwest Water Laboratory, 66p.

Schlicker, Herbert., and Deacon, Robert, 1967. Engineering Geology of the Tualatin Valley Region, Oregon. Portland, Department of Geology and Mineral Industries, Bulletin 60, 80p.

Schwantes, Carlos, 1989. The Pacific Northwest; an Interpretive History. Lincoln, University of Nebraska, 426p.

Scott, Leslie M., 1923. John Work's Journey from Fort Vancouver to Umpqua River, 1834. Oregon Historical Society, v.24, pp.238-268.

Sever, Megan, 2004. Western Aquifers under Stress. Geotimes, May, pp.32-33.

Shepard, W.B., and Doubleday, D.J., 1977. Political Efficiency and Political Effectiveness in Water-Related Policy Areas: A Report of Research Results on Three State Agencies in Oregon. Corvallis, Oregon State University, 132p.

Sisemore, Linsy, ed., 1941. History of Klamath County, Oregon. Klamath Falls, n.p., 598p.

Smith, Frank, ed., 1971. Conservation in the United States; a Documentary History. New York, Chelsea House, 782p.

Smith, Helen K., ed., 1948. With Her Own Wings; Historical Sketches. Compiled by the Fine Arts Dept. of the Portland Federation of Women's Organizations. Portland, Beatie and Co., 243p.

Sobel, Elizabeth, 1992. Background and Preliminary Inventory of Archaeological … Klamath Marsh, Klamath County, Oregon. Chiloquin, Klamath Forest National Wildlife Refuge, et al., 130p.

Spencer, Omar C., 1950. The Story of Sauvies Island. Portland, Binfords & Mort, 134p.

Stacey, Robert., 1973. The State Land Board: A Study in Administrative Negligence. Eugene, OSPIRG (Oregon Student Public Interest and Research Group), 94p.

Starbird, Ethel A., 1972. A River Restored: Oregon's Willamette. National Geographic, v.141, no.6, pp.816-835.

Stewart, Earle K., 1950. Steamboat on the Columbia: the Pioneer Period. Oregon Historical Quarterly, v.51, pp.21-42.

Stone, Norman F., 1985. Bountiful McKenzie; the Story of the Eugene Water & Electric Board. Eugene, Parkstone Co., 245p.

Strategic Water Management Group, 1995. Oregon's Watershed Health Program. Salem? vol. 1, various pagings.

Strite, Daniel D., 1976. Hurrah for Garibaldi. Pt. 2, Oregon Historical Quarterly, v.77, pp.341-368.

Stroud, Ellen, 1995. A Slough of Troubles: An Environmental and Social History of the Columbia Slough. Eugene, Masters, University of Oregon, 89p.

Swift, Lon., 1909. Land Tenure in Oregon. Oregon Historical Quarterly, v.10, pp.31-137.

Taylor, George, and Hannan, Chris, 1999. The Climate of Oregon. Corvallis, Oregon State University Press, 211p.

—and Hatton, Raymond, 1999. The Oregon Weather Book. Corvallis, Oregon State University Press, 242p.

Taylor, Joseph E., 1999. Making Salmon; an Environmental History of the Northwest Fisheries Crisis. Seattle, University of Washington Press, 421p.

Thornton, J. Quinn, 1973. Oregon and California in 1848. New York, Arno, 379p.

Tillamook County, Port of Bay City, and Port of Tillamook Bay, 1972. Development Program for Tillamook Bay, Oregon. Portland, Thomas J. Murray & Associates, 82p.

Tillamook County Performance Partnership, 2002. Remediation of Agricultural Contributions of Fecal Coliform Bacteria, Sediment, and heat in the Tillamook Basin ..., E&S Environmental Restoration, Inc., Corvallis, 61p.

—2004. Performance and Flexibility; Tillamook Bay National Estuary Project. Internet, May, 2004, 4p.

Towle, Jerry C., 1974. Woodland in the Willamette Valley: an Historical Geography. Eugene, Phd., University of Oregon, 159p.

Tualatin River Watershed: TMDL Case Study. Internet, May 16, 2004, 5p.

Tualatin Valley Water District, 2004. About our District. Internet, August 23, 4p.

Tweedell, Bob, 1949?. Old Millrace; How it was Born. Eugene, Register Guard Publ., 48p.

U.S. Army Corps of Engineers, Portland District, 1958. Water Resource Development of the Columbia River Basin. Portland, 5 vols.

—1971. Water Resource Development. Portland, 149p.

—1974. Corps of Engineers Actions Affecting Riverbanks and Channels in Willamette River Basin, Oregon; Draft Environmental Statement. Portland, various pagings.

—1975. Coos Bay, Oregon, Deep Draft Navigation Project; Environmental Impact Statement. Portland, various pagings.

—1976. Draft Environmental Impact Statement, Operation and Maintenance Dredging, Coos Bay and Coos and Millicoma River Navigation Project, Oregon. Portland, 2 vols.

—1977. North Jetty Rehabilitation, Yaquina Bay and Harbor, Oregon; Environmental Evaluation and Finding, Portland, various pagings.

—1979. An Environmental Impact Statement on Operations and Maintenance of the Willamette Reservoir System. Portland, various pagings.

—1979. Willow Creek Lake, Heppner, Oregon. Final Environmental Impact Statement. Portland, 72p.

—1980. Breakwater and Entrance Channel for the Proposed Bandon Small Boat Basin, Coquille River, Oregon. Portland, various pagings.

—1980. Lower Columbia River Bank Protection, Loop Extension Location, Multnomah County, Oregon. Portland, various pagings.

—1982. Historic Use of Six Reservoir Areas in the Upper Willamette Valley, Lane County Oregon. Eugene, Heritage Research Institute, 153p.

—1985. The Port of Portland, Oregon. Portland, 74p.

—1986. Clatsop County, Oregon; Diking & Improvement District No. 9; Flood Damage Reduction Study. Portland, 37p.

—1987. Elk Creek Lake, Rogue River Basin, Oregon. Master Plan for Resource Use. Portland, various pagings.

—1988. Coos Bay, Oregon, Dredged Material Disposal Site Designation; Final Environmental Impact Statement. Portland, various pagings.

—1992. Columbia Slough; Reconnaissance Study. Portland, various pagings.

—1994. Coos Bay, Oregon, Navigation Improvements; Final Feasibility Report and Environmental Impact Statement. Portland, 2 vols., various pagings.

—1994. Feasibility Report on Navigation Improvements. Portland, 87p.

—1994. Tillamook Bay Ocean Dredged Material Disposal Site Evaluation; Final Report. Portland, various pagings.

—1999. Integrated Feasibility Report for Channel Improvements and Environmental Impact Statement; Columbia & Lower Willamette River… Portland, 2 vols.

—2000. Water Resources Development in Oregon, 2000. Portland, 96p.

—2001. Ports on the Oregon Coast. Port Series No.33, Revised. Portland, 58p.

U.S. Bureau of Land Management, 2001. Analysis of the Management Situation (AMS) for the Upper Deschutes; Resource Management Plan and Environmental Impact Statement (RMP/EIS), Prineville, 236p.

—2001. John Day River Management Plan, Two Rivers, John Day and Baker Resource Management Plan. Prineville, 268p.

—2002. Cascade-Siskiyou National Monument; Draft Resource Management Plan/Environmental Impact Statement. Medford, 308p.

U.S. Bureau of Reclamation, 1957. Bureau of Reclamation Project Feasibilities and Authorizations. Washington, D.C., 1046p.

—2001. Analysis of the Management Situation (AMS) for the Upper Deschutes Resource Management Plan and Environmental Impact Statement (RMP/EIS); Executive Summary. Prineville, 236p.

—2001. Proposed Southeastern Oregon Resource Management Plan and Final Environmental Impact Statement. Vale, 3 vols.

U.S. Department of Agriculture, Economic Research Service, 1964. Report on Water and Related Land Resources; Middle Coast Drainage Basin, Oregon. Washington, D.C.?, 138p.

—and the Oregon Department of Agriculture, 2002. 2001-2002 Oregon Agriculture & Fisheries Statistics. Salem, Oregon Department of Agriculture, 80p.

U.S. Environmental Protection Agency, 2004. Constructed Wetlands for Wastewater Treatment and Wildlife Habitat, Cannon Beach, Oregon. Internet, July 4, 2004, 2p.

—2004. Constructed Wetlands for Wastewater Treatment and Wildlife Habitat, Hillsboro, Oregon – Jackson Bottom Wetlands Preserve. Internet, July 4, 2p.

—2004. Source Water Protection, Salem, Oregon. Internet, April, 2p.

U.S. Geological Survey, 1969. Mineral and Water Resources of Oregon. Printed for the 90th Congress, 2nd Session, Committee on Interior and Insular Affairs, Washington, D.C., General Printing Office, 462p.

—1990. National Water Summary, 1987 – Water Supply and Use: Oregon. Water-supply paper.

—1993. National Water Summary, 1990-91 – Stream Water Quality: Oregon. Water-supply paper.

—2002. Pharmaceuticals, Hormones, and Other Organic Wastewater Contaminants in U.S. Streams, 1999-2000: A National Reconnaissance. Open-file Report 02-94, 19p.

—2004. National Water-Quality Assessment (NAWQA) Program. Internet, May, 4, 2p.

—2004. Tualatin River Basin Water Quality Assessment. Internet, May 16, 4 p.

U.S. Senate. 106th Congress, Committee on Energy and Natural Resources, 1999. Report 106-60: Sewage Treatment Facility in Sisters, Oregon, 6p.

U.S. Works Progress Administration, 1930?. Flax in Oregon. Portland, 16p.

Vale, Thomas R., ed., 2002. Fire, Native Peoples, and the Natural Landscape. Washington, D.C., Island Press, 315p.

Vancouver, George, 1926. The Exploration of the Columbia River by Lieutenant W.R. Broughton, October, 1792. An Extract from the Journal of Captain George Vancouver. Longview, Washington, Longview Daily News, 39p.

Vaughan, Thomas, ed., 1981. High & Mighty; Select Sketches about the Deschutes Country. Portland, Oregon Historical Society, 309p.

Wagner, Norman., 1949. Ground-water Studies in Umatilla and Morrow Counties. Portland, Department of Geology and Mineral Industries, Bulletin 41, 100p.

WaterWatch of Oregon, 2004. Deschutes River Basin. Internet, July, 4p.

Wentz, Dennis A., *et al.*, 1998. Water Quality in the Willamette Basin, Oregon, 1991-96. U.S. Geological Survey, Circular 1161, 34p.

Whistler, John, and Lewis, John, 1916. John Day Project; Irrigation and Drainage. U.S. Bureau of Reclamation, 185p.

Whittlesey, Norman, ed., 1986. Energy and Water Management in Western Irrigated Agriculture. Boulder, Westview Press, 415p.

Wilkes, Charles, 1852. Narrative of the United States Exploring Expedition. London, Ingram, Cooke, and Co., 2 vols.

Will, Clark, 1958. How Salem Got its Water. Salem, Marion County Historical Society, Marion County History, v.4, pp.29-35.

Willamette Restoration Initiative, 2001. Restoring a River of Life; the Willamette Restoration Strategy Overview. Salem? 26p.

Willamette River Basin Task Force, 1997. Recommendations to Governor John Kitzhaber. Salem?, 59p.

Williams, Elsie H., 1983. A Pictorial History of the Bend Country. Norfolk, Virginia, The Donning Company, 206p.

Willingham, William F., 1983. Army Engineers and the Development of Oregon; a History of the Portland District ... Portland, U.S. Army Corps of Engineers, 258p.

Wilson, Tillie, and Scott, Alice, 1974. That Was Yesterday. Sisters, Authors, 113p.

Wilsonville, Oregon. Public Works Department, 2004. Willamette River Water Treatment Plant. Internet, July 4, 3p.

Wollner, Craig, 1990. Electrifying Eden. Portland, Oregon Historical Society Press, 325p.

Worth, Veryl., and Worth, Harry, 1989. Early Days on the Upper Willamette. Rev. ed., Oakridge, Fact Book, 142p.

Zwart, Michael J., 1990. Groundwater Conditions in the Stage Gulch Area, Umatilla County, Oregon. Salem, Oregon Water Resources Dept., 44p.

INDEX